MECHANISMS
OF
MICROBIAL PATHOGENICITY

Other Publications of the
Society for General Microbiology

THE JOURNAL OF GENERAL MICROBIOLOGY
(Cambridge University Press)

AUTOTROPHIC MICRO-ORGANISMS
FOURTH SYMPOSIUM OF THE SOCIETY
(Cambridge University Press)

ADAPTATION IN MICRO-ORGANISMS
THIRD SYMPOSIUM OF THE SOCIETY
(Cambridge University Press)

THE NATURE OF VIRUS MULTIPLICATION
SECOND SYMPOSIUM OF THE SOCIETY
(Cambridge University Press)

THE NATURE OF THE BACTERIAL SURFACE
FIRST SYMPOSIUM OF THE SOCIETY
(Blackwell's Scientific Publications Limited)

MECHANISMS
OF
MICROBIAL PATHOGENICITY

FIFTH SYMPOSIUM OF THE
SOCIETY FOR GENERAL MICROBIOLOGY
HELD AT THE
ROYAL INSTITUTION, LONDON
APRIL 1955

CAMBRIDGE
Published for the Society for General Microbiology
AT THE UNIVERSITY PRESS
1955

PUBLISHED BY
THE SYNDICS OF THE CAMBRIDGE UNIVERSITY PRESS
London Office: Bentley House, N.W. 1
American Branch: New York
Agents for Canada, India, and Pakistan: Macmillan

Printed in Great Britain at the University Press, Cambridge
(Brooke Crutchley, University Printer)

CONTRIBUTORS

AINSWORTH, G. C., Department of Botany, University College, Exeter.

BRIAN, P. W., Imperial Chemical Industries Limited, Butterwick Research Laboratories, Welwyn.

BURROWS, T. W., Microbiological Research Department, Ministry of Supply, Porton, Wilts.

DUBOS, R. J., Rockefeller Institute for Medical Research, New York.

GARNHAM, P. C. C., Department of Parasitology, London School of Hygiene and Tropical Medicine.

HAWKING, F., National Institute for Medical Research, Mill Hill, London.

HOARE, C. A., Wellcome Laboratories of Tropical Medicine, London.

KEPPIE, J., Microbiological Research Department, Ministry of Supply, Porton, Wilts.

KEYWORTH, W. G., National Vegetable Research Station, Wellesbourne, Warwicks.

MACFARLANE, Marjorie G., Lister Institute of Preventive Medicine, London.

MAEGRAITH, B. G., Department of Tropical Medicine, Liverpool School of Tropical Medicine.

MILES, A. A., Lister Institute of Preventive Medicine, London.

NEAL, R. A., Wellcome Laboratories of Tropical Medicine, London.

PAPPENHEIMER, A. M., Department of Microbiology, New York University College of Medicine.

SMITH, H., Microbiological Research Department, Ministry of Supply, Porton, Wilts.

VAN HEYNINGEN, W. E., Sir William Dunn School of Pathology, University of Oxford.

WOOD, R. K. S., Plant Pathology Laboratory, Imperial College of Science and Technology, London.

WRIGHT, G. PAYLING, Department of Pathology, Guy's Hospital Medical School, London.

CONTENTS

EDITORS' PREFACE

Discussions on how micro-organisms produce disease are very apt to follow a circular course to platitudinous conclusions. In the hope of producing something more useful, the organizers of this fifth Symposium of the Society for General Microbiology asked contributors to concentrate as much as possible upon the parasites and their attributes even at the risk of some neglect of the hosts and their reactions. Not surprisingly, it has proved impossible to discuss pathogenicity without reference to the host, but the distinguished contributors to this volume have broken out from the familiar circle of inconclusive discussion.

This Symposium deals with a range of bacteria, protozoa and fungi pathogenic to man, animals and plants; viruses were excluded because the second Symposium was devoted entirely to them. This volume contains an analysis of the terms commonly used in writing about pathogenicity, virulence, resistance and susceptibility, and it proposes clear definitions whose adoption would greatly add to the precision and logic of future communications. More than one contribution discusses what might reasonably be described as the philosophy underlying the design and interpretation of experiments on microbial pathogenicity. Throughout, there is clear evidence both of the great variety inherent in different host-parasite relations and of the vastly different levels of knowledge and understanding that we have attained about different organisms and the diseases they cause. It appears that some host reactions to a parasite may be so biologically disadvantageous that they contribute more to the pathology of the infection than any inherently aggressive mechanism of the invader. The interesting conclusion from one line of evidence is that virulent mutants of an avirulent strain of bacteria may exercise some of their pathogenic effects because they have lost the power to stimulate the normal primary defence reaction of the host—a necessary reminder that we are prone to err if we think about our natural parasites only as enemies liable at any time to become possessed of unusually formidable armaments. Their losses may sometimes be ours also.

The pathology of some infections is still so poorly defined that future work should obviously concentrate on this basic essential. Our knowledge of other infections has advanced so far that progress is now in the hands of the biochemist seeking to identify the exact site and precise nature of the chemical interactions between a purified toxin and enzyme systems of the host. Obviously the subject of discussion is not exclusively in the province of any single group of microbiologists.

The sixteen contributions within will form the basis for a discussion meeting of the Society for General Microbiology to be held in the Royal Institution, Albemarle Street, London, on 19 and 20 April 1955.

J. W. HOWIE

A. J. O'HEA

Bacteriology Department of the University
and Western Infirmary of Glasgow
15 *March* 1955

THE MEANING OF PATHOGENICITY

A. A. MILES

Lister Institute of Preventive Medicine, London

There is a well-established tradition that discussions of 'pathogenicity' begin with an examination of its meaning and its relations to the numerous manifestations of the parasitic state. The tradition reflects past confusion in the use of the word 'pathogenicity' and of its synonyms and near-synonyms; and since the confusion continues—though to a much lesser extent than formerly—it may be useful to conform with tradition and briefly examine the verbal problem. We need waste no time in trying to rationalize the various attributes applied to microbes by microbiologists and pathologists—*pathogenicity*, *virulence*, *invasiveness*, *toxigenicity* and so forth—by an appeal to etymology. *Virulence*, for example, has no more necessary connexion with the orthodox idea of a poison than *toxin* has with bow-and-arrows. These words are dead metaphors, and all we need do about them is define them rigorously enough to be useful, and not so rigorously that we risk unrewarding debates about their legitimate use in borderline cases.

PATHOGENICITY AND PARASITISM

A microbe must be a parasite if it is to cause an infectious disease; but, as Theobald Smith (1934) pointed out, disease of the host is an incident, and a not invariably occurring incident, in the development of the parasitic state. Smith insisted that parasitism, being a common phenomenon in biology, could not be regarded as a pathological phenomenon, or as a deviation from the normal processes of nature. This is true if we choose to interpret *normal* in a purely statistical sense. It is not true if by *normal* we mean typical—and this second sense of normal is fundamental in all considerations of parasitism and pathology.

Parasitism by definition is the close association of two distinguishable organisms, and cannot in any instance be regarded as incontrovertibly established unless at least one of the two organisms is demonstrably capable of an independent existence. In other words, unless we recognize an independent type species that is normal in the taxonomic sense, we cannot recognize the peculiar kind of deviation from a taxonomic norm that parasitism undoubtedly is. It may be contended that Smith's view has a greater value, because a statistical norm is a less arbitrary invention than a taxonomic norm. This is true, but not important. The recognition of parasitism as a statistical norm serves only to emphasize its ubiquity; but we cannot begin to collect the statistics until we have set up taxonomic norms.

We are not, however, primarily interested in the career of a microbe as it evolves towards a parasitic life. Our interest is in the qualities that make it pathogenic at any given stage in this career. Here again we need a norm based on something more subtle than simple frequency, because all analysis of pathogenicity depends on the recognition, or at least the assumption, of a healthy norm in the host. The establishment of a healthy norm is a far more complex and indeterminate problem than that of setting up a type species; and for the most part is never done with any precision or universality. One man's normal mouse is another's pox-ridden runt from a back-street dealer, according to their standards of health or rigorous experiment. Nevertheless, it is from the 'norms' we abstract from such highly variable material as mice that pathogenicity—the capacity of the parasite to cause disease—is estimated. Pathogenicity is an estimate made from the viewpoint of the host, just as the host might from the viewpoint of the parasite be measured for tastiness, nutritive value, or security of tenure. The point, though obvious, is not as trivial as it may first appear. The observed fact is a more or less diseased host. We can discuss the severity of the disease either in terms of the resistance of the host or of the pathogenicity of the parasite. But we can do neither unless we take the quite artificial and arbitrary step of defining, in the first case, a reasonably invariant parasite, and in the second, a reasonably invariant host.

PATHOGENICITY AND RESISTANCE

The artificiality of the procedure is evident when we consider the relation between pathogenicity of the microbe and resistance of the host. Pathologists would generally agree that the pathogenic manifestation of a microbe varies according to the state of the host; the greater the resistance, the less the pathogenicity, and conversely. The relation has even been generalized in a pseudo-mathematical statement

$$P \propto 1/R.$$

It emphasizes the fact that we are dealing with complex biological relationships between two organisms, but if it is to be of any use to us in the analysis of microbial pathogenicity, we must invent some way of ignoring the host if we are to avoid fruitless circular arguments. Because to indicate as things which determine pathogenicity the features of the host that predispose it to the attack of the parasite is to say in effect that the parasite's power to derange the normal life of the host depends on the susceptibility to derangement of the host's life; an unexceptionable statement, but not outstandingly informative.

We shall perhaps be readier to ignore the host if we accept the fact that the inverse relation between pathogenicity and resistance does not express some subtle *biological* relation between host and parasite. Much as we may like to believe the contrary, the relationship is not established empirically from the observation of numerous microbial infections. Like Newton's law that action and reaction are equal and opposite, it is a logical invention—a truism—designed to simplify the analysis of a particular sort of interaction, in this case infective disease. We start with an estimate of the severity of a derangement of the host's economy, and abstract from it measures of pathogenicity or resistance according to our particular interests.

Pathogenicity then is an index of the behaviour of a microbe either within the tissues or on the surface of a given host in a certain agreed or defined state of health. The term might be extended to cover factors like the parasite's survival outside the host, and its numerical and topographical distribution in the host's environment; all of which determine the opportunity for, and consequently the prevalence of, an infective disease. The high resistance of the anthrax spore, and the capacity of the malarial parasite or the potato mosaic virus to survive in certain insects, are cases in point. The same kind of factors, however, determine an opportunity for infection by non-pathogenic microbes that cannot take advantage of it, or by microbes that parasitize without inducing obvious disease. In a final analysis, therefore, even this aspect of general pathogenicity depends on behaviour in or immediately on the host; and factors in the external ecology of the microbe are best excluded from considerations of pathogenicity.

PATHOGENICITY AND VIRULENCE

It is a common practice, at least in animal and human pathology, to use pathogenicity and virulence as synonyms. Some writers still distinguish virulence as an indication of a pathogen's invasiveness, its toxigenicity or its cytotoxicity. These distinctions, which are confusing in their multiplicity, deserve to be dropped. None the less, a useful distinction between pathogenicity and virulence can be made—a distinction which to some extent conforms with modern usage. It is simply a distinction of the scope of the two terms. *Pathogenicity* is best regarded as an attribute of a species, a genus, or some other grouping of parasites.

We can then describe *Phytomonas polycolor* as pathogenic for certain plants, or *Streptococcus pyogenes* as pathogenic for certain mammals, without necessarily implying that all strains of these two species produce disease in their respective hosts. Pathogenicity thus becomes a potentiality we predict of a microbe when we have identified it, and the prediction is valid even when the identification does not include a demonstration of pathogenicity in a suitable host. *Virulence*, on the other hand, is conveniently reserved for the pathogenicity of a given stable homogeneous strain of a microbe, as determined by observation of its action on the host in relation to which the statement about virulence is made. For the purposes of this definition, it does not matter that in practice we more often assume than prove we are dealing with a stable homogeneous population of the parasite. Only rarely can we preserve a strain so as to ensure that at no time it undergoes significant variation. For the most part we hope that the environment we provide is sufficiently constant to discourage unwanted populational changes. In such circumstances 'homogeneity' may be little more than absence of gross heterogeneity. The same criticism applies with equal force to the population of host organisms we maintain for measurement of virulence. In both cases the assumption of homogeneity in the absence of demonstrable heterogeneity is a perfectly valid technical procedure, though it does not excuse the experimenter from a constant scrutiny of his populations for signs of significant heterogeneity.

Virulence then is a quality inferred from the observed behaviour, in stated conditions, of individual strains of a parasite; and the frequency with which we discover virulent strains in a group of organisms determines whether we apply the term pathogenic to that group. In other words, pathogenicity is no more than the disposition to virulence of a class of parasitic microbes.

The definitions preserve the near-synonymity of *pathogenicity* and *virulence*, at least to the extent that any explanation of virulence is necessarily one of pathogenicity; but they make a distinction such that descriptions like 'a non-virulent strain of the pathogenic species *Bacillus anthracis*' are both convenient and good sense.

THE MEASUREMENT OF VIRULENCE

Restricting our inquiry to a particular host, we can class all microbes as virulent or not, according to their effect on it. Here *virulence* is almost a qualitative statement. Something more precise is required when we wish to assign degrees of virulence to the microbes that *are* infective. At the outset it is important to realize that, however precise the tests applied, the measurement cannot be made primarily in terms of a host; it is always comparative—of one parasite in terms of another, or in terms of another strain of the same parasite. It may be objected that when a reasonably stable and homogeneous population of the test host is available, the pathogenicity of a parasite can be estimated without reference to any other parasite. This would be true if we could rely from day to day on the stability of the test population. But the variations in non-specific resistance associated with environmental changes, diet, breeding, and so forth, and the changes in specific resistance that may follow undetected exposure to related parasites, make this course impossible. Even if one laboratory maintains a near-ideal population, any extension of its work on virulence to a second laboratory entails a test of the second population with a strain of parasite agreed on by the two laboratories, to determine how far observed differences in experimental results are due to differences in resistance. The flaw in this procedure, of course, is the potential variability of the strain of parasite used to characterize resistance. However, dried preparations of bacteria and fungi, deep-frozen preparations of viruses, and protozoa maintained *in vivo*, can be distributed with reasonable expectation of temporary stability of the factors that make for virulence, and for this reason are preferred as standards against which to measure and allow for variation in different populations of test host, rather than the alternative of attempting to maintain and distribute a 'standard' host. The standard parasite, however, is never so stable that it can be relied on in the sense that a standard preparation of a chemical substance can. The best estimates of the virulence of one parasite in terms of another are those made at one time, on as homogeneous a batch as possible of test objects. In such a batch, we hope that the day-to-day variations in resistance are small; and by repeated tests on a carefully maintained population with a 'standard' strain of pathogen, we may find so little variation that it is sufficient to include the standard pathogen in the test only from time to time. But for any crucial measurements, especially those where the factors determining virulence are in question, we shall be wise if we make a simultaneous test of the standard strain and the strain under investigation. The standard, of course, need not be some widely recognized, authentic strain of the microbe, and indeed may be no more than a strain used in a single experiment; but some one strain or other must in effect be the standard, in terms of which the virulence of strains under test is stated.

In summary, there is an actual or implied comparison of the effect of one microbe with that of another in all valid measures of virulence.

It may be that both host and parasite are so unstable that the validity does not extend beyond the experiments forming part of a single investigation. Virulence measures of this kind are exportable, as it were, only on paper—in the published experiment. Most measurements, however, *are* exportable: sometimes because material can be exchanged between workers, but more often because we assume that an identifiable species of rabbit, potato plant, influenza virus, or rust fungus, is very much the same, in respect of resistance or virulence, all over the world. The assumption may be justified, but I suspect that we are not more often caught out because our measurements of virulence are so crude that we habitually build our pathological sciences on differences so large that they override the variations in resistance occurring in the generality of each particular host species.

The restriction of valid measures of virulence to comparisons, actual or implied, of two or more strains of microbe, is essential if we are to know how much observed differences in the behaviour of the infected host are referable to variable factors in the microbe, and how much to factors in the host. Given (temporarily at least) a stable host population, there are two ways of making a numerical comparison of virulence: (i) to estimate the dose of each microbe that produces the same indicating effect, and (ii) to measure differences in the indicating effect produced by similar doses of each microbe.

There is a wide variety of indicating effects, both general and local, to choose from, and it does not matter which effect is used, provided that it bears a reasonably constant relation to the severity of the disease. In this respect, death (expressed as mortality-rates, time-to-death, etc.) is obviously unexceptionable, when there are means of proving that it is directly due to the microbe injected and not, for example, to intercurrent infection. Death is a host-effect; other host-effects include the number of specific infective lesions resulting from either a local or general application of the microbe. Lesion counts must be more suspect than specific death, because a visible lesion, for example, may be the expression of successful defence against a moderately virulent microbe, whereas absence of lesion might result from overwhelming infection with a highly virulent microbe. Parasite-effects, of which the most obvious is survival or multiplication in the tissues, are even more equivocal indexes of pathogenicity. Proliferation is a direct index of the extent and degree of parasitism, but even high degrees of parasitism may be manifested in the host by very minor deviations from the healthy norm; it is an index of virulence only when it is demonstrably associated with severity of disease. The Gram-negative bacilli Bisset (1946) found in the tissues of healthy fish kept at 10°, though surviving therein, were not virulent. Nor were they necessarily virulent when they began to proliferate on transference of the host to temperatures of 20° or more, because in some cases they were destroyed by the antibacterial mechanisms of the fish, which were also activated by the increased temperature.

The measurement of dose. The estimation of dosage of microbes presents no difficulty when the potentially infective unit, as in many protozoa, is large and sufficiently distinctive in morphology to be counted directly, or when, as with many bacteria, it is cultivable *in vitro* and therefore susceptible to a viable count; although in both cases we may have to make some adjustments about proportion of healthy-looking or of cultivable units that are potentially capable of infection. The ease with which these operations are performed with many microbes tends to obscure the fundamental point that they provide an estimate of dose that is independent of the pathogenic effect. The point is more readily appreciated with viruses, which, being small and strictly parasitic, are at first detectable only as pathogenic material. At this stage, the only measure of virus content of fluids from an infected host may be the limiting dilution of the material which is infective for other hosts. In these circumstances, no comparison of virulence of two such preparations is possible. We may find that one produces the indicating effect when diluted 10^{-3}, the other at 10^{-4}. But the two dilution series represent scales of measurement that are 'floating' with respect to each other. Until we can see the virus particle, weigh the virus protein, measure the amount of virus antigen, or estimate some other substance or activity we believe characterizes the virus, we cannot fix the points on the two scales that represent equal numbers of potentially infective units. (At this early stage in the elucidation of a virus, the only numerical information that can be extracted from the infected host is a comparison of resistance; because, independently of actual virus content, the observation that one batch of susceptible animals succumbs to a 10^{-3}, and the other to a 10^{-4} dilution of a single virus preparation, is a significant fact about the two batches of animals.)

The dosage-response to infective agents. Whether we compare doses producing the same indicating effect, or the effects produced by the same dose, the interpretation of the result will depend on the type of response the host makes to graded doses of the microbe. No collection of animal, plant, or microbial hosts, however carefully selected, is so homogeneous in its reaction to infection that all individuals survive a given dose of microbes, and all die after a slightly larger dose. With constant increments of dose, it is usual to find that death-rates in similar batches of a population of test animals increase relatively slowly in the ranges of 1–10 %, and 90–99 %, and most rapidly in the region of 50 %. For this reason we can estimate the 50 % killing dose more precisely than say, the 5 % or the 95 %, for the expenditure of a given number of animals. This point was emphasized by Trevan (1927) in his pioneer work on dosage-response; and, as a consequence, the median or 50 % lethal dose, the LD 50, is now established as one of the most convenient and useful indicating effects in the estimation of virulence. Another point made by Trevan, the implications of which are less well heeded by microbiologists, is that the rate of increase of mortality with increasing dose is as important a characteristic of the dosage-response as the LD 50.

In mice infected with a type I pneumococcus, the range of doses that cover the 1–99 % mortality may be 5–100 organisms; whereas the equivalent dose-range with a strain of *Salmonella typhi-murium* may be 10 to 10^6 organisms. When the death-rates are plotted against the logarithm of the dose, the resulting curves with both organisms are roughly sigmoid, the one steep, the other shallow, and are compared with difficulty. But by suitable arithmetical manipulations, the percentage death-rates may be transformed into quantities that fall on roughly straight lines when plotted against log. dose (see Gaddum, 1933; Bliss, 1935; Finney, 1952); and the slope of the straight line fitted to these points can be expressed as a single, easily compared figure, which would be large for the pneumococcus and small for the salmonella.

One consequence of the difference in slope is that if we wished to compare the virulence of these two bacteria in the mouse, the result would vary with the response level at which the comparison was made. Comparing the LD 10, we might find a ratio of 10 pneumococci and 200 salmonellas (1 : 20); at LD 50 we might find 20 : 3400 (1 : 170); and at LD 90, 45 : 50,000 (1 : 1100). If we agree on LD 50 as the response at which all killing power is to be compared, we can ignore differences in slope, and fix this particular virulence ratio (with due regard for the errors of its determination) at 1 : 100. We must, however, always bear in mind that it is valid only for the LD 50. The importance of this restriction may be illustrated as follows. The LD 50 is often used, and sometimes rather blindly, as a unit dose, and experiments made with, say, five LD 50. In the above example five LD 50 of the pneumococcus would probably kill all of a large batch of mice, whereas five LD 50 of the salmonella would kill only 78 % of a batch; so that comparisons involving multiples of LD 50 will be misleading unless the slopes of the two responses are the same, or the consequences of differences in slope can be estimated.

Comparison of the effects produced by similar doses are also affected by differences in slope. Thus 80 pneumococci might kill 98 % of the mice, and 80 salmonella 4 %; but the corresponding death-rates for 15 organisms might be 37 and 0·5 %.

Clearly we shall get comparisons of more general significance when the slopes of the dosage-response of the two microbes are similar.

THE BIOLOGICAL SIGNIFICANCE OF
A VIRULENCE RATIO

When we have determined the dosage-response of two organisms, and have found, by orthodox statistical analysis, that the slopes and the error of the slopes are similar, we arrive at a ratio of the two LD 50's. We also determine the error of the ratio, and find whether the ratio is large enough to be considered statistically significant. Alternatively, we might express the difference in virulence as the death-rates produced by a selected dose of the two organisms, and determine whether the difference between the two percentages, like the virulence ratio, is statistically significant. Suppose the virulence ratio for organisms A and B is 100:1, and alternatively that 100 cells of A kill 5 % and 100 cells of B kill 95 % of the test mice. Which measure of the difference in virulence best indicates the relative pathogenic powers of the two organisms? Owing to the curvilinear slope of the dosage-response curve, direct comparison of percentage death-rates is misleading. The figures have to be transformed—into, say, 'normal equivalent deviations' (Gaddum, 1933) or 'probits' (Bliss, 1935)—to yield a linear scale for direct comparison; and only practising biometricians are capable of thinking easily in terms of probit scales and the like. Moreover, percentage values are reliable only when they are > 1 or < 100, because 0 and 100% are each obtained with an indeterminate range of doses; and when the slopes are steep, even small changes in virulence may shift the percentage into the indeterminate dose-range. These technical restrictions do not apply to the ratio of the LD 50's, which is measured on a simpler scale of numeration and is readily determined for both large and small differences. But, technical limitations apart, most people will feel that they apprehend the difference in virulence of two organisms more directly from the statement 'one LD 50 is 100 times the other', than from 'similar doses of the two organisms kill 5 and 95 %'. The preference for the ratio of LD 50's is put in this guarded way to emphasize our ignorance of what the number of organisms needed for infection really means. If we find that two strains of pneumococci with a steep dosage-response curve have a ratio of 100, it clearly indicates a greater difference in virulence as

killing power than a ratio of 100 for two salmonellas with a slope so
shallow that a 100-fold increase in dose means perhaps a 20 % increase
in death-rate. But what determines the slope? According to the classical
analysis by Trevan and his successors, the steep slopes may be interpreted in terms of a narrow, and shallow slopes in terms of a wide,
scatter of degrees of resistance in a host population reacting to a homogeneous dose of organisms. Peto (1953), on the other hand, derives
another kind of dosage-response equation leading to a linear relation
between dose and the logarithm of the proportion surviving, which is
based on the assumption that the population is homogeneous, and that
each of the organisms in the dose injected acts independently and has
a low probability of killing the host. There is at present no evidence to
decide between these two models, nor, indeed, is there evidence that
either model represents what happens in reality. During the course of an
infection from primary lodgement of the parasite to death of the host,
the moment when the number of infecting organisms is crucial, in the
sense of determining death, may in some diseases occur *at* the primary
lodgement, when we put in the counted dose; but in others it may take
place much later, when some virulence factor, up to this point useless
in promoting infection, becomes effective. And although the probability
that this late-acting factor will be effective in the individual animal must
in part depend on the dose originally given, the dependence will not
necessarily be of the same numerical order as that of an early-acting
factor. In such a case the advantage to an organism conferred by
a late-acting factor, in comparison with a variant that lacked it, might
not be reflected in the ratio of initial doses in the same way that the
possession by one of them of an early-acting factor would.

Analogous reasoning will apply to any attempted discovery of a larger
biological significance of a virulence ratio. There can be little doubt that
we can put more faith in the general biological significance of large
ratios than of small; but though we can rank microbes and microbial
factors in this way on a scale of virulence, we cannot give them any
precise meaningful position on that scale. Only in the restricted circumstances of its determination has a virulence ratio a reliable numerical
significance.

A virulence ratio, in terms of doses that produce an indicating reaction,
may of course be insufficient to express what we want to measure.
There is, for example, a sense of virulence expressed in the fact that
a group C streptococcus and a strain of toxigenic *Clostridium welchii*
both produce generalized infection of similar acuity and severity in the
guinea-pig, though the respective LD 50's of washed organisms are of

the order of 10^3 and 10^8. If 'virulence' is to include the capacity to produce nasty effects once the parasite gets a firm foothold, as well as the capacity to get that foothold, clearly two measurements about a microbe are required—one of the minimal generally infecting dose, and a second of the severity of that infection, as indicated by some measurable pathological effect or syndrome.

We return to the implications of our discussion of virulence and resistance. Virulence is in fact what you choose to measure, and the analysis of the significance of that measure, at any rate in the present state of pathology, can go little further than the experiments designed to explore it. As far as quantitative studies of virulence and factors determining virulence in laboratory animals are concerned, we probably know more about the pneumococcus than about any other microbe. Much of it is applicable to the virulence of pneumococci for man in the world at large. Nevertheless, the step from the experiment to the natural state is in some respects a blind one. The white mouse, upon which many fruitful studies have been made, may die when five Type I pneumococci are injected intraperitoneally. But pneumococci of this and many other types clearly lack a virulence factor of prime importance, since they cannot establish a primary lodgement in the mouse (as they obviously do in man) by natural contact. The factors, either in the coccus or the host, which determine natural infectivity for man, are still unknown. (It is perhaps our good fortune that this particular mouse-virulence factor is lacking, for if it were not, natural selection would long ago have eliminated the highly susceptible white mouse, and presented us with a much more resistant and therefore much less useful animal for the study of pneumococci.)

THE RECOGNITION OF MICROBIAL FACTORS THAT DETERMINE VIRULENCE

When a pathogenic microbe produces a potent toxin with a specific pharmacological action that mimics the natural disease; when other strains of the same species fail to produce the toxin and are at the same time non-virulent; and when treatment of the animal host with specific antitoxin protects it against both the natural disease and the experimental intoxication: we are safe in identifying the toxin as a virulence factor. This is the happy state of affairs with *Clostridium tetani* infections, and exemplifies several important points in the analysis of virulence: association of a factor with virulent strains or variants of a species; isolation of the factor and demonstration of significant action in the host tissues; and specific neutralization of the factor *in vivo*. The example, however, is misleadingly simple. It is seldom that we are handed the answer as easily as we were in tetanus. The microbial toxins that mimic the syndrome of the natural infection by the corresponding organisms are very few. If we pursue toxic substances in most microbes, we usually find general poisons, not very potent in the isolated state, and with little that is peculiar in their action. Moreover, they often occur in non-virulent species of bacteria. The protein-lipopolysaccharide and the lipopolysaccharide 'endotoxins' of many Gram-negative bacilli have the same order of toxicity for mice, yet among these *Escherichia coli* is non-pathogenic and *Salmonella typhi-murium* highly pathogenic. We get nearer the mark by finding little or no endotoxin in non-virulent R forms of the latter, and that mice immunized with the endotoxin are immune to *S. typhi-murium* infection. The endotoxic material of this bacillus is therefore associated with virulence; but we do not know that it determines virulence because it is a *toxin*. The endotoxic antibody may, for example, protect by opsonizing the bacilli, since endotoxin is also a surface antigen. Moreover, as Hill, Hatswell & Topley (1940) showed, mice selectively bred for resistance to the relevant endotoxin, are not more resistant to oral infection by *S. typhi-murium*.

The serological proof of significance, if it comes off, is as good as we can expect. Negative results are not conclusive: among other reasons, *in vivo*, the factor may act in places inaccessible to antibody; the antibody may not be potent enough; or the experiment may be too crude to reveal small but real changes in the severity of the disease. It has other limitations. It is inapplicable to non-antigenic factors, and applicable only in hosts capable of a humoral immune response. The plant pathologist has no such resources for his analysis of virulence, lacking this means to make specific alterations in host resistance. There is an analogous indirect approach, via non-specific immunity, by which a host may be selectively bred for resistance to a pathogen, and the tissue reactions compared during infection of susceptible and resistant stocks. This, by giving some idea of where the microbe is attacking most effectively, may indicate the nature of the virulence factors. The chief limitations of this method arise from our ignorance of what we are doing in selective breeding. Even when the selection of a single gene variant can be presumed the tissue reactions which in the parent stock appeared to have survival value may in the variant have the opposite effect, owing to changes in the sum total of genic interactions (cf. Weir, Cooper & Clark, 1953).

In the absence of specific inhibitors, serological or other, we must rely on association of presumed factors with virulent forms, and on the demonstration of their significant action. Most of our definitive knowledge of virulence factors stems from the study of variants, or of closely related microbial varieties and species. Mere association, however, is obviously not crucial. The next criterion, the significance of a factor in the natural infection, is much harder to satisfy. As the example of the *S. typhi-murium* infection shows, we cannot incriminate a microbial substance that proves to be toxic for the host unless we show that it acts as such in the natural infection. There is little evidence, one way or the other, that bacterial haemolysins, so readily demonstrable *in vitro*, contribute to virulence by attacking the red blood cells of the infected animals. Infections present a subtle problem in 'internal' ecology, where the parasite, at least in a complex metazoan host, is in varying relation with all kinds of cells and fluids of widely differing functions; and any virulence factor must be proved relevant in ecologically significant conditions. The classical exotoxins apart, most virulence factors, like the capsular substance of the pneumococci, are probably non-toxic in the ordinary sense; and it is in the interplay of such factors—the so-called auxiliary pathogenic factors—we are likely to find the prime causes of virulence.

In the researches on virulence of the past twenty years, the emphasis has been shifting from toxins to enzymes and their substrates; and to the interaction of complex biochemical systems in the host and the parasite. Here again we must look to the significant ecological conditions. It is tempting to conclude that the possession of pectinase (Elrod, 1942) determines the virulence of certain coliform bacilli that produce soft rots in carrots and the like; and that the hyaluronidase of certain animal pathogens promotes infection in the tissues; because in both instances the host contains an appropriate substrate. Even if these enzymes passed the test of constant association with the virulent form of the pathogen, they might only be accidentally associated with virulence. Indeed, this appears to be the case with hyaluronidase, because the crucial test of mitigation of infections by anti-hyaluronidase serum has so far failed (see Miles, 1951–2). Again, the cholera vibrio produces an enzyme that desquamates epithelium (Burnet & Stone, 1947) and primarily infects in a situation, the lumen of the gut, where the removal of the presumably protective layer of gut epithelium would clearly be advantageous to it. Nevertheless, as Burnet & Stone point out, the enzyme appears to act only on dead intestinal tissues; an *in vivo* action remains to be shown. We must in fact beware of the Fallacy of the Appropriate Substrate. The variety of biochemical structures in nature is not vast enough to warrant our reading a deep significance into every correspondence between a parasite enzyme and a host substrate, or between a host enzyme and a parasite substrate. It *may* indeed be significant that *Staphylococcus aureus* readily produces breast abscesses in the lactating female in part because it synthesizes a lactase; but it is an association that many would think unprofitable for investigation in the present state of our ignorance about the minutiae of virulence factors in the staphylococcus.

To be aware of a fallacy, however, does not mean that we should be afraid of manœuvring ourselves into positions where we might commit it. The suggestion about staphylococcal lactase in mastitis is not so very far fetched when we consider recent examples of the effect of small-molecular metabolites on the course of infection. Thus, the presence of threonine in infected tissue is associated with the suppression of S forms of *Brucella abortus* (Page, Goodlow & Braun, 1951); malonate greatly enhances the virulence of certain pathogens when injected with them, apparently by interfering with the tricarboxylic acid cycle in the host's tissues (Berry, Merritt & Mitchell, 1954); and the virulence for mice by the intraperitoneal route of certain nutritionally exacting variants of *Salmonella typhi* is greatly increased when the essential nutrient they are unable to synthesize—for example, *p*-aminobenzoic acid—is present in adequate amounts in the peritoneal cavity (Bacon, Burrows & Yates, 1950).

The analysis of virulence will clearly take us far beyond the traditional observations of cell death or host death in the presence of toxins. We have to explore the capacity of the pathogen to interfere with and de-range the structure and the metabolic processes of the host; and these derangements are likely to be as complex, and, considered separately, as uncharacteristic of any one disease, as those, for example, in shock or in the cachexia of malignant disease. We are dealing, in fact, with a complex field of relatively non-specific events, and before we can pin down this or that feature of a pathogen as contributory to virulence, it will be more necessary than ever to be sure that in essentials our experi-mental systems approach as closely as possible to the conditions of natural infection.

CONCLUSIONS

There are two main aspects of the meaning of pathogenicity; one is verbal, the other technical.

The *verbal* problem, which is the lesser, may be settled by codifying the meaning of the various words, especially 'virulence', used in the study of pathogenicity. I suggest that the term *virulence* be restricted to the observed infective capacity of individual strains of the pathogen studied, on application to the tissues of the host; and the term *pathogenicity* be reserved for the disposition to virulence of a class (species, variety, or other group) of pathogens. The proportional frequency of individual virulent strains determines the pathogenicity of the group.

The more important, technical problem concerns the *measurement* of virulence, which can be done only in highly artificial conditions, and interpreted in the light of a number of arbitrary assumptions. The observed fact is the severity of derangement of the health (itself an arbitrary concept) of the host, resulting from infection. Both host and pathogen are naturally highly variable organisms, and virulence of the pathogen is an abstraction from the interaction of the two whose measurement demands (*a*) the establishment of a sample of the host species with resistance that can be considered stable at least for the duration of the experiment and (*b*) comparison with the virulence of another parasite, determined on a similar sample of the host species. Estimates of virulence, it should be noted, are formally independent of resistance in the host. Resistance and virulence in given types of infection vary inversely with respect to each other; but this relation is not an empirical fact reflecting any fundamental biological relation. It is an *a priori* invention designed to simplify the measurement of one or the other. Only by specifying resistance, however temporarily, can estimates be made of the relative virulence, the virulence ratio, of two or more pathogens.

The commonest estimate of the virulence ratio of two pathogens is made in terms of doses producing any chosen indicating effect, like death or the number of specific lesions. By the application of biometric methods devised in the first place for the assay of drugs, these ratios can be estimated, in theory at least, with some accuracy. But the highly artificial conditions of the test, so far removed from those of natural infection, preclude much direct application of the figures to virulence in the natural state. They can be taken only as a very rough indication of virulence in general. As numerical estimates their validity does not usually extend beyond the conditions of the test employed. Broadly speaking, in our present state of knowledge 'virulence' is little more than what one chooses to measure.

These considerations apply with even greater force to the detection of microbial virulence factors, when, in addition to estimating differences in virulence, it is necessary to ensure that the experimental system in essentials represents the natural infection, if we are to avoid merely creating laboratory problems in order to solve them. Aside from a few classical exotoxins and endotoxins, and some non-toxic antigenic factors whose role in infections of vertebrates can be assessed by specific immunological tests, few factors peculiar to microbial metabolism have been conclusively identified, particularly in regard to their mode of action. In these circumstances virulence must be analysed in terms of biochemical features which, considered separately, will not necessarily be peculiar to the pathogen and will not grossly interfere with the host metabolism, but which together contribute decisively to the capacity of the organisms to proliferate in the infected tissues.

REFERENCES

BACON, G. A., BURROWS, T. W. & YATES, M. (1950). The effects of biochemical mutation on the virulence of *Bacterium typhosum*: The virulence of mutants. *Brit. J. exp. Path.* **31**, 714.

BERRY, L. J., MERRITT, P. & MITCHELL, R. B. (1954). The relation of the tricarboxylic acid cycle to bacterial infection. III. Comparison of survival time of mice infected with different pathogens and given Krebs cycle inhibitors and intermediates. *J. infect. Dis.* **94**, 144.

BISSET, K. A. (1946). The effect of temperature on non-specific infections of fish. *J. Path. Bact.* **58**, 251.

BLISS, C. I. (1935). The calculation of the dosage-mortality curve. *Ann. Appl. Biol.* **22**, 134.

BURNET, F. M. & STONE, J. D. (1947). Desquamation of intestinal epithelium *in vitro* by *V. cholerae* filtrate. Characterization of mucinase and tissue disintegrating enzymes. *Aust. J. exp. Biol. med. Sci.* **25**, 219.

ELROD, R. P. (1942). The Erwinia-coliform relationship. *J. Bact.* **44**, 433.

FINNEY, D. J. (1952). *Statistical Methods in Biological Assay.* London: Griffen.

GADDUM, J. H. (1933). Methods of biological assay depending on a quantal response. *Spec. Rep. Ser. med. Res. Coun., Lond.*, no. 183.

HILL, A. B., HATSWELL, J. M. & TOPLEY, W. W. C. (1940). The inheritance of resistance, demonstrated by the development of a strain of mice resistant to experimental inoculation with a bacterial endotoxin. *J. Hyg., Camb.*, **40**, 538.

MILES, A. A. (1951–2). *Lectures on the Scientific Basis of Medicine*, p. 192. London: Athlone Press.

PAGE, L. A., GOODLOW, R. J. & BRAUN, W. (1951). The effects of threonine on population changes and virulence of *Salmonella typhimurium*. *J. Bact.* **62**, 639.

PETO, S. (1953). A dose response equation for the invasion of microorganisms. *Biometrics*, **9**, 320.

SMITH, T. (1934). *Parasitism and Disease.* Princeton University Press.

TREVAN, J. W. (1927). The error of determination of toxicity. *Proc. roy. Soc.* B, **101**, 483.

WEIR, J. A., COOPER, R. H. & CLARK, R. D. (1953). The nature of genetic resistance to infection in mice. *Science*, **117**, 328.

THE ROLE OF TOXINS IN PATHOLOGY

W. E. VAN HEYNINGEN

Sir William Dunn School of Pathology, University of Oxford

INTRODUCTION

In this contribution the word 'pathogenic', when applied to bacterial toxins, will refer to their action in causing the symptomatology of disease; the word 'aggressive' will refer to their action in assisting the parasite to establish or extend its infection by killing the host's tissues, by preventing phagocytosis, and by breaking down mechanical barriers. I have been asked to discuss the pathogenic role of toxins, as distinct from the aggressive. It is seldom easy to make this distinction, particularly as very few experiments have been designed specifically to this end.

My task would be easier if appeal to authority had any weight in scientific discussion. The pathogenic role of toxins has always been taken for granted by the leading authorities ever since their discovery more than sixty years ago. It is clear, however, that in many infectious diseases, probably in most of them, there are alternative and additional pathogenic factors, doubtless of the greatest importance. These factors are ill-defined, but fortunately for me they do not come within my terms of reference and I am not obliged to enumerate and discuss them.

The idea that the harm caused by infectious diseases might be due to microbial poisons is obvious. It is not surprising that it was entertained long ago, even before the germ theory of disease was established. Both endo- and exotoxins were foreseen in 1713 by Vallisnieri, who suggested on one page of his *Riposta* that 'the little worms of the most atrocious pests are of themselves of a poisonous nature', and on another that 'as often as they enter the humoral mass [they] defile it with their excrement, adulterate it, pollute it'. For many centuries there was also the belief that poisonous substances originated from putrefaction of the host's tissues. After the discovery of disease germs this idea was revived by Brieger with his doctrine of ptomaines, or toxic amines, which were supposed to result from the microbial decomposition of proteins. Brieger's doctrine did not survive the demonstration that his ptomaines were only feebly toxic, but we shall see that it may, after all, be due for a limited revival. In the meantime Klebs had suggested, in 1872, that chemical substances, or 'sepsins', were responsible for the lesions produced by staphylococci; but the first practical demonstration of a bacterial toxin came nearly twenty years later. Loeffler, who discovered the diphtheria bacillus in 1884, was impressed by the fact that in animals that died after experimental infection the organism was localized at the seat of inoculation and totally absent from the internal organs. The animals nevertheless were considerably affected with 'haemorrhagic oedema, effusion into the pleural cavities, lobar consolidation of the lungs, catarrhal inflammation of the kidneys and deep reddening of the suprarenal capsules'. These observations 'clearly indicated that a poison produced at the seat of inoculation must have circulated in the blood'. After an unsuccessful attempt to isolate the poison in 1887, Loeffler continued his investigations in the following year, using methods of extraction suitable for enzymes, since the action of the poison resembled that of the enzyme-like plant poison, abrin. A 4- to 5-day culture of the bacillus was extracted with glycerol and a precipitate obtained by the addition of alcohol. When a few hundred milligrams of the precipitate were injected into guinea-pigs 'the animals bristled up their hair and raised themselves up on their feet, uttering loud cries', It is unlikely that diphtheria toxin was responsible for this particular reaction by the guinea-pigs, but it is probable that Loeffler's preparation did contain at least a trace of toxin. However, the credit for the discovery of the toxin is generally given to Roux & Yersin (1888). They showed in the same year that the older the culture the more toxic was the filtrate. By precipitation from old alkaline cultures with calcium chloride they obtained a preparation that was lethal to guinea-pigs in a dose of half a milligram. They also concluded that the poison was 'a kind of enzyme'.

This discovery encouraged Roux to the belief that the harmful effects of all pathogenic bacteria were due to poisons. He stated in his Croonian Lecture on Preventive Inoculation (Roux, 1889) that many pathogenic bacteria, including those of typhoid fever, Asiatic cholera, blue pus, acute experimental septicaemia and diphtheria, manufactured poisonous substances. By administering gradually increasing doses of these poisons to animals, in such a way as gradually to accustom them to their presence, it was possible to render them refractory, not only to toxic doses which originally would have caused death, but even to the microbe itself. He expressed the hope that 'when once we are thoroughly acquainted with these poisonous substances formed by pathogenic microbes we shall perhaps be in a position to find antidotes for them capable of paralysing their action even within the tissues themselves; but in offering this suggestion I perceive that I have deserted the domain of fact for that of hypothesis, and that it is therefore time I drew my remarks to a close'. Roux need not have been so timid. Within two years von Behring & Kitasato (1890) discovered tetanus toxin and announced that 'the immunity of rabbits and mice, immunized against tetanus, consists in the power of the cell-free blood fluid to render innocuous the toxic substance which the tetanus bacilli produce'. The immune serum could be transferred to the body of another animal and protect it against the toxin. A week later von Behring announced similar results with diphtheria toxin.

A few years later van Ermengem (1896) discovered a third powerful bacterial poison, the toxin of botulism. Little wonder, then, that the idea should prevail at that time that the harmful effects of all infectious diseases were due to toxins, and that medical research should be dominated by the conception of antitoxic serum therapy. It soon became clear, however, that these hopes were not be to fulfilled. It is probably more than a coincidence that the first three toxins to be discovered should be the only ones that are unequivocally responsible for the harmful effects of the diseases in which they are concerned. In the following decade there was much injecting of bacteria and their products, and of other substances, into animals, and mixing of the resultant immune sera with all kinds of preparations. This led to a great expansion of the new science of immunology, but added little to the understanding of the role of toxins in the pathology of infectious diseases. In the half-century that has followed there has been no fundamental progress, although many more bacterial toxins have been discovered and some have been purified and studied in detail. What is written to-day in text-books of pathology and bacteriology about the mechanisms of pathogenesis differs little from the editorial views expressed nearly seventy years ago by Watson Cheyne (1886) in a publication of the New Sydenham Society.

CRITERIA FOR ASSUMING PATHOGENIC ACTION

What are the criteria for judging that a toxin is responsible for the harmful effects of an infectious disease? Ideally they are fulfilled when: (a) the organism is known to produce a toxin; (b) virulent variants produce the toxin and avirulent do not; (c) injection of the toxin separately from the germs produces symptoms that mimic the disease; (d) the infecting organism produces the disease without multiplying profusely or spreading extensively, the blood is sterile, and organs at a distance from the seat of infection are affected; (e) the disease can be prevented by immunization against the toxin.

It is clear that a toxin may play a pathogenic role without fulfilling all these criteria. We shall now examine them in more detail.

(a) *Toxin production.* A failure to demonstrate toxin production *in vitro* does not necessarily mean that the organism is incapable of producing a toxin. Anybody with experience of toxin production knows that it is seldom easy to find the correct conditions for the production of a particular toxin, and that these are not necessarily the same as the conditions for luxuriant growth of the organism. The wrong strain of organism may be employed, or the wrong culture medium, or the wrong test animal, and it may be extremely difficult to hit upon the right combination. For example, if a non-lysogenic rather than a lysogenic strain of the diphtheria bacillus were used, or if a lysogenic strain were grown in a medium containing a concentration of iron normally encountered in culture media, or if the filtrate of a lysogenic culture in iron-free medium were injected into mice rather than guinea-pigs, it would not seem that there was such a thing as diphtheria toxin. Even after exhaustive attempts to demonstrate toxin production *in vitro* have failed it may still be unwise to assume that a toxin may not be produced under the natural conditions of infection. The case of anthrax illustrates this point. For many years investigators have attempted to demonstrate toxin production in order to account for the pathogenesis of this disease, but always without success. Now recent work suggests that in infected guinea-pigs the organism does indeed produce a toxin, but this can only be found *in vivo* in the plasma of animals in which the number of organisms in the blood has reached at least three million chains per ml. (Smith & Keppie, 1954).

The difference between laboratory and natural conditions may be due to the presence of toxigenic factors in the host which are not present in artificial media, but possibly to other factors as well. For example, a situation may be envisaged in which an organism produces a proteolytic enzyme which destroys the toxin as fast as it is formed *in vitro*; but *in vivo* the proteolytic enzyme is inhibited by a component of normal serum, as is often the case, and the toxin is thus allowed to survive. No actual case has been recorded to illustrate this situation, but it is a reasonable possibility. Conversely, a toxin which is demonstrable *in vitro* may not be produced so readily *in vivo*. For example, the production of several toxins is inhibited by iron in the culture medium, and the level of iron in the body tissues is higher than that which is optimal for toxin production in artificial media.

There is also the possibility that an organism may produce a substance that would be toxic if it were not inhibited by some substance in the host's tissues, or denied access to susceptible substances in some other way. The lecithinases of *Bacillus cereus* (Chu, 1949) and *Clostridium bifermentans* (Miles & Miles, 1950) illustrate this point. These enzymes are relatively non-toxic to mice, although an enzyme from *Cl. welchii* with an identical catalytic action *in vitro* is highly toxic. The *B. cereus* lecithinase has a low toxicity because it is inhibited by normal serum, but the cause of the low toxicity of the *Cl. bifermentans* lecithinase is not known. However, we need not concern ourselves for the present with substances of this nature—if they are not toxic they are not toxins.

A more relevant question is whether the organism in the course of an infection produces enough toxin to do harm. It was a consideration of this question, and the one raised in the previous paragraph, that led Miles (1953) to accept as a toxin only a substance that 'observably damaged living organisms in ecologically significant conditions'. Since it is generally extremely difficult to observe whether a bacterial product (a suspected 'toxin') is doing damage under natural conditions of infection—indeed, this is the burden of my essay—I suppose the number of substances that Miles will accept as toxins is not greater than three or four. I prefer to follow the French legal practice of assuming guilt until innocence is proved, and suggest that it is reasonable, even wise, to assume, in the absence of evidence to the contrary, that all poisonous bacterial substances play a pathogenic role in ecologically significant conditions—that is, are 'toxins'—but that it is unwise to assume that they always play an exclusive, or even an important, part.

(*b*) *Toxin production by virulent strains.* Even when there is a perfect correlation between virulence and toxin production, as with the diphtheria bacillus, it is likely that the toxin is functioning as much as an aggressive as a pathogenic factor. There would not be enough growth of the organism to produce a lethal dose of toxin if the toxin did not break down the host's defence mechanism and allow the organism to grow (see Amies, 1954). On the other hand, absence of correlation between virulence and toxin production does not necessarily mean that the toxin does not produce harmful effects. This is largely because other, comparatively non-toxic, factors can determine virulence, as the following examples show. Rough strains of *Shigella shigae* produce an extremely potent neurotoxin (van Heyningen & Gladstone, 1953) but are completely avirulent because they lack the O antigen. In *Clostridium welchii* virulence is generally correlated with α-toxin production, but some feeble toxin producers are virulent and some active toxin producers are avirulent (Evans, 1945*a*). In the staphylococci, virulence is associated as much with the non-toxic coagulase as with the α-haemolysin (Cruickshank, 1937).

(c) *Mimicry of the natural disease.* This criterion is relevant only when the toxin is practically the sole pathogenic agent of the disease, and therefore fits only botulism, tetanus, diphtheria and the rash of scarlet fever. In other cases the harmful effects produced by more than one toxin acting together, and by the other pathogenic agencies, will confuse the issue; and this will be further complicated by the peculiar features which result from the variation in the organs particularly attacked by different bacteria.

(d) *Restricted growth.* Ideally the organism that produces harmful effects by means of a toxin remains localized at its portal of entry into the body and there manufactures its poison which circulates to distant organs and tissues. In so doing it upsets part of Koch's first postulate, which states: 'The organism should be found in all cases of the disease in question, *and its distribution in the body should be in accordance with the lesions observed*' (Wilson & Miles, 1946, my italics). Indeed, it was the failure of the diphtheria bacillus to comply with Koch's demands in this respect that caused his pupil Loeffler to exercise great caution in putting forward the claim that he had isolated the causative bacillus. On the other hand, it cannot be assumed that the organism that spreads extensively in the body, and even produces septicaemia, does not produce ecologically significant toxins.

(e) *Protection by immunization.* The diseases whose pathogenicity is entirely due to toxins (e.g. diphtheria, tetanus) are preventable by active immunization and prophylactic passive immunization against the toxin, and curable by therapeutic passive immunization if it is applied soon enough. But protection against a disease by immunization against a toxin cannot be taken as proof that the toxin is responsible for the pathogenic effects of the disease. The role of the toxin may be purely aggressive, and the action of the antitoxin concerned with preventing the organism from establishing and extending a foothold, rather than with neutralizing a pathogenic factor.

On the other hand, negative results in protective experiments with active or passive immunization do not necessarily mean that a toxin is not exerting a pathogenic effect. (i) The toxin may not in fact be antigenic. The streptococcal haemolysin, streptolysin S, is the only non-antigenic toxin I know of, but others may yet be discovered. (This begs the question of what is meant by a toxin—streptolysin S is generally and inconsistently included among the toxins although it appears to be tacitly agreed that toxins are antigenic poisons.) (ii) The toxin may be antigenic, but the antibody may not be capable of completely neutralizing its activity. This is the case with the toxic polymolecular O antigens of many Gram-negative bacteria, and with many enzymes of non-bacterial origin. The possibility remains that simple protein toxins may yet be discovered which will behave in the same way, although none are known at present. (iii) The efficacy of passive antitoxin falls off rapidly as the time between infection and the application of antitoxin is delayed. This is owing partly to its not reaching the toxin lesion for mechanical reasons, and partly to the combination between toxin and its susceptible substance being rapid and not reversible by antitoxin (see Miles, 1951–2).

We shall now examine a number of diseases in the light of these criteria. It will be instructive to start with the case of gas gangrene. Here we have a disease in which practically all the criteria for regarding toxin as the agent of pathogenesis are fulfilled; yet closer examination of the facts will illustrate the difficulty of assigning pathogenic roles to toxins in infectious diseases.

CASES CONSIDERED ON THEIR MERITS

(i) Gas gangrene

Gas gangrene is a rapidly spreading oedematous myonecrosis resulting from the infection of severe wounds and the invasion of muscle by spore-bearing toxin-producing anaerobic organisms of the genus *Clostridium*, particularly *Cl. welchii*, *Cl. oedematiens* and *Cl. septicum*. The most serious effect of the disease is a profound toxaemia and prostration. R. G. Macfarlane & MacLennan's (1945) description of this condition is worth quoting:

'The patient lies collapsed and obviously desperately ill. He has a livid pallor, the extremities are cold, and sometimes the veins cannot be filled sufficiently to make venepuncture possible. The pulse is often impalpable; it is feeble and irregular, and we have noticed it to be markedly dicrotic in some cases. The blood-pressure, particularly the diastolic pressure, is low. In some cases there is a very large pulse-pressure, with systolic readings of about 100 mm. of mercury, while the diastolic pressure is too low to be recorded. Mentally the patient is unusually alert and clear, anxious, even terrified, and apparently fully aware of his danger. Sometimes he lapses into coma or delirium before death, but more often he dies suddenly, particularly during some disturbance, such as being moved or anaesthetized. Death appears to be due to circulatory failure.'

This state of affairs is commonly ascribed to bacterial toxins, which is understandable since the clostridia produce, *in vitro* at any rate, a formidable array of toxins. *Cl. septicum* produces a rapidly acting haemolytic toxin (Bernheimer, 1944); *Cl. oedematiens* produces a potent necrotizing toxin and small amounts of haemolysins of different kinds, including lecithinases and lipases (Oakley, Warrack & Clarke, 1947); *Cl. welchii* type A produces (*a*) α-toxin, a lecithinase (M. G. Macfarlane & Knight, 1941) which is lethal, haemolytic, and necrotizing to tissues, (*b*) θ-toxin, which is haemolytic and cardiotoxic (Bernheimer & Cantoni, 1945), (*c*) κ-toxin, or collagenase, a proteolytic enzyme which specifically attacks the collagen fibres of muscle, leaving the myofibrils intact (Bidwell & van Heyningen, 1948), (*d*) μ-toxin, a hyaluronidase which breaks down the polysaccharide cementing substance present in most tissues (McClean, Rogers & Williams, 1943). Of these organisms *Cl. welchii* occurs with the greatest frequency in gas-gangrene cases, and of the *Cl. welchii* toxins the α-toxin appears to be the most important. Evans (1943*a*, *b*, 1947) showed that prophylactic passive immunization with α-antitoxin, in the absence of antibody to θ-toxin, hyaluronidase or collagenase, was completely effective in protecting guinea-pigs against experimental infection with *Cl. welchii*. On the other hand, antitoxins to the other toxins, administered in the absence of α-antitoxin, are completely ineffective, and have no enhancing effect on immunization with α-antitoxin, even when this is given in doses which are too small to give more than partial protection. Evans (1945*a*) also found that virulence for the guinea-pig of thirty strains of *Cl. welchii* was positively correlated with ability to produce α-toxin *in vitro* and not correlated with an ability to produce other toxins.

In gas gangrene due to *Cl. welchii* the organism grows profusely over a fairly extensive but circumscribed area and produces large amounts of potent α-toxin. Probably at least as many, if not more, lethal doses of toxin are produced as in a fatal case of diphtheria or tetanus. The disease, moreover, is characterized by a toxaemia, and is preventable by active (Robertson & Keppie, 1943) or passive (Evans 1943*a*, 1945*b*) immunization against the toxin. It is not unreasonable, therefore, to suppose that the toxin is directly responsible for the toxaemia and the fatal outcome of the disease. Nevertheless, observations and experiments made during the war reopen the question of the direct responsibility of the α-toxin for the toxaemia of gas gangrene (R. G. Macfarlane & MacLennan, 1945; McLennan & R. G. Macfarlane, 1945; Robb-Smith, 1945).

Doubts about the systemic action of the toxin might have arisen from Bull & Pritchett's (1917) original paper on the discovery of the toxin. They noticed that when a toxic filtrate was injected intravenously into pigeons there was extensive haemolysis and death; but intramuscular injection of the same amount of filtrate produced no haemolysis, although it caused death in the same time. They concluded that they were dealing with separable haemolytic and lethal entities, but since these are now known to be identical another explanation must be found. Similar results have been obtained by others. R. G. Macfarlane & MacLennan (1945) gave a series of seventeen injections of culture filtrate, aggregating 8·5 lethal doses, into the hind limb of a rabbit over a period of 2 days and observed no haemoglobinuria and only a transient trace of intravascular haemolysis which disappeared after the third injection. Frazer, Elkes, Sammons, Govan & Cooke (1945) injected massive doses of toxin intramuscularly into guinea-pigs and observed no haemolysis up to 16 hr. after injection. On the other hand, numerous observers have confirmed Bull & Pritchett's original finding that severe intravascular haemolysis is seen after the toxin is injected directly into the blood stream. The parallel to these laboratory findings is seen in clinical gas-gangrene infection in man. MacLennan & R. G. Macfarlane (1945) could find no intravascular haemolysis, and no toxin in the blood of soldiers suffering from severe gas gangrene. But in cases of septic abortion, when *Cl. welchii* invades the blood stream and causes septic-aemia, there may be extensive haemolysis for some hours before other signs of toxaemia appear (see Hill, 1950).

If there is no intravascular haemolysis there can hardly be a lethal quantity of toxin in circulation, because the amount of toxin required to produce haemolysis on intravenous injection is less than the lethal dose. On the other hand, it is hardly conceivable that the organism growing so profusely in the damaged muscle should not produce a considerable amount of toxin. R. G. Macfarlane & MacLennan (1945) suggested that the toxin is prevented from getting into the blood stream by being adsorbed on living tissues. They studied twenty-six cases of *Cl. welchii* gas gangrene in Normandy, and in twenty-two were unable to find any α-toxin in wound exudates or extracts of infected tissue; in four cases they found very slight traces of toxin but, in three of these, samples were taken post-mortem. It is true that many of these patients had had anti-toxin, but seven had not. Moreover, in the cases where antitoxin had been given, heating of the samples failed to liberate toxin, although it did so with known toxin-antitoxin mixtures. Nor was it likely that other components of the samples were inhibiting the toxin, because addition of serum, exudate or extract were shown to have no effect on the toxin. It appeared, therefore, that the toxin was not present in the exudates or extracts. When toxin was injected into the muscles of rabbits, and the animals subsequently killed, it could not be extracted from the injected muscle; but it could readily be extracted after injection into the muscle of a dead rabbit. This suggested that toxin was absorbed only on living tissue. Other observations showed that even when the toxin did get into the blood stream it disappeared rapidly. When R. G. Macfarlane & MacLennan injected toxin intravenously into rabbits they could not detect it although the blood was haemolysed and the amount of toxin injected was such that the concentration after dilution by the blood should have been sufficient for a strongly positive test. McClean *et al.* (1943) found that, when guinea-pigs were infected in the hind limb with *Cl. welchii*, α-toxin could never be detected in the circulating blood, although it could be found in oedema fluid and in extracts of infected muscle. The finding of toxin in oedema fluid and tissue extract of guinea-pigs is in contrast to the observations of R. G. Macfarlane & MacLennan on man and rabbits. The guinea-pig is considered by many (e.g. Oakley, 1954) to be an unsuitable animal for gas-gangrene experiments, particularly because the muscle masses available for infection are relatively thin.

It is possible, however, to interpret R. G. Macfarlane & MacLennan's observations in another way. The toxin produced in the muscle may not be adsorbed on living tissues, but drained from them by the lymphatic system at the same rate as it is produced. In dead muscle there is no lymphatic drainage. This would account for the absence of toxin from extracts of living tissue and its presence in dead tissue. The toxin could be passed from the lymphatic system to the circulating blood, and be absorbed from the blood as fast as it appears by some vital organ, such as the liver. In this way the blood level need never rise to a high enough concentration to produce haemolysis, and yet a lethal amount of toxin may in time be transported by the blood from the infected tissue to a vital organ. This possibility appears to be ruled out by an experiment of MacLennan (private communication). He canalized the lymphatics draining living rabbit muscles into which large quantities of α-toxin had been injected, and failed to detect any toxin in the lymph.

Whether or not the toxin is transported in this way, it does not appear to be the chief agent of toxaemia. MacLennan & R. G. Macfarlane (1945) found in some cases of gas gangrene that there was enough antitoxin circulating to neutralize an amount of toxin equivalent to 20 l. of laboratory culture, and yet the patients were suffering from toxaemia. In nine cases an excess of antitoxin for as long as 92 hr. before death failed to prevent a fatal outcome. It might be argued that the reaction of the toxin with its susceptible substance is rapid and irreversible, and that access of antitoxin to toxin is delayed by mechanical factors (see Miles, 1951–2), so that the toxin can produce a fatal lesion which the antitoxin cannot affect. In that event nothing could be done to save the patient. But he can be saved. It is recognized that radical surgery is the most effective, if not the only, means of saving life in severe cases of gas gangrene (see M. G. Macfarlane, 1943, 1945). Whenever the affected tissue can be excised, by amputation of a limb or otherwise, life can be saved; but in the cases where for various reasons the affected tissue cannot be removed the outcome is almost invariably fatal. The recovery that takes place when radical surgery is performed on a prostrate gas-gangrene patient is dramatic, heartening and instructive. A source of poison appears to have been removed, and this poison does not seem to be the α-toxin.

If not α-toxin, what is it? It passes into the circulation from the infected muscle, and if it does not come from the infecting organism it must be derived from the muscle. It cannot be a normal component of muscle, for such a toxic agent has been sought in vain in order to account for the toxic effects of traumatic shock (e.g. Abraham, Brown, Chain, Florey, Gardner & Sanders, 1941). Whenever shock-producing substances have been obtained from traumatized muscles of living experimental animals, *Cl. welchii* and related organisms have been found in the tissues (Pope, Zamecnik, Aub, Brues, Dubos, Nathanson & Nutt, 1945). It seems possible, therefore, that the poison formed in a *Cl. welchii* infected muscle is either some as yet unrecognized and non-antigenic product of the organism, or something formed by the action of the organism or its products on constituents of muscle. This latter view is a revival of Brieger's doctrine of the formation of poisonous substances from the tissues of the host by the parasite, although the chemical nature of the substances is not specified.

Whether the muscle is brought into this dangerous state by one of the toxins, or by some other action of the organism, is not known. Intramuscular injection of cell-free toxic filtrate causes death without intravascular haemolysis, but we do not know how relevant this is to the natural conditions of infection. The injected toxin may possibly act by producing the hypothetical poison from muscle tissue, but theoretically there is an equal possibility that it may act directly on a vital organ after being transported there via the lymphatic system and the blood stream. We have already discussed how this could happen without the concentration of toxin in the blood reaching a high enough level to produce intravascular haemolysis.

The following possibilities are open: (*a*) The hypothetical muscle poison is produced by the organism independently of the α-toxin, which has nothing to do with the toxaemia of gas gangrene. (*b*) The action of the α-toxin results in the production of the muscle poison. (*c*) The toxaemia is due both to the α-toxin and the muscle poison. (*d*) The muscle poison does not exist and the α-toxin does not act systemically, but the extreme oedema and the constant and profuse serous ooze from the infected tissue result in a profound disturbance of the blood electrolytes such as is seen in severe burning. (*e*) The observations we have discussed are susceptible of another interpretation and the α-toxin is the sole agent of the toxaemia.

The moral to be drawn from a consideration of gas gangrene is that it is unwise to assume either that prevention of death by active immunization against a toxin necessarily implicates the toxin as the lethal agent, or that failure to prevent death by passive immunization exonerates it. In the former case the toxin may play the role of an aggressive factor and be responsible for the establishment, but not the effects, of an infection; in the latter it may be the cause, but not the direct agent, of toxaemia.

(ii) *Botulism*

Little need be said about botulism, for there is not the slightest doubt that the pathogenic effects of this disease are due to a toxin. It is an extreme case of an organism acting at a distance, because it produces a lethal toxin *outside* the body of its victim. It is not an infectious disease because *Cl. botulinum*, except in rare cases, is incapable of establishing an infection in a mammalian host. It results from the ingestion of food in which the organism has grown and produced toxin, and the contaminated food need not contain any living organisms to produce a fatal effect. There is no question therefore of other agencies being at work in the production of the pathogenic effects of the disease. The toxin ranks with tetanus and Shiga neurotoxins in being the most potent poisons known.

(iii) *Tetanus*

Tetanus is the ideal case of an infectious disease producing its pathogenic effects by means of a toxin. The bacillus remains strictly localized at the portal of entry, a powerful toxin is produced, and organs at a distance are affected. The disease can be prevented by prophylactic active or passive immunization against the toxin. Fig. 1 shows the effect of passive and active prophylactic immunization against the toxin on the incidence of tetanus in the British Army in two world wars. In the first three months of the First World War the incidence of tetanus was nearly 7 per 1000 wounded, but when prophylactic antiserum for all at risk was introduced towards the end of 1914 there was a dramatic fall to an average incidence of just over 1 per 1000. In 1938 active immunization with toxoid was introduced, and practically every soldier in the 21st Army Group was immunized. In the Second World War the incidence of tetanus was a tenth of that in the first. There were in fact only thirty-five cases of tetanus in the entire British Army, and fifteen of these were in soldiers who had not been immunized.

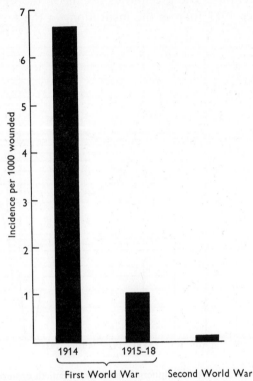

Fig. 1. Incidence of tetanus in the British Army in two world wars. Prophylactic passive immunization against the toxin was introduced towards the end of 1914, active immunization before the second world war. (Adapted from Bruce, 1920; Boyd, 1946.)

The toxin appears to act on the nervous system only and is not generally toxic to tissues or phagocytes. It is therefore unlikely to assist the organism in establishing or maintaining the infection, and antitoxic immunity is directed against the toxin purely as a lethal agent.

(iv) *Diphtheria*

Diphtheria is also an undoubted instance of pathogenesis by a toxin, but perhaps not as ideal a case as tetanus. Again the infection remains localized at the seat of infection in the throat, organs at a distance are affected, avirulent strains do not produce the toxin, and immunization

against the toxin affords protection or cure. The almost complete elimination of diphtheria in the United Kingdom and certain other countries
is probably due to active immunization against the toxin, but this claim
must be advanced with care. Fig. 2 shows the mortality trends for
diphtheria for England and Wales and for Sweden for the first half of
the twentieth century. The precipitous decline in the trend in England
and Wales after 1941 follows the institution, in the previous year, of

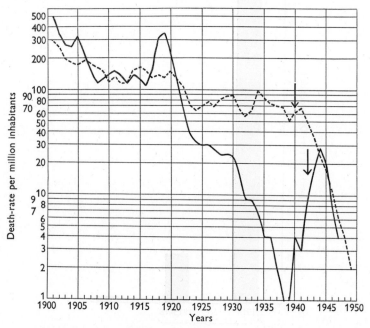

Fig. 2. Trend of mortality from diphtheria during the twentieth century in England and
Wales (broken line) and Sweden (solid line). Arrows indicate the times of introduction of
programmes of active immunization against the toxin. (Adapted from Pascua, 1951.)

a widespread campaign for active immunization. However, the figures
from Sweden show that such a sharp decline can happen for other
reasons. The death-rate for Sweden had dropped to as low as 1 per
million by 1938, although there had been no immunization up to this
time. Immunization was introduced into Sweden on a large scale in
1942, after there had been a big increase in the attack rate, possibly as
a result of the influx of refugees from other countries. The mortality
trends for Holland, Switzerland and Denmark are similar to that of
Sweden. England, too, had a period in the past when the incidence of
diphtheria was very low. In 1858 Sir John Simon (quoted by Creighton,
1891–4), medical officer to the Privy Council, wrote (as we might write

to-day): 'diphtheria is a disease which (though it has been experienced in former times) is well-nigh unknown to the existing generation of British medical practitioners.' He spoke too soon, for the disease returned in force in the same year (Creighton, 1891–4). There is, however, no doubt that active immunization is largely, if not entirely, responsible for the present low death-rate from diphtheria. This can be seen in a comparison between immunized and non-immunized children in Table 1; and from Logan's (1952) calculation that the chances of a non-immunized child under 15 years dying of diphtheria is 22 times as great as that of an immunized child in the same community.

Table 1. *Case fatality rates from diphtheria in immunized and non-immunized children under* 15. (From Thompson, 1951)

Case fatality rate per 1000

	Non-immunized	Immunized
1945	68·9	8·1
1946	62·0	5·5
1947	68·6	12·4
1948	73·0	7·6
1949	66·5	9·2

The *gravis* type of *Corynebacterium diphtheriae* is said to cause a more severe form of the disease than the *mitis* (see McLeod, 1943), although there does not appear to be any difference in the toxin produced (Zinnemann, 1946). It is possible that under the natural conditions of infection the *gravis* type produces more toxin, or produces it faster, than the *mitis*. The production of diphtheria toxin is inhibited when iron is present in the culture medium, and the level of iron in the tissues of the throat is high enough to depress toxin production quite considerably, but *gravis* strains are less affected than *mitis* (Mueller, 1941). Greater toxin production may also be due simply to greater growth, for Orr-Ewing (1946) has shown that the *gravis* type has a greater resistance to phagocytosis.

The role of diphtheria toxin is not, however, purely pathogenic. Unlike tetanus toxin, it attacks tissues generally and produces necrosis. Moreover, Amies (1954) believes that it inhibits the local inflammatory response of the infected tissues and so counteracts a defence mechanism of the host.

(v) *Streptococcal toxins*

The haemolytic streptococcus produces a number of toxins, including the erythrogenic toxin; streptolysin O, which may be identical with a leucocidin; and streptolysin S. Nevertheless, cultures of streptococci are not particularly toxic, the lethal dose of filtrate for a rabbit being 5–10 ml. This comparatively low toxicity is probably due not so much to low concentration of the active components as to their low activity per unit weight. For example, the lethal dose of streptolysin O for the mouse is about 40 μg. (Herbert & Todd, 1941), which is at least 400 times greater than that of *Clostridium welchii* α-toxin; and the erythrogenic toxin is so innocuous that it is used unmodified in the active immunization of human beings, although as little as 5 picograms (1 pg. = 1 μμg.) will produce a reaction in the skin (Stock & Verney, 1952).

Of these toxins the erythrogenic toxin is the only one that can be implicated with any certainty as an agent of pathogenesis. The red rash of scarlet fever results from the absorption of this toxin from the lesion in the throat and its action on susceptible tissues. However, it is not clear whether the toxin is responsible for the other clinical manifestations of scarlet fever. Circulating antitoxin protects against the rash, but not against the local lesion, the concomitant acute tonsillitis. There is no evidence that immunity to the erythrogenic toxin confers any resistance to the invasive powers of the streptococcus. Nor is there any evidence that active or passive immunization against streptolysin O, the oxygenlabile cardiotoxic haemolysin, has any effect on the outcome of a streptococcal infection. No such evidence can be considered in the case of streptolysin S, the oxygen-stable haemolysin, since this toxin is not antigenic. When injected into experimental animals it causes death by intravascular haemolysis, but it is unlikely that this ever takes place on an effective scale in natural infection.

(vi) *Staphylococcal toxins*

The staphylococcus also produces a large number of toxins, including the α-, β- and γ-haemolysins and the Panton-Valentine leucocidin. The α- and γ-haemolysins are associated with strains that are pathogenic to humans, and the β with strains isolated from animal sources. The α-haemolysin produces necrosis in all tissues of the body and is also said to destroy rabbit, but not human, leucocytes. The Panton-Valentine leucocidin attacks both rabbit and human leucocytes, and is lethal to rabbits (Valentine, 1936). In addition, staphylococci also produce numerous other substances, such as coagulase and fibrinolysin, but these are not particularly toxic.

Attention was first focused on staphylococcal toxins by Burnet's (1929) investigation of the Bundaberg disaster of 1928, when twelve children died after being injected with a diphtheria toxin-antitoxin mixture infected with staphylococci. The Commission of Investigation came to the conclusion that 'a massive production of toxic substances must have taken place in the fatal cases if staphylococci were the responsible agents'. Previous to this, attempts had been made to treat staphylococcal infections with antisera against whole cultures, but these did not prove to have any value. Hopes were now placed in active and passive immunization against the toxins, but they were not to be realized. Experimental animals can be protected from infection by active immunization against the toxins, but protection is variable. In acute infections in man, benefit is often but not invariably derived from antiserum, the value of the antiserum possibly deriving more from its content of antibodies to Panton-Valentine leucocidin than to α-toxin (Valentine & Butler, 1939). In fatal cases of acute osteomyelitis mortality is associated with septicaemia rather than toxaemia, and factors other than the known bacterial toxins appear to operate (Butler & Valentine, 1943). In chronic infections there are occasional successes from treatment with toxoid, but many apparently suitable cases are quite resistant.

The case for staphylococcal toxins being responsible for the harmful effects of infection is thus far from being established. Even those successful instances of immunization may mean only that the toxins have an aggressive, as distinct from a pathogenic, function.

(vii) Toxins of gram negative bacteria

Complex toxins. Polymolecular complexes of phospholipid, polysaccharide and protein account in whole or in part for the toxicity of smooth strains of a number of Gram-negative organisms, including the salmonellae, shigellae, brucellae, neisseriae, cholera and coliform organisms. Besides this, they are also somatic antigens, and on inoculation many of them will confer immunity against the parent organisms. This immunity, however, is antibacterial rather than antitoxic, since the antibodies do not neutralize the toxic activity of their antigens. Indeed, in the course of disease antibodies, by hastening the destruction of the bacteria and bringing about rapid liberation of the endotoxins, may have the apparent effect of increasing toxicity.

The effects produced by these toxins on their injection into animals are numerous; they include pyrexia followed by shock, diarrhoea and prostration, hyperglycaemia followed by hypoglycaemia, congestion, oedema and haemorrhages into the abdominal viscera and lungs. Since these effects are produced by all the polymolecular toxins, irrespective of their parent organisms, it cannot be said that each toxin mimics the particular effects of the natural disease caused by the parent. But they may be responsible for the fever and intoxication which is common to all these diseases even though their characteristic features may differ. Experimental animals die when the organisms in an inoculum have multiplied and attained the same number as that in a lethal dose of dead organisms. It is reasonable therefore to suppose that the animals killed by injection of living and dead organisms have died of the same cause, namely, the endotoxin. It must not be assumed, however, that the endotoxin is the only cause of pathogenic effects in natural infection. Hill, Hatswell & Topley (1940) showed that a strain of mice that had inherited a resistance to the endotoxin of the mouse-typhoid bacillus were nevertheless no more resistant than control mice to the lethal effects of infection by live bacilli.

Shiga neurotoxin. Rough strains of *Shigella shigae* differ from rough strains of all other Gram-negative bacteria in containing a toxin. This toxin is also present in smooth strains of *S. shigae* but differs from the O antigen in being a simple protein, in being about ten million times as toxic, and in producing paralytic symptoms that are quite different from those produced by the O antigen. Although the isolated protein is as potent as botulinus and tetanus toxins, cultures of *S. shigae* are not nearly as toxic as those of the clostridia because a far smaller weight of toxin is produced per cell (van Heyningen & Gladstone, 1953).

The question now arises whether this toxin plays any part in dysentery. Some of the evidence suggests that it does not: the neurological symptoms that appear after the injection of the toxin into animals do not form a typical part of the syndrome of human dysentery; symptoms resulting from an infection by *S. shigae* are similar to those caused by other shigellae, and these do not produce the neurotoxin; antibody to the neurotoxin does not protect against the disease, whereas the somatic antigen is protective in small quantity (see Weil, 1947). On the other hand, treatment of dysentery patients with anti-neurotoxic serum results in clinical improvement due to a reduction in the toxicity, but this is only transient since the serum has no antibacterial effect (Fairley & Boyd, 1943). This suggests (*a*) that the neurotoxin is responsible for pathogenic effects that are preventable with antitoxin, (*b*) that the O antigen produces additional pathogenic effects which, not surprisingly, are not preventable by anti-neurotoxin, and (*c*) that the neurotoxin does not have an aggressive action, which is to be expected since it is not generally toxic to cells.

(viii) *Food poisoning*

The mode of action of micro-organisms in causing food poisoning is not always understood. There seem to be two types of food poisoning: (1) the 'infection' type that follows the multiplication within the body of pathogenic organisms conveyed by the food, and (2) the 'toxin' type that follows ingestion of food in which poisonous substances have been formed as a result of bacterial proliferation (see Dack, 1953).

The infection type has an incubation period of 8–24 hr. and is generally caused by salmonellae, but occasionally by shigellae. The gastro-intestinal disturbances due to these organisms are caused by living organisms and apparently not by their toxic O antigens. Feeding of bacterial bodies or of the isolated O antigens to human volunteers produces no signs of gastro-intestinal distress. In food poisoning, therefore, the means by which salmonellae exert their harmful effect is different from that in systemic infections. How they act in food poisoning appears to be entirely unknown.

Food poisoning due to heat-resistant *Clostridium welchii* (see Hobbs, Smith, Oakley, Warrack & Cruickshank, 1953) appears to belong to the 'infection' type, since ingestion of culture filtrates by volunteers produced no ill effects. The organisms produced traces of lecithinase, collagenase, hyaluronidase and desoxyribonuclease, but no other toxins. However, the possibility of endotoxins, though hitherto unknown in these organisms, cannot be excluded.

The 'toxin' type of food poisoning has a shorter incubation period, usually about 3 hr., and can be subdivided into two groups: (1) that caused by pathogenic organisms known to produce toxins, and (2) that caused by organisms not usually considered to be pathogenic, but which are presumed to produce substances with an irritating effect on the human gastro-intestinal mucosa.

The organisms in the first group are *Cl. botulinum* and the staphylococcus. Botulinus toxin has already been considered. The symptoms of botulism are paralytic and thus entirely different from the gastro-intestinal disturbances of other forms of food poisoning. Staphylococcal food poisoning is due to an enterotoxin which is probably, but not certainly, distinct from any of the haemolytic toxins produced by this organism.

The 'non-pathogenic' group of food-poisoning organisms include *Escherichia coli*, *Proteus vulgaris*, *Proteus morgani*, *Streptococcus faecalis* and *Bacillus cereus*. Poisoning is often associated with food heavily infected with these organisms, and the inference is that they produce non-specific toxic substances with an irritating effect on the human gastro-intestinal mucosa. There is no concrete evidence for this toxin formation, but Wilson & Miles (1946) express the belief that the epidemiological and bacteriological evidence is now coming in favour of this Briegerian view and that 'the pendulum is in fact slowly swinging in the direction of the old "ptomaine" theory with the distinction that the poisons now regarded as responsible are not the results of advanced protein decomposition but result from the growth of types of bacteria which can proliferate enormously without greatly altering the appearance and taste of the food. What the nature of these products is remains in doubt.' They suggest that they may be breakdown products of food, or enzymes with a special affinity for some constituent of the human gastro-intestinal tract.

(ix) *Anthrax and pneumococcal infections*

These infections are examples of diseases in which a lethal effect is not produced until there has been a considerable multiplication of organisms in the body of the host. Until recently it has been supposed that the causative organisms are not toxin producers, but this idea may now have to be modified. It is true that no potent toxins have been detected in laboratory cultures, but the fact that great multiplication is necessary for a fatal outcome suggests that it may be useful to look for feeble toxins. A large amount of modest toxin may be just as harmful as a small amount of spectacular toxin.

Evans & Shoesmith (1954) have shown that filtrates of old cultures of *Bacillus anthracis* and *B. subtilis* contain a substance which in rather large doses (20–50 μg.) produces necrosis in the skin of a rabbit, and in larger doses (500 μg.) produces lesions similar to those occurring in cutaneous anthrax infections. What role this toxin plays in pathogenesis of natural infection is not clear. It does not seem to be the same as the toxin recently reported by Smith & Keppie (1954) which is detectable only *in vivo* and which will be discussed by them in this Symposium. It remains to be shown that anthrax toxins have a pathogenic function in natural disease.

The pneumococcus is known to produce a feeble toxin *in vitro*—an oxygen-labile haemolysin which has a toxic effect on the heart and is similar to the O-labile haemolysins of *Clostridium welchii*, *Cl. tetani* and *Streptococcus pyogenes* (Bernheimer & Cantoni, 1945). This toxin is produced intracellularly or extracellularly, according to the method of culture (Cowan, 1934). It is generally assumed not to play a part in the pathogenesis of pneumococcal infections, largely because haemolysis is never a feature even of overwhelming infection. But the toxin has cardiotoxic and doubtless other effects besides the haemolytic, and these may be important. We have seen how the haemolytic α-toxin of *Clostridium welchii* appears to play an important role in pathogenesis, without producing intravascular haemolysis.

REFERENCES

ABRAHAM, E. P., BROWN, G. M., CHAIN, E., FLOREY, H. W., GARDNER, A. D. & SANDERS, A. G. (1941). Tissue autolysis and shock. *Quart. J. exp. Physiol.* **31**, 79.

AMIES, C. R. (1954). The pathogenesis of diphtheria. *J. Path. Bact.* **67**, 25.

BERNHEIMER, A. W. (1944). Parallelism in lethal and hemolytic activity of the toxin of *Clostridium septicum*. *J. exp. Med.* **80**, 309.

BERNHEIMER, A. W. & CANTONI, G. L. (1945). The cardiotoxic action of preparations containing the oxygen-labile hemolysin of *Streptococcus pyogenes*. 1. Increased sensitivity of the isolated frog's heart to repeated application of the toxin. *J. exp. Med.* **81**, 295.

BIDWELL, E. & VAN HEYNINGEN, W. E. (1948). The biochemistry of the gas gangrene toxins. 5. The κ-toxin (collagenase) of *Clostridium welchii*. *Biochem. J.* **42**, 140.

BOYD, J. S. K. (1946). Tetanus in the African and European theatres of war. *Lancet*, i, 113.

BRUCE, D. (1920). Tetanus. *J. Hyg., Camb.*, **19**, 1.

BULL, C. G. & PRITCHETT, I. W. (1917). Toxin and antitoxin of and protective inoculation against *Bacillus welchii*. *J. exp. Med.* **26**, 119.

BURNET, F. M. (1929). The exotoxins of *Staphylococcus pyogenes aureus*. *J. Path. Bact.* **32**, 717.

BUTLER, E. C. B. & VALENTINE, F. C. O. (1943). Further observations on acute staphylococcal infection. *Lancet*, i, 194.

CHU, H. P. (1949). The lecithinase of *Bacillus cereus* and its comparison with *Clostridium welchii* α-toxin. *J. gen. Microbiol.* **3**, 255.

COWAN, S. T. (1934). Pneumococcal haemolysin; its extracellular nature, production and properties. *J. Path. Bact.* **38**, 61.

CREIGHTON, C. (1891–4). *A History of Epidemics in Britain*. Cambridge University Press.

CRUICKSHANK, R. (1937). Staphylocoagulase. *J. Path. Bact.* **45**, 295.

DACK, G. M. (1953). Food poisoning. *Ann. Rev. Microbiol.* **7**, 327.

EVANS, D. G. (1943*a*). The protective properties of the alpha antitoxin and theta antihaemolysin occurring in *Cl. welchii* type A antiserum. *Brit. J. exp. Path.* **24**, 81.

EVANS, D. G. (1943*b*). The protective properties of the alpha antitoxin and anti-hyaluronidase occurring in *Cl. welchii* type A antiserum. *J. Path. Bact.* **55**, 427.

EVANS, D. G. (1945*a*). The in-vitro production of α-toxin, θ-haemolysin and hyaluronidase by strains of *Cl. welchii* type A, and the relationship of in-vitro properties to virulence for guinea-pigs. *J. Path. Bact.* **57**, 75.

EVANS, D. G. (1945*b*). The treatment with antitoxin of experimental gas gangrene produced in guinea pigs by (*a*) *Cl. welchii*, (*b*) *Cl. oedematiens* and (*c*) *Cl. septicum*. *Brit. J. exp. Path.* **26**, 104.

EVANS, D. G. (1947). Anticollagenase in immunity to *Cl. welchii* type A infection. *Brit. J. exp. Path.* **28**, 24.

EVANS, D. G. & SHOESMITH, J. G. (1954). Production of toxin by *Bacillus anthracis*. *Lancet*, i, 136.

FAIRLEY, N. H. & BOYD, J. S. K. (1943). Dysentery in the Middle East with special reference to sulphaguanidine treatment. *Trans. R. Soc. trop. Med. Hyg.* **36**, 253.

FRAZER, A. C., ELKES, J. J., SAMMONS, H. G., GOVAN, A. D. T. & COOKE, W. T. (1945). Effect of *Cl. welchii* type A toxin on body tissues and fluids. *Lancet*, i, 457.

HERBERT, D. & TODD, E. W. (1941). Purification and properties of a haemolysin produced by group A haemolytic streptococci. *Biochem. J.* **35**, 1241.

HILL, A. B., HATSWELL, J. M. & TOPLEY, W. W. C. (1940). The inheritance of resistance, demonstrated by the development of a strain of mice resistant to experimental inoculation with a bacterial endotoxin. *J. Hyg., Camb.*, **40**, 538.

HILL, A. M. (1950). The changing face of obstetric infection. *Med. J. Aust.* **2**, 782.

HOBBS, B. C., SMITH, M. E., OAKLEY, C. L., WARRACK, G. H. & CRUICKSHANK, J. C. (1953). *Clostridium welchii* food poisoning. *J. Hyg., Camb.*, **51**, 75.

LOGAN, W. P. D. (1952). Diphtheria immunization. *Mon. Bull. Minist. Hlth Lab. Serv.* **11**, 50.

McCLEAN, D., ROGERS, H. J. & WILLIAMS, B. W. (1943). Early diagnosis of wound infection with special reference to gas gangrene. *Lancet*, i, 355.

MACFARLANE, M. G. (1943). The therapeutic value of gas gangrene antitoxin. *Brit. med. J.* ii, 636.

MACFARLANE, M. G. (1945). Case-fatality rates of gas gangrene in relation to treatment. *Brit. med. J.* i, 803.

MACFARLANE, M. G. & KNIGHT, B. C. J. G. (1941). The biochemistry of bacterial toxins. 1. The lecithinase activity of *Clostridium welchii* toxins. *Biochem. J.* **35**, 884.

MACFARLANE, R. G. & MACLENNAN, J. D. (1945). The toxaemia of gas gangrene. *Lancet*, ii, 328.

MACLENNAN, J. D. & MACFARLANE, R. G. (1945). Toxin and antitoxin studies of gas gangrene in man. *Lancet*, ii, 301.

McLEOD, J. W. (1943). The types *mitis, intermedius* and *gravis* of *Corynebacterium diphtheriae*. A review of observations during the past ten years. *Bact. Rev.* **7**, 1.

MILES, A. A. (1951–2). Some aspects of antibacterial immunity. P. 192 in *Lectures on the Scientific Basis of Medicine*. London: Athlone Press.

MILES, E. M. & MILES, A. A. (1950). The relation of toxicity and enzyme activity in the lecithinases of *Clostridium bifermentans* and *Clostridium welchii. J. gen. Microbiol.* **4**, 22.

MUELLER, J. H. (1941). Toxin production as related to the clinical severity of diphtheria. *J. Immunol.* **42**, 353.

OAKLEY, C. L. (1954). Gas gangrene. *Brit. med. Bull.* **10**, 52.

OAKLEY, C. L., WARRACK, H. & CLARKE, P. H. (1947). The toxins of *Clostridium oedematiens* (*Cl. novyi*). *J. gen. Microbiol.* **1**, 91.

ORR-EWING, J. (1946). The relative susceptibility to phagocytosis of *gravis* and *mitis* types of *C. diphtheriae. J. Path. Bact.* **58**, 167.

PASCUA, M. (1951). Evolution of mortality in Europe during the twentieth century. *WHO Epidemiological and Vital Statistics Report*, **4**, 36.

POPE, A., ZAMECNIK, P. C., AUB, J. C., BRUES, A. M., DUBOS, R. J., NATHANSON, I. T. & NUTT, A. C. (1945). The toxic factors in experimental traumatic shock. 6. The toxic influence of the bacterial flora, particularly *Clostridium welchii*, in exudates of ischemic muscle. *J. clin. Invest.* **24**, 856.

ROBB-SMITH, A. H. T. (1945). Tissue changes induced by *Clostridium welchii* type A filtrates. *Lancet*, ii, 362.

ROBERTSON, M. & KEPPIE, J. (1943). Gas gangrene active immunization by means of concentrated toxoids. *Lancet*, ii, 311.

Roux, E. (1889). (On behalf of L. Pasteur.) The Croonian Lecture on Preventive Inoculation. *Brit. med. J.* i, 1269.

Roux, E. & Yersin, A. (1888). Contribution à l'étude de la diphthérie. *Ann. Inst. Pasteur*, **2**, 629.

Smith, H. & Keppie, J. (1954). Observations on experimental anthrax: Demonstration of a specific lethal factor produced *in vivo* by *Bacillus anthracis*. *Nature, Lond.*, **173**, 869.

Stock, A. H. & Verney, E. (1952). Properties of scarlet fever toxin of the NY 5 strain. *J. Immunol.* **69**, 373.

Thompson, D. (1951). Ten years of diphtheria immunization. *Mon. Bull. Minist. Hlth Lab. Serv.* **10**, 132.

Valentine, F. C. O. (1936). Further observations on the role of the toxin in staphylococcal infection. *Lancet*, i, 526.

Valentine, F. C. O. & Butler, E. C. B. (1939). Specific immunity in acute staphylococcal osteomyelitis. *Lancet*, i, 973.

van Ermengem, E. (1896). Recherches sur des cas d'accidents alimentaires. *Rev. Hyg. Police sanit.* **18**, 761.

van Heyningen, W. E. & Gladstone, G. P. (1953). The neurotoxin of *Shigella shigae*. 1. Production, purification and properties of the toxin. *Brit. J. exp. Path.* **34**, 202.

von Behring, E. & Kitasato, S. (1890). Ueber das Zustandekommen der Diphtherieimmunität und die Tetanusimmunität bei Tieren. *Dtsch. med. Wschr.* **16**, 1113.

Watson Cheyne, W. (1886). Preface to *Recent Essays by various authors on Bacteria in relation to Disease*. London: New Sydenham Society.

Weil, A. J. (1947). Medical and epidemiological aspects of enteric infection. *Ann. Rev. Microbiol.* **1**, 309.

Wilson, G. S. & Miles, A. A. (1946). Topley and Wilson's *Principles of Bacteriology and Immunity*, 3rd ed. p. 1002. London: Edward Arnold and Co.

Zinnemann, K. (1946). Neutralisation of *C. diphtheriae* type toxins with standard antitoxins, as determined by skin reactions in guinea-pigs. *J. Bact. Path.* **58**, 43.

THE PATHOGENESIS OF DIPHTHERIA

A. M. PAPPENHEIMER, Jr.

Department of Microbiology, New York University College of Medicine

I. FACTORS CONCERNED IN VIRULENCE

During the years 1919–22 a remarkable study on the epidemiology of diphtheria was carried out at the Royal Naval College in Greenwich by Sir Sheldon F. Dudley, then a Surgeon Commander in the Royal Navy. In his classic monograph Dudley (1923) reported that several Schick-positive boys at the College were found to be carriers of avirulent diphtheria bacilli; but despite the simultaneous prevalence of carriers of virulent strains, in no instance was a virulent (i.e. toxigenic) strain isolated from an individual known to be Schick-positive at the time of culture. Dudley noted that one boy developed clinical diphtheria caused by a virulent bacillus similar *in all other respects* to the avirulent organism which he had been known to carry for the previous two months. He pointed out that he could find no record of *avirulent* and *virulent* organisms ever having been isolated from the same throat swab* and regretted that no greater effort was made to see if avirulent organisms could be present in throats of diphtheria cases.

It is interesting to look back on these astute observations of Dudley in the light of Freeman's (1951) recent discovery that non-toxigenic diphtheria strains may be converted to toxigenicity and lysogenicity by infection with a temperate bacteriophage. One cannot escape the suspicion that perhaps a bacterial virus may have been the agent which precipitated diphtheria in the Schick-positive boy who carried an avirulent diphtheria bacillus in his throat.

It has been recognized for a very long time that some outbreaks of diphtheria are attended by a much higher mortality rate than others. Moreover, there is a good deal of evidence to show that strains of *Corynebacterium diphtheriae* which exhibit the cultural characteristics of the *gravis* or *intermedius* type, tend, in general, to produce a type of disease which is clinically more severe than that observed in cases caused by the *mitis* variety (McLeod, 1943). The symptoms of diphtheria, except for those caused by mechanical obstruction by the pseudomembrane,

---

* Later, Okell (1929) succeeded in demonstrating the simultaneous presence of both virulent and avirulent diphtheria bacilli of the same serological type in a few individuals during an epidemic.

are due to the production of a single well-characterized toxic protein which is produced by all *virulent* strains of *C. diphtheriae*. The recent work by Freeman (1951) and by others (Hewitt, 1952; Groman, 1953; Barksdale & Pappenheimer, 1954) suggests that only the diphtheria bacilli which are lysogenic are capable of producing diphtheria toxin.* We may well ask whether the nature of the specific phage can determine the degree of virulence. Are *gravis* strains more virulent because the phage which they carry is different from that carried by *mitis* strains? Admittedly there may exist many different specific diphtheria phages; however, we are inclined to believe that the degree of virulence of a strain is mainly determined by the bacteria themselves. The capacity of a given virulent strain to produce toxin depends on how efficiently it can grow when its iron supply becomes exhausted. As will be discussed below, it is only under conditions of iron deficiency that diphtheria toxin can be demonstrated in culture filtrates, where it is always accompanied by equivalent concentrations of a porphyrin (Pappenheimer, 1947) identified by Gray & Holt (1948) as coproporphyrin III. It has been observed that, under the same conditions, avirulent diphtheria bacilli produce the same amount of porphyrin, but no toxin. The capacity to grow and produce porphyrin in an iron-deficient medium is not altered when a given avirulent strain is converted to lysogenicity and toxigenicity by infection with a temperate phage (Pappenheimer & Barksdale, unpublished).

The higher virulence of *gravis* and *intermedius* strains has frequently been attributed to their greater 'invasive' powers. Burnet (1953) is inclined to favour this view, and O'Meara (1940) has obtained some evidence that *gravis* strains may form a substance which differs from ordinary diphtheria toxin and which is concerned in spread of the infection. Actually, even completely non-toxigenic strains may not be entirely lacking in pathogenicity. Thus the avirulent C4 and C7 strains produce purulent local lesions resembling those caused by staphylococci when injected into the skin of laboratory animals; but even after conversion to toxigenicity by infection with β-phage, the C4(β) and C7(β) strains remain localized after intradermal injection. Although 'invasiveness' may play some part in determining relative virulence of *gravis* and *mitis* strains, it is questionable whether such variations are of sufficient magnitude to account for observed differences in clinical severity. It must be recalled that, since Loeffler's original observations, there have

* The converse is not always true; in other words, there are certain phages which can convert avirulent strains to lysogenicity but not to toxigenicity (Groman, 1954; Barksdale, personal communication).

been only a few scattered instances, even including the most severe cases of so-called 'bull-neck' diphtheria, where diphtheria bacilli could be isolated from the blood or any of the tissues other than the original superficial lesion.

The simplest explanation of why *gravis* strains cause a more severe type of disease than do *mitis* strains would be, of course, that they produce more toxin *in vivo*. However, attempts to demonstrate in the laboratory a correlation between toxin-producing capacity of diphtheria bacilli and the clinical severity of the cases from which they were isolated have been unsuccessful. Mueller (1941) pointed out that, because of their high iron content, conditions in the tissues or in a diphtheritic membrane are far from being favourable for toxin production. Thus if any correlation is to be found between the amount of toxin produced and clinical severity, strains must be tested for toxin production in media containing an excess of iron. Mueller proceeded to test three non-*gravis* strains under these conditions and found that they produced approximately 3 M.L.D./ml. as compared with 40 M.L.D./ml. produced by a *gravis* type, the Halifax strain. In the same medium containing a critically low iron concentration, one of the non-gravis strains (P.W.8) produced far more toxin than did the Halifax strain.

No extensive attempt to test Mueller's hypothesis has been undertaken, and indeed any such attempt would be difficult, since not only toxin production at iron concentrations comparable to those in the tissues must be determined, but also the amount of growth, the growth rate and even the type of growth must be considered. The situation in a diphtheritic membrane probably resembles that in a still culture where the diphtheria bacilli grow clumped together in a heavy pellicle on the surface of the nutrient medium. In order to reach the outermost layer of growing organisms, nutrients, including inorganic iron, must diffuse through a thick layer of competing bacteria. Thus even when the medium contains an excess of iron, there will always be a significant proportion of organisms which receive a suboptimal supply of this metal and will consequently form toxin. We have observed that even the Halifax (*gravis*) strain produces but a few skin-test doses of toxin per ml. in well-shaken cultures* grown in excess iron. Moreover, the recent experiments of Mitsuhashi, Kurokawa & Kojima (1949) show that at the low iron concentrations usually considered optimal for toxin production, no appreciable toxin is produced by well-shaken cultures of the P.W.8 strain until termination of the logarithmic growth phase, when the

---

* It is necessary to add a protective colloid such as gelatin to shake cultures in order to avoid surface denaturation of extracellular proteins.

exogenous iron supply presumably has been exhausted.* In Fig. 1 we have replotted the data of the Japanese workers. It can be seen that the curve showing toxin production per unit growth (Lf/mg.) cuts the abscissa at 17 hr. and this time approximately coincides with the end of the rapid-growth phase. We have obtained similar results with other strains in our laboratory. It would thus appear that toxin is produced only during the growth of the organisms which occurs *after* all of the exogenous iron supply has become exhausted. Under the non-homogeneous conditions existing in a diphtheritic membrane, the number of organisms failing to receive an adequate supply of iron will depend on

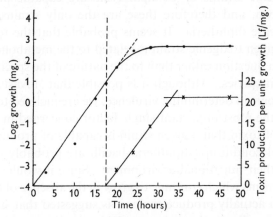

Fig. 1. Toxin production and growth of the P.W. 8 strain of *C. diphtheriae* in shake culture as a function of time. (Plotted from the data of Mitsuhashi, Kurokawa & Kojima, 1949.) Crosses: toxin production in Lf per unit growth in milligrams. Circles: logarithmic growth curve.

the growth rate of the particular strain in question. It is interesting that the Halifax strain (*gravis*) has a growth rate which is nearly three times that of the P.W. 8 strain (*mitis*). The division times are about 60 and 160 min. respectively.

Before concluding this section, it seems worth while to comment briefly on a recent paper by Amies (1954). Amies seems to feel that the term 'virulence' has little meaning as applied to the diphtheria bacillus; a strain is either toxigenic or it is not. According to Amies, the severity of the disease in a completely non-immune population is determined by

* The 6-fold increase in growth observed by Mitsuhashi *et al.* (1949) during the period of declining growth rate but rapid toxin production agrees well with our own observations in still cultures (Pappenheimer & Hendee, 1947). Under the latter conditions the P.W. 8 organisms harvested from cultures grown at iron concentrations optimal for toxin production contain only about one-sixth the iron and cytochrome b_1 contents of bacteria from cultures grown in excess iron.

the effectiveness of the host's inflammatory response; if this is slow and the bacteria gain a foothold, inhibition of the cellular response will be caused by the toxin which they produce and a malignant form of the disease will result. In my opinion, this merely begs the question, for it does not explain why in some epidemics a far greater proportion of the population show an ineffective inflammatory response than in other epidemics, nor why one cultural type of *C. diphtheriae* is commonly associated with the malignant form of the disease.

Conclusions regarding virulence

Only lysogenic strains of *C. diphtheriae* are capable of producing diphtheria toxin, and therefore these are the only strains which will cause the disease diphtheria. It seems probable that the relative virulence of any given toxigenic strain is related to the metabolic properties of the strain in question rather than to the nature of the specific bacteriophage which it carries. Although it is possible that 'invasiveness' may play a minor part in determining virulence, we are inclined to agree with Mueller that the most important single factor concerned in virulence is the quantity of toxin that a given strain is capable of producing *in vivo*. Under natural conditions, diphtheria bacilli are probably not in equilibrium with their nutritional environment. Since it would appear that only the organisms which continue to grow in the absence of an adequate supply of iron actually produce toxin, it is suggested that strains of the *gravis* type generally produce more toxin *in vivo* because they divide at a faster rate than do *mitis* strains. A faster growth rate will result in a greater proportion of organisms which fail to receive their optimal supply of iron diffusing out from the underlying tissues.

II. MODE OF ACTION OF DIPHTHERIA TOXIN

Diphtheria toxin has been isolated in highly purified form on numerous occasions (Eaton, 1936; Pappenheimer, 1937; Agner, 1950; Lepow & Pillemer, 1952). At neutral pH it is a relatively stable protein with a molecular weight of 72,000, and its chemical and physical properties have been reasonably well characterized. Recently Pope & Stevens (1953) have succeeded in isolating the toxic protein in crystalline form, a noteworthy achievement despite the apparently low yields of crystalline material. It seems likely that the difficulties encountered by previous workers who attempted to crystallize the toxic protein were due to the fact that diphtheria toxin in culture filtrates does not exist as a homogeneous protein. It is probable that prior to Pope & Stevens's work, purified preparations of the toxin consisted of a mixture of molecules transformed in varying degrees into toxoid owing to peroxidative activity of the crude culture (Agner, 1950).

The early naïve hope that isolation and chemical analysis of the purified toxic protein would reveal unusual chemical groupings and thus lead to an understanding of its mode of action has not been realized. However, studies of the metabolism of the diphtheria bacillus in relation to toxin production have furnished evidence which strongly suggests that the toxin acts by interfering in some way with the normal functioning of one or more components of the cytochrome system in the tissues of susceptible animals.

The diphtheria bacillus is an aerobic organism which forms toxin only when grown in the presence of an abundant supply of oxygen and an inadequate supply of iron. Bacteria harvested from cultures of the P.W.8 strain which have produced maximal yields of toxin contain only one-sixth the iron content of organisms grown in the presence of excess iron.* Catalase and all of the iron-containing respiratory enzymes are proportionately reduced in bacteria of low iron content. Culture filtrates from such organisms contain toxin and coproporphyrin III in a molecular ratio approximately 1 to 4. Within the bacteria themselves, about 90 % of the haem iron appears to be bound to the principal respiratory pigment of the cell, i.e. cytochrome b_1.† As estimated from the intensity of its Soret band, the amount of cytochrome b_1 present in bacteria of high iron content is approximately equivalent to the amount of porphyrin found in culture filtrates from the same mass of cells of low iron content. These quantitative relationships which exist between bacterial cytochrome b_1 content on the one hand and toxin and copro-porphyrin on the other suggested a possible relationship between toxin and the protein moiety of cytochrome b_1, and further suggested the possibility that the toxin might cause injury to the cells of the susceptible animal by interfering with their cytochrome system (Pappenheimer, 1947; Pappenheimer & Hendee, 1947).

As yet there is no decisive evidence to substantiate the postulated relationship between diphtheria toxin and cytochrome b_1. Purified diphtheria cytochrome b_1 remains firmly attached to large particulate

* It is because of its ability to continue growing until its cellular iron content falls to these very low levels that the P.W.8 strain produces such unusually high yields of toxin in the laboratory. Most other strains have about the same iron content as P.W.8 when grown in media containing excess iron, but unlike P.W.8 they cease to grow when their iron content is lowered 30–40 % and the maximal yields of toxin possible are correspondingly small.

† The spectrum of diphtheria cytochrome b_1 lies 3–4 mμ. to the left of mammalian cytochrome b. Cytochrome b_1 also appears to be more readily autoxidizable than b. Both the mammalian and diphtheria pigments are involved in succinate oxidation (Pappenheimer & Hendee, 1949; Smith, 1954).

material, probably fragments of the cytoplasmic membrane (Weibull, 1953); it undoubtedly contains bound lipids in addition to protohaem and other materials. It seems unlikely that the toxin could represent more than a fraction of the protein of these particles. In view of the complex nature of particles containing diphtheria cytochrome b_1, it is not surprising that no immunological cross-reaction between the pigment and toxin has been demonstrated. For the same reason, we do not feel that Lepow's (1952) failure to find spectrophotometric evidence for any unusual binding of protohaem by solutions of the toxin can be considered a serious objection to the theory.

In considering the action of diphtheria toxin certain facts should be kept in mind. It may easily be calculated that only a few molecules, perhaps only one or two, suffice to kill a susceptible cell. Moreover, even large amounts of toxin cause no obvious damage to the tissues until after a latent period of many hours. Finally, if the toxin does indeed interfere with the cytochrome system, its action cannot be a direct one, since even an enormous excess of toxin added to tissue slices or homogenates fails to inhibit respiration within a reasonable length of time. It has therefore been proposed that diphtheria toxin acts by specifically blocking synthesis of one or more components of the host's cytochrome system. Cytochrome b, because of its close similarity to cytochrome b_1, would appear to be the component most likely to be affected.

Revealing evidence substantiating the suggestion that diphtheria toxin brings about a derangement of the susceptible host's cytochrome system has been obtained through the happy choice of an experimental animal whose biological properties appear to be uniquely suited to this purpose. The large American silkworm, *Platysamia cecropia*, undergoes striking and predictable changes in its cytochrome system at certain periods during its life cycle. After 6–8 weeks' growth and four larval moults, the cecropia caterpillar attains a weight of 15–20 g. and spins a cocoon of silk within which it undergoes a final moult and transforms into a diapausing pupa. This metamorphosis is attended by the almost complete disappearance of the succinoxidase system and of cytochromes b and c (Williams, 1948; Sanborn & Williams, 1950). Only in the intersegmental muscles of the abdomen do these cytochromes persist in appreciable concentrations during the pupal diapause (Pappenheimer & Williams, 1952). In other pupal tissues, such as heart muscle, fat body, wing hypodermis, etc., only cytochromes b_5 and $a+a_3$ can be detected (Shappirio & Williams, unpublished). With the advent of warm weather in late spring, renewed endocrine activity of the brain and prothoracic glands triggers the initiation of adult development which can be followed day by day through transparent plastic windows placed in the animal's face or abdomen (Williams, 1946). At 25° development follows a rigid time schedule requiring 21–22 days from its initiation until final emergence of the adult moth. Coincident with the onset of adult development, rapid synthesis of cytochrome *c* occurs, and this component approaches its maximal content on about the 10th day at a time when the thoracic flight muscles are being formed. Only after the rate of cytochrome *c* synthesis has already begun to decline do the syntheses of cytochromes *b* and oxidase attain their maximal rates. Fig. 2 illustrates the changes in various cytochrome components during development.

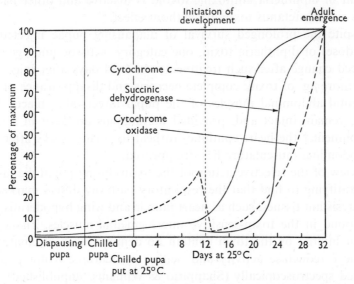

Fig. 2. Changes in the total contents of certain components of the cytochrome system during metamorphosis of the cecropia silkworm (from Williams (1948), and unpublished data of Sanborn, Schneidermann & Williams).

Injection of purified diphtheria toxin even in small amounts (0·1–1 μg.) into cecropia larvae and into developing adults results in delayed death after 5–15 days or longer (Pappenheimer & Williams, 1952). Even much larger doses of toxin cause no recognizable degenerative changes before the third or fourth day. After this latent period, the animals gradually become flaccid and soft and the blood darkens and finally turns black. Although degenerative changes in developing pupae occur only after a latent period of several days, adult development is brought to a prompt standstill within a matter of hours or less following injection of purified toxin. In sharp contrast to this response of larvae and developing adults, diapausing pupae survive doses of 100 μg. or more of toxin for many weeks; death, when it finally occurs, results from desiccation, due to loss of water vapour through the spiracles.

It is of interest that of a large series of drugs and poisons which have been tested by injection into cecropia, only a few have been found which exert a selective inhibition of adult development, similar to that caused by diphtheria toxin. *All* of these compounds are known inhibitors of the classical cytochrome system and include KCN, high pressures of CO, deuterohaem, and certain imidazole compounds (Schneidermann & Williams, 1954). It may be added that the effects of diphtheria toxin on cecropia are highly specific, since they are neutralized by the calculated amount of diphtheria antitoxin; toxoid is inactive and other bacterial toxins such as tetanus toxin are without effect.*

Despite the prolonged survival of diapausing pupae injected with large doses of diphtheria toxin, one category of tissue undergoes pronounced change after such treatment. At 6–14 days after injection of 10 or more μg. of toxin, complete necrosis and disappearance of intersegmental abdominal muscles of the pupal insect takes place. Other tissues remain intact and, provided the animals are kept in a humid environment,† the heart continues to beat for many weeks after all of the abdominal musculature has disappeared.

In view of the selective action of the toxin during pupal diapause, it was gratifying to find that the respiratory pathway differs markedly in toxin-resistant tissues, such as heart muscle and wing hypodermis, from that found in the toxin-sensitive intersegmental muscles. Tissues that are *not* injured by the toxin contain no demonstrable succinate cytochrome c reductase activity and neither cytochrome b nor c can be detected spectroscopically (Shappirio & Williams, unpublished). They contain cytochromes b_5, a and a_3 as major components and electron transfer in diphosphopyridine nucleotide (DPN) linked oxidations occurs via the following pathway (Pappenheimer & Williams, 1954; Chance & Pappenheimer, 1954):

$$\text{DPN} \rightarrow \text{flavoprotein} \rightarrow \text{cytochrome } b_5 \rightarrow c \rightarrow a \rightarrow a_3 \rightarrow O_2.$$
$$? \qquad \downarrow ?$$
$$O_2$$

Cytochrome b_5 is a newly defined respiratory pigment that is widely

---

* Williams (unpublished) has recently tested crystalline botulinum toxin and found it to be without effect on cecropia. The alpha toxin or lecithinase of *Clostridium welchii*, however, is equally toxic for diapausing as for developing pupae.

† The tiny muscles which control the closing of the spiracles and thus prevent undue loss of water vapour are presumably destroyed by the toxin.

distributed in animal and plant tissues.* It is a *major* component not only in insects but in both adrenal cortex and medulla (Pappenheimer, Hendee & Williams, 1955), in liver where it is the principal pigment of the microsomal fraction (Strittmatter & Ball, 1952; Chance & Williams, 1954), and in most other mammalian tissues. Its concentration in mammalian heart and skeletal muscle is low, and in these tissues its α-band is visible only at low temperatures.

The DPNH oxidase system involving cytochrome b_5 has been carefully studied in cecropia larval midgut which contains the pigment in unusually high concentration (Pappenheimer & Williams, 1954). The system is insensitive to antimycin A and therefore does not involve the Slater factor which acts between succindehydrogenase or diaphorase and cytochrome c, which is sensitive to BAL and combines stoichiometrically with antimycin A (Potter & Reif, 1952). It is still uncertain whether cytochrome b_5 is truly autoxidizable and acts as a KCN and CO insensitive terminal oxidase. Tissues such as diapausing heart muscle may contain minute traces of cytochrome c, not detectable spectroscopically but sufficient to allow oxidation to proceed at a slow rate which is not greatly diminished even when most of the large excess of oxidase $(a + a_3)$ is inhibited by KCN or CO. Addition of cytochrome c to the system greatly accelerates DPNH oxidation and renders the system sensitive to cyanide. There is reason to believe that cytochrome c makes its appearance and adds to the system *in vivo* during the early stages of adult development.

Cytochrome b_5 is present as a minor component in toxin-sensitive tissues such as the intersegmental muscles. Intersegmental muscle homogenates resemble the mammalian heart preparation and contain an active succinoxidase system with cytochromes b, c, a and a_3 as major components. Electron transfer proceeds mainly according to the now familiar pathway (Slater, 1950; Chance, 1952) modified as shown below:

$$DPN \rightarrow flavoprotein \rightarrow cytochrome\ b_5 \rightarrow O_2$$

Slater factor $\rightarrow$ cytochrome $c \rightarrow a \rightarrow a_3 \rightarrow O_2$

succinate $\rightarrow$ succindehydrogenase

antimycin A HCN CO

cytochrome b

In the above scheme, representing the oxidative pathway in the toxin-sensitive intersegmental muscles during diapause, KCN and CO are

* Cytochrome b_5 may be identical with the cytochrome e which Keilin & Hartree (1949) observed at liquid-air temperatures in the thoracic flight muscles of bees and in other tissues.

4

potent inhibitors. Antimycin A inhibits succinate oxidation completely
and DPNH oxidation 80–85 %. Inhibition of DPNH oxidation by
antimycin is incomplete because cytochrome b_5 is present as a minor
component.

We feel that the experiments with cecropia provide strong circumstantial evidence that diphtheria toxin acts primarily upon the cytochrome system. Clearly, cytochromes b_5 and oxidase are not involved
since tissues containing only these components are not attacked by the
toxin. The most likely target of the toxin would thus appear to be that
portion of the succinoxidase system which lies below cytochrome c. The
prompt fashion in which toxin arrests adult development, a process
depending on continued cytochrome synthesis, as opposed to the prolonged latent period required for toxin to bring about necrosis of tissue
that already contains an intact and functioning succinoxidase system,
is in keeping with the hypothesis that it is the formation or synthesis
of one of the succinoxidase components that is blocked by diphtheria
toxin. It is realized that other hypotheses could be devised to account
for these observations. For example, it is possible that oxidative phos-
phorylation linked to succinate might be interfered with, due to action
of the toxin (see Pinchot & Bloom, 1950). In any event, we feel that
the properties of the succinoxidase system itself must be clearly understood before it will be possible to define more precisely the way in which
toxin interferes with its function.

Consequently, before attempting further deliberations about the
exact point of attack of diphtheria toxin, it is well to consider the
succinate cytochrome c reductase system in some detail. The role of
cytochrome b in succinate oxidation remains a mystery. There appears
to be a close parallelism between cytochrome b content* and ability to
oxidize succinate even in tissues from widely different sources (Pappenheimer & Hendee, 1949). No clear-cut separation of succindehydrogenase from cytochrome b (or b_1) has been reported,† although from
time to time preparations with succindehydrogenase activity (i.e. which
catalyse reduction of dyes, ferricyanide, or cytochrome c by succinate)
have been described which have been said to contain little or no cytochrome b (Clark, Neufeld & Stotz, 1951; Green, Kohout & Mii, 1954).
Recently, however, good evidence has been obtained that succindehydrogenase and cytochrome b represent distinct components of the
system (Tsou, 1951). Moreover, the kinetic studies of Chance (1952)

* Cytochrome b_1 must be included if bacteria are considered.

† After completion of this manuscript the paper by Neufeld, Scott and Stotz, *J. Biol.
Chem.* **210**, 869 (1954), appeared, describing the almost complete separation of succindehydrogenase from haemoproteins.

have shown that in the Keilin–Hartree heart-muscle preparation, reduction of cytochrome b is slow in comparison with all of the other cytochromes. In the presence of KCN, reduction is so slow that only 2 % of the oxidase activity could be carried through cytochrome b; the latter, therefore, can scarcely lie on the main pathway to oxygen. Chance proposes the following scheme:

succinate → succindehydrogenase → Slater factor → c
fast oxidation ↓ ↑ slow reduction
cytochrome b

Likewise, in the diphtheria bacillus, recent evidence indicates that succindehydrogenase and cytochrome b_1 are separate components of the succinoxidase system. In the bacterial system, electron transfer from both succinate and DPNH pass through cytochrome b_1 (Gump & Pappenheimer, unpublished). Nothing is known as yet of the intermediate steps (if any) between cytochrome b_1 and oxygen:

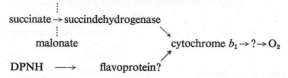

Purified preparations of diphtheria cytochrome b_1 are completely reduced by either succinate or DPNH as determined by the intensity of the difference spectrum observed in the Soret region, o.d. 430 minus o.d. 410 mμ. Reduction of cytochrome b_1 by succinate is almost completely inhibited by 0·1 M-malonate, but on adding DPNH to the mixture the 430 mμ. band appears at full intensity. This suggests that the competition between succinate and malonate is for some component other than cytochrome b_1.

Since succindehydrogenase and cytochrome (b or b_1) are separate components of the succinoxidase system, and since cytochrome b apparently does not lie on the main pathway between succinate and cytochrome c, it is obvious that determination of succindehydrogenase activity does not necessarily measure the cytochrome b content of a tissue. Under normal conditions, cytochrome b seems to be invariably present wherever there is a succinoxidase system. However, if a reagent can be found which is capable of specifically removing or destroying cytochrome b, then, according to Chance's scheme, its addition to the system should cause no decrease in succinoxidase activity. Diphtheria toxin may possibly provide such a reagent.

In normal diapausing cecropia pupae, cytochrome b is spectroscopically visible only in the intersegmental muscles of the abdomen.

At least 90 % of the total succinoxidase and succinate cytochrome c reductase activity of the entire animal is localized within this group of muscles. When pupae which received large doses of diphtheria toxin 10–14 days previously are examined, it is found that all traces of these muscles have disappeared. However, when homogenates of such intoxicated animals are prepared in isotonic sucrose, the washed mitochondrial fraction shows the same succinate cytochrome c reductase activity per pupa as normal animals containing intact musculature. Table 1 shows that there is no significant difference between the activities of cytochrome c oxidase, cytochrome b_5 or the complete succinoxidase system (containing added cytochrome c) in normal as opposed to intoxicated diapausing pupae. In fact, the only significant change observed in intoxicated animals, as is evident from Table 1, is in the rate of oxygen

Table 1. *Effect of diphtheria toxin on cytochrome system of diapausing cecropia pupae*

	Micromoles cytochrome c oxidized or reduced per pupa per minute*	
	Normal	Intoxicated†
Succinate cytochrome c reductase	0·067	0·062
DPNH cytochrome c reductase‡ (antimycin A)	0·057	0·058
Cytochrome c oxidase	0·36	0·42
	Microlitres oxygen consumed per pupa per hour§	
Succinoxidase (no added cytochrome c)	10–15	0–2
Succinoxidase (2×10^{-4} M cytochrome c)	30–40	30–40

* Followed in Beckman spectrophotometer at 550 mμ.

† 10 Lf purified diphtheria toxin injected per pupa about 2 weeks before the experiment. Results on both normal and intoxicated animals represent the average of several experiments performed with homogenates from two to four pupae.

‡ Antimycin resistant DPNH cytochrome c reductase activity is considered as a measure of cytochrome b_5 content. Rates were 30–50 % faster in the absence of antimycin A. Inhibition of succinate cytochrome c reductase by antimycin A was 100 %.

§ Succinate oxidation was followed in the Warburg apparatus at 25°.

uptake from succinate *without* added cytochrome c. Washed particles from whole intoxicated animals show little or no succinoxidase activity unless cytochrome c is added. It would thus appear that neither succindehydrogenase nor the Slater factor are affected by the toxin. Barring the unlikely possibility that cytochrome c is split off from the succinoxidase system through *direct* action of the toxin, we are left with cytochrome b as the only remaining known cytochrome component that has not yet been ruled out as a possible target for the toxin. An effect on cytochrome b content can be established only by direct spectrophotometric observations on homogenates from normal and intoxicated pupae. Such observations are, of course, crucial. At the present time, however, the experiment presents considerable technical difficulty owing to the small amount of cytochrome b in homogenates from whole normal diapausing pupae and the high turbidity of the preparations. But even if selective destruction of cytochrome b can be demonstrated in intoxicated animals, we shall still be faced with the problem of determining the role of cytochrome b in oxidative metabolism.

CONCLUSIONS

Diphtheria, once a leading cause of death, has become an almost extinct disease within our lifetime. The almost complete disappearance of clinical diphtheria can be attributed largely to the present practice of mass-active immunization of children with diphtheria toxoid. There are few other infectious diseases whose pathogenesis is so well understood as diphtheria; yet, as we have seen, many aspects of the problem remain clouded in mystery. In this article we have tried to show how progress towards the complete understanding of the biology of an infectious disease depends upon the *simultaneous* probing into the metabolic processes of both host and parasite. We feel that we are beginning to understand the factors concerned in virulence of the diphtheria bacillus and in how its toxin causes injury to the host.

Decisive experiments are often difficult to formulate and to execute. For example, the problem of relating the virulence of a given strain of *Corynebacterium diphtheriae* to the clinical severity of the disease which that strain is capable of producing can never be solved with finality until we find a method for carrying out quantitative virulence tests in experimental animals or until we can measure with precision the severity of a case of clinical diphtheria in man.

The theory that dipthheria toxin is related in some way to the protein moiety of diphtheria cytochrome b_1, and that its high toxicity is due to interference with a related component of the cytochrome system in the cells of higher animals, is an attractive one. The experiments with the cecropia silkworm provide evidence consistent with the theory. Thus the action of the toxin in diapausing pupae in bringing about selective destruction of tissues containing succinate cytochrome c reductase seems to suggest cytochrome b as the most likely point of attack of the toxin. The rapid arrest of adult development caused by the toxin, as opposed to the long latent period required before degenerative changes become evident, is in accord with the theory that it is the formation or synthesis of this component that is interfered with. So far as I am aware, there have been no serious objections raised to the theory. Nonetheless, here again, decisive evidence is lacking. There has been no direct demonstration of any impressive decrease in the cytochrome b content of intoxicated tissues. The function of cytochrome b remains obscure, so that no method other than direct spectrophotometric estimation is available for its assay. If diphtheria toxin does, in fact, block synthesis of cytochrome b, then the turn-over of this protein within the cell must be very rapid since in some tissues, effects of the toxin may become evident within a matter of hours. In other words, the theory demands rapid rates of formation and breakdown of cytochrome in the tissues, and there seems to be no evidence as yet bearing on this point.

None of these important problems appear to lie beyond experimental approach and many are being investigated in various laboratories at the present time. The resolution of any one of them can scarcely fail to further our understanding of the action of diphtheria toxin at the biochemical level.

REFERENCES

AGNER, K. (1950). Peroxidative detoxification of purified diphtheria toxin. *J. exp. Med.* **92**, 337.

AMIES, C. R. (1954). The pathogenesis of diphtheria. *J. Path. Bact.* **67**, 25.

BARKSDALE, W. L. & PAPPENHEIMER, A. M., Jr. (1954). Phage-host relationships in non-toxigenic and toxigenic diphtheria bacilli. *J. Bact.* **67**, 220.

BURNET, F. M. (1953). *The Natural History of Infectious Disease.* Cambridge University Press.

CHANCE, B. (1952). Spectra and reaction kinetics of respiratory pigments of homogenized and intact cells. *Nature, Lond.,* **169**, 215.

CHANCE, B. & PAPPENHEIMER, A. M., JR. (1954). Kinetic and spectrophotometric studies of cytochrome b_5 in midgut homogenates of cecropia. *J. biol. Chem.* **209**, 931.

CHANCE, B. & WILLIAMS, G. R. (1954). Kinetics of cytochrome b_5 in rat liver microsomes. *J. Biol. Chem.* **209**, 945.

CLARK, H. W., NEUFELD, H. A. & STOTZ, E. (1951). Cytochrome b. *Fed. Proc.* **10**, 172.

DUDLEY, S. F. (1923). The Schick test, diphtheria and scarlet fever. *Spec. Rep. Ser. med. Res. Coun., Lond.,* no. 75.

EATON, M. D. (1936). The purification and concentration of diphtheria toxin. *J. Bact.* **31**, 347.

FREEMAN, V. J. (1951). Studies on the virulence of bacteriophage infected strains of *C. diphtheriae. J. Bact.* **61**, 675.

GRAY, C. H. & HOLT, L. B. (1948). Isolation of coproporphyrin III from *C. diphtheriae* culture filtrates. *Biochem. J.* **43**, 191.

GREEN, D. E., KOHOUT, P. M. & MII, S. (1954). Purification of succinic dehydrogenase. *Fed. Proc.* **13**, 220.

GROMAN, N. B. (1953). Evidence for the induced nature of the change from non-toxigenicity to toxigenicity as a result of exposure to specific bacteriophage. *J. Bact.* **66**, 184.

GROMAN, N. B. (1954). The role of bacteriophage in converting non-toxin producing *C. diphtheriae* to toxin production. *Bact. Proc.* p. 48.

HEWITT, L. F. (1952). Diphtheria bacteriophages and their relation to the development of bacterial variants. *J. gen. Microbiol.* **7**, 362.

KEILIN, D. & HARTREE, E. F. (1949). Effect of low temperature on absorption spectra of hemoproteins. *Nature, Lond.*, **164**, 254.

LEPOW, I. H. (1952). Spectrophotometric studies on mixtures of purified diphtheria toxin and ferriprotoporphyrin. IX. *Proc. Soc. exp. Biol., N.Y.*, **80**, 529.

LEPOW, I. H. & PILLEMER, L. (1952). Studies on the purification of diphtheria toxin *J. Immunol.* **69**, 1.

McLEOD, J. W. (1943). The types *mitis, intermedius* and *gravis* of C. *diphtheriae*. *Bact. Rev.* **7**, 1.

MITSUHASHI, S., KUROKAWA, M. & KOJIMA, Y. (1949). Study on the production of toxin by C. *diphtheriae. Jap. J. exp. Med.* **20**, 261.

MUELLER, J. H. (1941). Toxin production as related to clinical severity of diphtheria. *J. Immunol.* **42**, 353.

OKELL, C. C. (1929). The relationship of virulent to avirulent diphtheria bacilli. *J. Hyg., Camb.*, **29**, 309.

O'MEARA, R. A. Q. (1940). C. *diphtheriae* and the composition of its toxin in relation to severity of diphtheria. *J. Path. Bact.* **51**, 317.

PAPPENHEIMER, A. M., JR. (1937). Diphtheria toxin. I. Isolation and characterization of a toxic protein from C. *diphtheriae* filtrates. *J. biol. Chem.* **120**, 543.

PAPPENHEIMER, A. M., JR. (1947). Diphtheria toxin. III. A reinvestigation of the effect of iron on toxin and porphyrin production. *J. biol. Chem.* **167**, 251.

PAPPENHEIMER, A. M., JR. & HENDEE, E. D. (1947). Diphtheria toxin. IV. The iron enzymes of C. *diphtheriae* and their possible relation to diphtheria toxin. *J. biol. Chem.* **171**, 701.

PAPPENHEIMER, A. M., JR. & HENDEE, E. D. (1949). Diphtheria toxin. V. A comparison between the diphtherial succinoxidase system and that of beef heart muscle. *J. biol. Chem.* **180**, 597.

PAPPENHEIMER, A. M., JR., HENDEE, E. D. & WILLIAMS, G. R. (1955). Cytochromes of the adrenal glands (in preparation).

PAPPENHEIMER, A. M., JR. & WILLIAMS, C. M. (1952). Effects of diphtheria toxin on the cecropia silkworm. *J. gen. Physiol.* **35**, 727.

PAPPENHEIMER, A. M., JR. & WILLIAMS, C. M. (1954). Cytochrome b_5 and the dihydrocoenzyme I-oxidase system in the cecropia silkworm. *J. biol. Chem.* **209**, 915.

PINCHOT, G. B. & BLOOM, W. L. (1950). Alterations in the level of muscle phosphocreatine of guinea pigs produced by the injection of diphtheria toxin. *J. biol. Chem.* **184**, 9.

POPE, C. G. & STEVENS, M. (1953). Isolation of a crystalline protein from highly purified diptheria toxin. *Lancet*, ii, 1190.

POTTER, V. R. & REIF, A. E. (1952). Inhibition of electron transport component by antimycin A. *J. biol. Chem.* **194**, 287.

SANBORN, R. C. & WILLIAMS, C. M. (1950). The cytochrome system in the cecropia silkworm with special reference to the properties of a new component. *J. gen. Physiol.* **33**, 579.

SCHNEIDERMANN, H. & WILLIAMS, C. M. (1954). Physiology of insect diapause. VIII. Qualitative changes in the metabolism of the cecropia silkworm during diapause and development. *Biol. Bull., Woods Hole*, **106**, 210.

SLATER, E. C. (1950). The components of the dihydrocozymase oxidase system. *Biochem. J.* **46**, 484.

SMITH, L. (1954). Bacterial cytochromes. *Bact. Rev.* **18**, 106.

STRITTMATTER, C. F. & BALL, E. G. (1952). Hemochromogen component of liver microsomes. *Proc. Nat. Acad. Sci., Wash.*, **38**, 10.

TSOU, C. L. (1951). On the cyanide inactivation of succinic dehydrogenase and the relation of succinic dehydrogenase to cytochrome *b*. *Biochem. J.* **49**, 512.

WEIBULL, C. (1953). Characterization of protoplasmic constituents of *B. megaterium*. *J. Bact.* **66**, 692.

WILLIAMS, C. M. (1946). Physiology of insect diapause. Role of the brain in the production and termination of pupal dormancy in *Platysamia cecropia*. *Biol. Bull., Woods Hole*, **90**, 234.

WILLIAMS, C. M. (1948). Extrinsic control of morphogenesis as illustrated in the metamorphosis of insects. *Growth*, supplement to vol. **12**, p. 48.

ON THE BIOCHEMICAL MECHANISM OF ACTION OF GAS-GANGRENE TOXINS

MARJORIE G. MACFARLANE
Lister Institute of Preventive Medicine, London

In the self-effacing opinion of Topley & Wilson (1946) 'only when the chemist has replaced the immunologist shall we be able to give an intellectually satisfactory account of what happens when a particular parasite invades a particular host'. This is maybe the scientist's version of '"Beauty is truth, truth beauty"—that is all ye know on earth, and all ye need to know'; it is certainly a tall order for the chemist. It is indeed somewhat ironical that, after several toxins of the gas-gangrene group of clostridia had been identified as lecithinases, further study showed that other clostridial lecithinases, with similar biochemical activity, are not toxic; the host-parasite relationship is still with us in the slightly simplified form of the accessibility of an enzyme to a substrate in a cellular matrix. Moreover, the isolation of the classical exotoxins as homogeneous proteins has not as yet clarified the mechanism of their action.

Though ultimately no doubt this mechanism is explicable in terms of chemistry and physics, or in a series of mathematical formulae, its elucidation depends on a variety of experimental sciences. Knowledge of the biochemical mechanism is not an end, but a beginning from which the morbid physiology—'the inner connexion of the phenomena of disease'—due to the toxin may be traced upwards through its effect on isolated tissues and organs to its lethal effect on the animal. As Marjory Stephenson pointed out at the first meeting of this Society in 1945, 'facts established at levels *A* and *B* provide the starting point for work at levels *C*, *D* and *E*; and results obtained at levels dealing with enzymes must be referred...for animal experiments'. In Fig. 1 are set out the different stages involved in tracing the mechanism of action of bacterial toxins, from the recognition of a characteristic disease to the understanding and rational treatment of its signs. Considering these stages, it will readily be conceded that, though we know much of the pharmacological action of the classical exotoxins, of their antigenicity and their reaction with antitoxins *in vitro*, and something of their chemical and physical properties, we know little more to-day of their biochemical action than did Roux and Yersin more than sixty years ago.

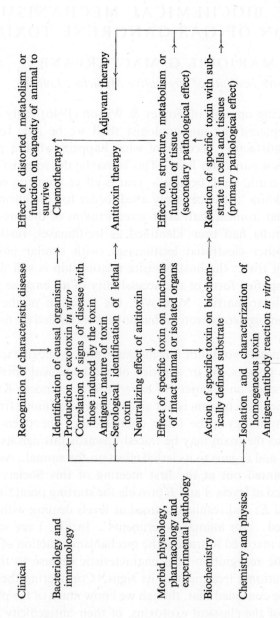

Fig. 1. Stages in elucidation of the mechanism of action of toxins.

Circumstance and fashion perhaps account in part for this gap in knowledge. Roux & Yersin (1888, 1889) carried out their classical research on diphtheria toxin with the catholic approach of their time. After establishing that the toxin was responsible for characteristic signs of the disease, they noted that the effect was apparently chiefly on the walls of blood vessels; they explored the chemical nature of the toxin and, being struck by the similarity between its behaviour and that of the diastases, examined its effect on sucrose and fibrin—surely the first of many negative experiments on the biochemical action of bacterial toxins.

Roux & Yersin intended to study the properties of the toxin further, but their third paper (1890) was wholly epidemiological. By 1894, after the discovery of diphtheria and tetanus antitoxins, Roux was engrossed in antitoxin and Yersin was investigating bubonic plague in Hong Kong. With antitoxin as a successful prophylactic and therapeutic agent there was presumably no pressure of clinical need for further inquiry into the mode of action of the toxin.

Fate in the shape of a severe epidemic of diphtheria in Paris may regrettably have diverted the fertile minds of Roux and Yersin from academic studies on the nature of toxins, but in the shape of war it stimulated research on the toxins of the gas-gangrene group of organisms. Gas gangrene was recognized as a clinical entity on the Western Front by the end of 1914, and in a remarkably short time, considering the complicated bacteriological picture and the difficulties of field investigations, the chief causative organisms were identified, and in turn the production of specific toxins by Clostridium oedematiens, Cl. septicum and Cl. welchii was established (Weinberg & Séguin, 1915; Nicolle, Cesari & Raphael, 1915; Bull & Pritchett, 1917; Weinberg & Séguin, 1918; Report to Medical Research Committee, 1919). Gas gangrene is characteristically a disease of war, and with war in the offing in 1938 measures for its prevention and treatment were presumably being reinvestigated in many countries, for the methods of vaccination worked out between the wars for the control of animal diseases caused by the gas-gangrene organisms are not suitable for use in man. In 1939 Seiffert in the Hygienische Untersuchungstelle des Wehrkrieses and Nagler in Sydney reported independently that Cl. welchii type A produced an opalescence in human sera, and Nagler showed that this activity was due to the specific lethal toxin. Pursuing this clue R. G. Macfarlane, Oakley & Anderson (1941) found that the toxin produces a similar opalescence in saline extracts of egg yolk, which they ascribed to the enzymic splitting of a lipoprotein, and M. G. Macfarlane & Knight (1941) then identified the enzyme as a lecithinase.

Between 1887 and 1939 great strides were made in biochemistry, particularly in protein chemistry and enzymology, and in immuno-chemistry, so that by 1940 it was almost axiomatic for biochemists meditating on the mode of action of toxins to envisage an immuno-logically specific toxin as a protein of specific structure whose action has the same order of specificity as that of an enzyme, whether the toxin is actually an enzyme attacking some tissue constituent or metabolic re-action, or whether it acts stoichiometrically as an inhibitor of some metabolic reaction. Where practically all is speculation it can hardly be said that one hypothesis is better than another. The fact that one bacterial toxin has been identified as an enzyme does not make it more likely that all toxins are enzymes, but this hypothesis is perhaps helpful because the known facts of enzymology can be used for guide and touch-stone in experiments and conclusions.

Pappenheimer (1947), however, considers it unlikely that tetanus, botulinus and diphtheria toxins are enzymes; his views may be most fairly stated by quotation: 'When administered in 1–2 M.L.D. doses, each of the three toxins show a prolonged latent period (18–72 hours or even longer) during which no symptoms or lesions can be demonstrated. Yet it is certain that some irreversible damage is caused within a few minutes or seconds after the toxin has been injected. Thus even 1000 units of diphtheria antitoxin injected 15 minutes after 1/50 M.L.D. of toxin has been injected in the skin at the same site fails to prevent a positive reaction from appearing 24–48 hours later. Yet only 0·001 unit of anti-toxin mixed with this small amount of toxin *before* injection suffices to neutralize its toxic action. The characteristic latent period and the extraordinary potency of these toxic proteins suggest that they do not act by direct inhibition of enzymes nor as enzymes themselves but rather perhaps, by interfering with the synthesis of some essential enzyme. Toxic symptoms, then, would not be manifested until the excess of essential enzyme has been depleted.'

But are the facts really incompatible with an enzymic action? Is the failure to neutralize toxin by subsequent injection of antitoxin adequate proof that the toxin *has already caused irreversible damage*? It would certainly be expected that a toxic enzyme would not be 'fixed' to its substrate but continuously decomposing it, and that therefore it should be possible to neutralize it at any time. But two factors may intervene. Firstly, the toxin molecule may have penetrated where the antitoxin cannot follow; the existence in natural membranes of a selective per-meability to different kinds of antitoxin has been shown by Hartley (1951). Secondly, as was shown by Zamecnik & Lipmann (1947) with

Cl. welchii lecithinase, in the presence of the substrate much larger quantities of antitoxin are necessary to neutralize the toxin than in the absence of substrate, because of competition between the substrate and the antibody for the toxin; this problem has been further studied by Cinader (1953). These two factors together may make it impossible to get an effective concentration of antitoxin in the right place, but failure to neutralize does not appear to be incompatible with the possibility that the toxin is an enzyme.

In considering the significance of the latent period of toxins it should be taken into account that though the action of an enzyme may be the primary cause of death, it is not the immediate cause. Between the administration of a toxic enzyme and the death of an animal, time has to be allowed for a number of consecutive events:

(1) *Distribution of the toxin and arrival at the significant organ or tissue.*

(2) *Entry into the susceptible cell.* This rate may perhaps vary considerably according to the nature of the toxin; *Cl. welchii* toxin, for instance, appears to be 'fixed' more rapidly than diphtheria toxin (Wright & Hopkins, 1946).

(3) *Action on specific substrate.* It seems possible, from the comparative rates of hydrolysis by *Cl. welchii* lecithinase of lecithin present in intact red cells and lecithin in aqueous emulsion, that enzymic attack on a substrate fixed in some cell structure may be considerably slower than would be expected from cell-free reactions.

(4) *Manifestation of damage to the cell.* It is clear from the work of Bernheimer (1947) on the kinetics of haemolysis by *Cl. septicum* toxin, and also from the phenomenon of 'hot-cold lysis' with *Cl. welchii* toxin, that there can be an appreciable gap in time between primary and secondary damage in a cell. The length of this period may be dependent upon the maintenance of favourable conditions, and this depends in turn on the capacity of the host to repair both the primary and the secondary damage. The rate at which damage becomes manifest is the result of an imbalance, a race between damage and repair. If the capacity to repair is itself affected by the toxin, as seems probable with *Cl. welchii* toxin, since it can affect the energy-producing reactions of the cell, the gap between normality and disease may widen more rapidly, and therefore generally speaking more obviously, than if the toxin attacks some substance at a rate which barely outstrips the normal capacity for repair. With so many variable rates and without knowledge of the nature of the primary attack it appears difficult to judge what time would be a reasonable latent period for a toxic enzyme, or, for that matter, for the depletion of an essential enzyme.

It is easy to suggest the possibility that a toxin may be an enzyme, almost too easy perhaps, for there is a tendency to label any enzyme found in a culture filtrate as a 'toxin' without much regard for its biological significance; but to pin-point the action of a particular toxin *hoc opus hic labor est*. Whereas Roux and Yersin could practically cover the known fields of enzymology by testing a toxin for invertase and fibrinolysin, the order of inquiry to-day is probably literally that of looking for a needle in a haystack. Admittedly the search can be narrowed down, when the pharmacological action of the toxin is clearly on a specified tissue or function, as in tetanus and botulism. The gas-gangrene toxins, however, appear to affect such a variety of tissues that it is difficult to distinguish a primary effect; and although a toxin may be recognized as being, for instance, dermonecrotic or haemolytic or a capillary poison, so little is known of the intimate structure of the lipoprotein membranes or of cement substances and so forth, which obviously might be susceptible to attack, that many possible substrates are not yet sufficiently defined for biochemical tests.

In these circumstances, a casual observation, such as that of Nagler on the growth of *Cl. welchii* in human sera, may play a crucial part in the elucidation of the mechanism of action of a toxin, and I wish to emphasize the value of such observations, particularly to bacteriologists using a variety of media for cultural or diagnostic work. Nagler's work led not only to the identification of *Cl. welchii* α-toxin and *Cl. haemolyticum* toxin as lecithinases, but to the recognition by Miles & Miles (1947, 1950) that other clostridial lecithinases of similar biochemical action are not toxic. This somewhat disconcerting fact is a salutary reminder of the warning given by Theobald Smith (1934): 'The experimental method must not let too many machines get between it and the whole, and must find some way of putting the fragments surgically removed for experimental purposes back into the whole. The comparative method is frequently in position to restrain the generalizations deduced from the experimental procedures, and to keep the experimenter from steering away from the goal which is an understanding of the totality.'

It was suggested by the conveners of this symposium that so far as possible discussions of virulence and host defences should be avoided. Nevertheless, it appears impossible to discuss mechanisms of pathogenicity without reference to the host, for the mechanism is the turn of the key in the lock, to which the structure of the lock is as apposite as that of the key. The differences in the biological behaviour of the clostridial lecithinases, and the differences in the susceptibility of tissue functions to a particular lecithinase, may be as illuminating to an under-standing of mechanisms of pathogenicity in general as the identification of the specific biochemical action of more and more toxins; at present the unique interest of the lecithinases is not that their kind of activity is known, but that their biological activity can be referred quantitatively to a common basis—the enzymic activity in a standard test towards a chemically defined substance—instead of to a basis of relative virulence in different hosts.

This article therefore will be concerned mainly with the different aspects of these lecithinases, and briefly with possible mechanisms of the effect of the lethal toxins of *Cl. welchii* type A, *Cl. oedematiens* and *Cl. septicum*. Consideration of other toxins produced by organisms of the gas-gangrene group, about whose biochemical action little is known, and of the antigenic enzymes whose pathological significance is doubtful, will be excluded, for these various toxins and enzymes have been enumerated and their nature and significance discussed recently in articles by Oakley (1943, 1954) and by van Heyningen (1950, 1954*a*, *b*, and in this volume).

IDENTIFICATION OF THE LECITHINASES OF CLOSTRIDIA

The validity of any discussion of the comparative biological significance of these lecithinases depends upon their identification as lecithinases with the same biochemical action, and the identification of at least one of them as a lethal toxin; the evidence on these points will be considered first.

Clostridium welchii *lecithinase.* Nagler (1939) showed that toxins of all types of *Cl. welchii* produced an opalescence in human sera which was inhibited by *Cl. welchii* antitoxin, and that with a number of *Cl. welchii* antitoxins the capacity to neutralize this factor and the lethal factor ran parallel. R. G. Macfarlane *et al.* (1941) found that *Cl. welchii* toxins produced in clear extracts of egg yolk an opalescence due to the libera-tion of free fat; they showed by selective neutralization tests with a variety of *Cl. welchii* toxins and antitoxins that this activity (commonly called the lecitho-vitellin or L.V. reaction) ran parallel with the haemo-lytic and lethal activity of the α-toxin, the main lethal component in *Cl. welchii* type A toxins. These authors suggested that the activity was that of an enzyme splitting a lipoprotein and showed that ionized cal-cium was necessary for the reaction. M. G. Macfarlane & Knight (1941) found that *Cl. welchii* toxins contained an enzyme with an optimum pH in the range 7·0–7·6, designated as a lecithinase C, which split lecithin into phosphorylcholine and a diglyceride, and that the development of

opalescence in egg yolk was accompanied or preceded by decomposition
of the lecithin present. The lecithinase was activated by calcium ions
and inhibited by *Cl. welchii* antitoxins and the anti-lecithinase content
of the antisera run parallel with their anti-α-toxin content. Though the
identity of the lecithinase with the α-toxin and the L.V. factor has not
been formally proved by synthesis, the foregoing facts are generally
accepted as evidence of the identity of these factors, and so far these
activities have not been separated by purification procedures. It should,
however, be pointed out that a positive L.V. test is not *per se* evidence
of the presence of lecithinase.

Clostridium oedematiens *lecithinase*. Crook (1942) and Hayward
(1943) found that some strains of *Cl. oedematiens* gave a positive L.V.
reaction, and M. G. Macfarlane (1942) found that occasional samples
of *Cl. oedematiens* toxin contained a lecithinase. A comprehensive
analysis of the antigens present in *Cl. oedematiens* filtrates was made by
Oakley, Warrack & Clarke (1947), who found that two immunologically
distinct L.V. factors were produced by *Cl. oedematiens*, one, designated
as *Cl. oedematiens* γ-toxin, produced by type A strains, and the other,
designated as *Cl. oedematiens* β-toxin, produced by type B (*gigas*) strains.
In complementary work M. G. Macfarlane (1948) showed that the
type A and type B filtrates contained immunologically distinct lecithinases which produced phosphorylcholine and a diglyceride from
lecithin; these lecithinases were specifically neutralized by anti-γ- and
anti-β-sera respectively, and were immunologically distinct from *Cl.
welchii* lecithinase.

Clostridium haemolyticum *lecithinase*. Jasmin (1947), in an investigation of bacillary haemoglobinuria (red-water disease) in cattle and sheep,
followed up in the light of Nagler's work the observation of Records &
Vawter (1926) that the lethal factor was apparently a haemolysin, and
found that *Cl. haemolyticum* toxin gave strong Nagler and L.V. reactions;
the L.V. activity of culture filtrates ran parallel with the lethality in mice,
and was equal to or greater than that of various *Cl. welchii* toxins
examined. At the same time Oakley *et al.* (1947) found that *Cl. haemolyticum* filtrates contained an L.V. factor which was apparently identical
antigenically with *Cl. oedematiens* β-toxin, and M. G. Macfarlane (1950*a*)
verified that the L.V. factor was a lecithinase of the same biochemical
type (a lecithinase C) as *Cl. welchii* lecithinase.

Clostridium bifermentans *lecithinase*. Hayward (1943) found that
various strains of *Cl. bifermentans* and *Cl. sordellii* gave Nagler reactions
which were partially or completely neutralized by *Cl. welchii* antisera.
Miles & Miles (1947, 1950) showed that *Cl. bifermentans* produced

a lecithinase which was neutralized by homologous antisera. The enzymes prepared from several strains were also all neutralized by *Cl. welchii* antitoxin, and *Cl. welchii* lecithinase was neutralized by the *Cl. bifermentans* antisera; the antigenic relationship, however, is distant, as in terms of lethal doses *Cl. welchii* α-antitoxin is 500 times more effective against *Cl. welchii* lecithinase than against *Cl. bifermentans* lecithinase.

Miles & Miles (1947, 1950) found that the *Cl. bifermentans* enzyme differed from *Cl. welchii* lecithinase in certain biochemical properties, such as the lower pH optimum about 5 and the requirement for calcium ions, and differed notably in its biological properties. In view of certain discrepancies in the titres of this factor by L.V., lecithinase and lethal tests, Lewis & M. G. Macfarlane (1953) re-examined the biochemical properties of the *Cl. bifermentans* preparations used by Miles & Miles (1950), and verified that the lecithinase present was a lecithinase C, similar to that of *Cl. welchii*, and found that activation by calcium ions could be demonstrated in suitable conditions.

Thus four enzymes—designated as *Cl. welchii* α-toxin, *Cl. oedematiens* β-toxin, *Cl. oedematiens* γ-toxin and *Cl. bifermentans* lecithinase—have been identified as being lecithinases of a single biochemical type, but immunologically distinct except for the distant relationship between the *Cl. welchii* and the *Cl. bifermentans* lecithinases.

VARIATION IN PATHOGENICITY

The significance of the lecithinases as toxic agents can be considered from two aspects, firstly, the contribution of the lecithinase to the killing power of the organism in a natural infection, and secondly, the relative toxicity to animals of enzymically equipotent amounts of the different lecithinases.

Contribution to killing power in infections. There is adequate evidence, particularly from the work of Evans (1943 *a, b,* 1945, 1947), that in *Cl. welchii* type A infections the lecithinase (*Cl. welchii* α-toxin) is the most important lethal factor and the α-antitoxin is the significant antibody in the control of the disease. It seems very probable from Jasmin's work that the lecithinase is the main toxic factor in disease caused by *Cl. haemolyticum*, since the L.V. factor was correlated with the lethality of the toxin, and the L.V. titres of culture filtrates were considerably higher than those of representative strains of *Cl. welchii* type A, but the evidence of its importance in natural infections is not complete. Oakley *et al.* (1947) obtained no evidence that *Cl. oedematiens* filtrates contained lethal activity except that of the α-toxin, common to type A and type B

5

strains, whose mode of action is as yet unknown; the lecithinases were present in such small concentrations in culture filtrates that their killing power could not be determined and may be reckoned as probably only a very small factor in *Cl. oedematiens* infections. Nevertheless, *Cl. oedematiens* type B lecithinase (β-toxin) is legitimately described as a toxin, for it is apparently identical with the lethal agent in *Cl. haemolyticum* toxin, and it therefore cannot be wholly discounted as a factor in *Cl. oedematiens* infections. The *Cl. bifermentans* strains used by Miles & Miles, in contrast to the other lecithinase-producing species of clostridia, were practically non-pathogenic, so the contribution of the lecithinase to the killing power of this organism does not arise.

Toxicity of enzymically equipotent amount of different lecithinases. Miles & Miles (1947) found that preparations of *Cl. bifermentans* lecithinase were much less toxic to mice than might be expected from their lecithinase activity assessed by the egg-yolk test, and that, in the concentrations available, the lecithinase did not haemolyse human, horse, sheep and guinea-pig red cells, and only partially haemolysed rabbit and mouse cells. Later, Miles & Miles (1950) succeeded in preparing more concentrated preparations of *Cl. bifermentans* lecithinase and made a detailed study of the relative toxicities of enzymically equipotent doses of this enzyme and *Cl. welchii* lecithinase. They adopted as a unit of lecithinase activity the liberation of 50μg. P from lecithin in 15 min. at $37°$ and pH $7 \cdot 5$; these conditions were not optimal for *Cl. bifermentans* lecithinase, which has a pH optimum of about $5 \cdot 0$, but correspond approximately to the conditions in which the lecithinase would have to act *in vivo*, and therefore give a fairer basis for the comparison of the toxicities.

On this basis Miles & Miles (1950) compared the toxicity to mice and the haemolytic activity to mouse cells of lecithinases derived from three strains of *Cl. bifermentans*—M 58*e*, A 250*c* and M 10*g*—with those of two preparations of *Cl. welchii* lecithinase. They found that the most toxic *Cl. bifermentans* lecithinase, derived from M 58*e*, was only one-ninth as toxic as *Cl. welchii* lecithinase, and that the lecithinases of the strains A 250*c* and M 10*g* were 60 and 75 times less active than *Cl. welchii* lecithinase. The *Cl. bifermentans* lecithinases therefore differed significantly from each other, as well as from *Cl. welchii* lecithinase. The differences in toxicity were reflected in differences in the haemolytic activity. The haemolytic activity of the *Cl. bifermentans* lecithinases roughly paralleled their lethal activity, and neutralization tests with *Cl. welchii* α-antitoxin were sufficiently close to indicate the identity of the lecithinase and the haemolysin in these preparations.

Miles & Miles (1950) point out that, though haemolysis may not be the determining factor in toxicity, the red cell at least reflects the susceptibility of other tissues whose poisoning determines the death of the animal. It may be added that in the haemolytic tests the potential lecithinase activity of the samples of toxin used directly corresponded to the activity titrated on lecithin, as the conditions of the two *in vitro* tests were similar; the differences in haemolytic activity cannot be explained by some selective inhibition or activation by an agent external to the reactions, as might be the case *in vivo*. The haemolytic experiments therefore strengthen the conclusion that the observed differences in toxicity are real and, even allowing some latitude in a comparison based on an arbitrary unit of lecithinase activity *in vitro*, there seems little doubt that the differences in toxicity of *Cl. bifermentans* and *Cl. welchii* lecithinases are significant.

As yet there are no comparable data for the relative toxicity of the other immunologically distinct lecithinases, the β- and γ-toxin of *Cl. oedematiens*. Jasmin (1947), in his experiments with *Cl. haemolyticum* toxin, estimated the lecithinase activity by the end-point in turbidity tests with egg yolk, and though this sufficed to correlate the lethality of the samples with the lecithinase activity of the toxins, the activity cannot be accurately equated with the lecithinase activity of other toxins; by a rough comparison of the titres mentioned by this author for egg yolk and lethality it appears probable that *Cl. haemolyticum* lecithinase (i.e. *Cl. oedematiens* β-antigen) is rather less toxic for mice than *Cl. welchii* toxin.

Variation in haemolytic activity. There is evidence, however, that the two *Cl. oedematiens* lecithinases differ from each other and from *Cl. welchii* lecithinase in their haemolytic activity. Just prior to the first paper by Miles & Miles (1947), Oakley *et al.* (1947) pointed out that *C. oedematiens* β- and γ-toxins readily attack horse red cells, which are hardly attacked by *Cl. welchii* α-toxin, whereas sheep red cells, which are readily attacked by *Cl. welchii* toxin, are relatively insensitive to *Cl. oedematiens* γ-toxin. The differences noted were qualitative rather than quantitative, in that the haemolytic activity of the several lecithinases was not referred to an independent assay of the actual lecithinase activity, but it seemed obvious that these differences were essentially of the same nature as the difference in toxicity to the mouse of *Cl. bifermentans* and *Cl. welchii* lecithinases, with the additional complication that the species of the host, as well as the species of lecithinase, was a factor determining the degree of haemolysis.

Oakley *et al.* (1947) suggested that something besides the enzymic attack on lecithin was involved in the haemolysis of different types of

5-2

red cells. M. G. Macfarlane (1950*b*), however, showed that the rate of hydrolysis, measured chemically, of the phospholipid in intact red cells by enzymically equipotent amounts of different lecithinases could vary with the kind of lecithinase for one species of red cell, and also with the species of cell for one kind of lecithinase. Thus *Cl. welchii* α-toxin hydrolysed the phospholipid in sheep cells more rapidly than that in horse cells, but *Cl. oedematiens* γ-toxin hydrolysed the phospholipid in horse cells more rapidly than that in sheep cells. Haemolysis was always preceded by some decomposition of phospholipid. No difference was detected between the rate of attack of the different enzymes on phospholipid extracted from red cells and the rate of attack on egg lecithin by which the enzymes were assayed.

The differences in the rates of hydrolysis underlay the differences in the rates of haemolysis, and were consistent with the findings of Oakley *et al.* (1947) on the sensitivity of the different cells to the different haemolysins. There seems no reason to suppose that the differences in haemolytic activity are due to anything beyond differences in the structure of the several lecithinases on the one hand and the several species of red cells on the other. The differences in the rates can only be regarded as reflecting the 'goodness of fit' between the individual enzyme and the cell surface in which the substrate lecithin is embedded.

One is tempted by the coyness of these haemolytic systems to cry

> Who order'd that their longing's fire
> Should be, as soon as kindled, cool'd?—
> Who renders vain their deep desire?—

and the answer

> A God, a God their severance ruled;
> And bade betwixt their shores to be
> The unplumb'd, salt, estranging sea

is perhaps as enlightening and certainly more euphonious than any which can be offered in terms of the Michaelis constant, measuring the affinity of an enzyme for its substrate. Nevertheless, the measurement might be of interest.

Effect of cell concentration on rate of haemolysis. Haemolytic activity was measured by Oakley *et al.* (1947) and by Miles & Miles (1950) with the concentration of red cells usual in haemolysis tests, i.e. about 2–5 % (v/v) of packed cells and apparently without added calcium. With these conditions the statements of these authors, for example that *Cl. bifermentans* lecithinase is practically non-haemolytic to human and guineapig cells and that *Cl. welchii* lecithinase hardly attacks horse cells, are correct. If the concentration of cells is raised to 10 or 20 % (v/v), as was necessary in the experiments of M. G. Macfarlane (1950b) in order to get sufficient phospholipid for analysis, these lecithinases attack the 'resistant' cells, and, as was shown by Oakley & Warrack (1941), the minimum haemolytic dose for resistant cells is more markedly reduced by the addition of calcium ions than is that for 'sensitive' cells.

An experiment carried out by the writer to measure the rate of haemolysis with increasing concentrations of guinea-pig red cells by enzymically equal doses of *Cl. bifermentans* and *Cl. welchii* lecithinase is illustrated in Fig. 2. The cell concentrations at which half the observed

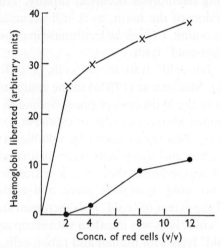

Fig. 2. Effect of cell concentration on amount of haemoglobin liberated from guinea-pig cells. Incubation 3 hr. at 37°, pH 7·4, Ca 0·001 M. ×—× 0·45 unit/ml. *Cl. welchii* lecithinase. ●—● 0·50 unit/ml. *Cl. bifermentans* lecithinase.

maximum rate of liberation of haemoglobin was reached was about 1·5 % (v/v) for 0·40 unit/ml. *Cl. welchii* enzyme and 6 % (v/v) for 0·5 unit/ml. *Cl. bifermentans* enzyme. On the assumption that these figures reflect the apparent Km, the affinity of *Cl. welchii* enzyme for guinea-pig cells was about four times that of *Cl. bifermentans* enzyme in these conditions. Considerable care would be necessary to devise fair conditions for comparison, but it appears that it would be possible to express the affinity of the different lecithinases for different cells in this way.

It would be interesting to correlate the virulence of different strains of *Cl. welchii* with the 'affinity' of the lecithinase, as well as with the toxigenic capacity. Evans (1945) found that a general relationship existed between production of lecithinase *in vitro* and ability to produce fatal infection in guinea-pigs, but there were some discrepancies. In view of the differences in strains of *Cl. bifermentans* found by Miles & Miles (1950), it is possible that, in relation to their enzymic activity, lecithinases from different strains of *Cl. welchii* also differ in toxicity towards guinea pigs.

Variation in secondary effect of lecithinase action in different cells. The liberation of haemoglobin from red cells treated with this type of lecithinase is clearly a secondary effect of the alteration in the cell membrane caused by the decomposition of the phospholipid. It was observed by van Heyningen (1941) that on incubation of sheep red cells with *Cl. welchii* lecithinase at 37° there might be no visible haemolysis, but that on cooling haemolysis occurred rapidly. This lysis was independent of the action of the toxin, as it still occurred when antitoxin was added before cooling. *Cl. welchii* lecithinase in consequence has been designated as a 'hot-cold' lysin.

The extent of 'hot-cold' lysis in red cells of different species was examined by M. G. Macfarlane (1950*b*) in the course of the experiments on the correlation of the hydrolysis of phospholipid in the red cells with haemolysis mentioned above, in order to establish conditions in which the measurement of haemolysis would be reliable. It was found that when *Cl. welchii* toxin and sheep cells were incubated at 37° and then cooled at different temperatures there was a critical temperature about 20° above which no 'cold' lysis took place, and as the temperature of cooling decreased the extent of 'cold' lysis increased steeply. With horse cells the extent of 'cold' lysis was less than with sheep cells, and there was practically no 'cold' lysis with human and rabbit cells. The results were similar with *Cl. haemolyticum* lecithinase. Although the phenomenon of 'hot-cold' lysis appears to be connected with the decomposition of lecithin, since not all haemolysins give this effect with sheep cells, these lecithinases cannot legitimately be called 'hot-cold' lysins, since the effect appears to be due to the ability of the cells to undergo this lysis.

This is an interesting example of the wide differences there may be in the secondary effect in different species after infliction of the same amount of primary damage; this no doubt reflects differences in the structure of the cells. Hillier & Hoffman (1953), from electron-microscope studies of red cell ghosts, suggest that the membrane consists of plaques situated on the outside of a fibrous network, to which they are joined by some ether-extractable lipid. The plaques are characterized as cylinders, about 30 A. thick, with a diameter roughly from 100 to 500 A. in different individuals and species; the cylinders are arranged in different groupings, so that different cell membranes have a characteristic texture. A study of the changes in appearance of these membranes after treatment with the different clostridial lecithinases should give interesting information on the structure of the red cell membrane, and possibly on the nature of the structures which determine the affinity of the different species of cell for different species of lecithinases and on the nature of hot-cold lysis.

The nature of 'toxicity' in a toxin

The comparative studies of the lecithinases produced by different species of clostridia show that toxicity, judged by the lethal capacity or the haemolytic capacity, is not inherent in lecithinases of a particular biochemical type, nor is susceptibility to this kind of lecithinase inherent in a cell containing lecithin. The toxicity is the resultant of the rate of action of the enzyme which is dependent primarily on the relationship between the enzyme and the substrate *in situ* in the cell. It involves the particular structure of the cell as well as that of the enzyme, and it appears that it could be expressed in the usual terms of the affinity of an enzyme for its substrate, by determination of the apparent *Km*.

It is of course well known that a particular toxin may be more toxic in one host than in another, and that toxins of the same character but different immunological specificity may differ in toxicity in the same host. The significance of the experiments with the lecithinases is that the mechanism of toxicity has been stripped, if not entirely, at least nearly to the bone. It has been shown that lecithinases of the same high biochemical specificity can vary in effect between virtual non-toxicity and high lethality. The primary mechanism has been observed, with an independent assay of the potential toxicity of the lecithinases used, and in conditions which rule out the intervention of 'vital forces' or the obscuring of the primary effect by differences in the secondary effect. The chemical basis of the differences determining toxicity is still unknown, but in the variation of toxicity there seems nothing foreign to biochemical concepts.

POSSIBLE MECHANISMS OF THE PATHOLOGICAL EFFECT OF THE GAS-GANGRENE TOXINS

Clostridium welchii, *type A*. Since lecithin occurs in cell membranes generally, it is to be expected that a toxic lecithinase will have a widespread effect in the body in addition to a haemolytic effect. Many of the effects of injection of *Cl. welchii* toxin into animals, such as oedema, haemorrhage, local necrosis and shock, as well as the signs of clinical gas gangrene, can reasonably be ascribed to the effect of the lecithinase on capillary permeability and on the permeability of cell membranes, leading to leakage of material from damaged cells, although in general it has not been shown that these effects are initiated or accompanied by decomposition of lecithin (see Oakley, 1943, 1954; Zamecnik, Nathanson & Aub, 1947).

The secondary effects can be more readily correlated with the effect of the lecithinase in the examination of biochemical functions. Wooldridge & Higginbottom (1938) showed that *Cl. welchii* α-toxin interfered with the aerobic oxidation of succinate by various minced tissues, and concluded that the effect was upon some intermediate link in the succinoxidase system. It is now known that many of the energy-producing oxidizing systems are congregated in the mitochondria of cells and the similar sarcosomes of muscle, and that these particles contain a large proportion of phospholipid. Some enzymes present, for instance, phosphatase, are not demonstrable in intact mitochondria, owing to the presence of a selectively permeable membrane, which limits access of substrates and confers osmotic properties; but in unfavourable conditions, e.g. incubation in a hypotonic medium, such enzymes may leak out (Berthet, Berthet, Appelmans & de Duve, 1952).

M. G. Macfarlane & Datta (1954) treated mitochondria, separated from livers of rats, mice, guinea-pigs and rabbits, with *Cl. welchii* toxin, and found that about half the phospholipid present (corresponding to the lecithin content) was readily decomposed. After decomposition of the lecithin, the succinoxidase activity was greatly decreased; this can be ascribed chiefly to damage to the factor transferring electrons from cytochrome *b* to cytochrome *c*, because the component enzymes cytochrome oxidase and succinic dehydrogenase were less readily affected. This intermediate factor is also concerned in the oxidation of dihydrocozymase (Slater, 1950) and is an important link in the oxidation systems of cells. The phosphatase activity of mitochondria was increased after the action of the lecithinase. No marked difference was observed in the susceptibility to the lecithinase of mitochondria from the different species of animals examined, though there were some minor differences in the rate at which the secondary damage became apparent. A similar effect on the succinoxidase activity of mitochondria has been shown with crystalline lecithinase A from snake venom by Nygaard & Sumner (1953).

It appears probable that *Cl. welchii* lecithinase by its ability to attack mitochondria, and presumably also sarcosomes, could grossly upset the enzymic balance of cells *in vivo*. A decrease in oxidizing power would lead not only to curtailment of the coupled processes of synthesis for repair, but to a replacement of the oxidation of carbohydrate by glycolysis with a consequent increase in acid production. This imbalance, together with the augmentation of autolytic processes by phosphatases leaking from the mitochondria, would give conditions favourable for the growth of the organism. This might be of special significance in the spread of infection in muscle; the systemic effects would appear to be due mainly to vascular damage.

Kielley & Meyerhof (1950) found that the unstable magnesium-activated adenosine-triphosphatase of muscle was inactivated by *Cl. welchii* toxin, though M. G. Macfarlane (1950c) found that the adenosine-triphosphatase of myosin was not altered after hydrolysis of the lecithin present. It is not clear whether the contractile process of muscle can be directly affected.

Clostridium oedematiens *toxin.* In clinical gas gangrene due to *Cl. oedematiens* there is generally intense toxaemia and marked oedema locally; a feeling of weight in the affected limb is often an early symptom (MacLennan, 1943). Culture filtrates of the organism are very toxic, producing on injection a gelatinous oedema and haemoconcentration with serous effusions into the lungs. The main lethal component, designated as the α-toxin, is the same in type A and type B strains (Oakley *et al.* 1947) and appears to be a capillary poison.

Aub, Zamecnik & Nathanson (1947) found that small intramuscular doses in dogs caused massive local oedema and haemoconcentration, while larger intravenous doses led to a rise in peripheral vascular resistance, a fall in cardiac output, and finally a decline in blood pressure to shock levels. In the heart-lung preparation (Krayer, Aub, Nathanson & Zamecnik, 1947) the toxin caused a marked loss of plasma and blood from the pulmonary vessels into the lungs; the heart was relatively slightly attacked. Miles & Miles (1952) found that intradermal injections of *Cl. oedematiens* toxin into the skin of guinea-pigs increased capillary permeability in a singular manner, for the effect of a single dose lasted more than 30 hr., much longer than the effect of histamine or *Cl. welchii* toxin.

Aub *et al.* (1947) suggested that the toxin affected the walls of blood vessels by some enzymic action destroying some architectural unit. There are several possibilities for a capillary poison, for the site of action may be on the cell wall proper or on the intracellular cement substance through which diffusion from the capillaries appears to take place; and the attack may be on some constitutent of the membrane or matrix, or on some metabolic function which maintains the normal permeability. With this last possibility in mind, Lewis & M. G. Macfarlane (1954) examined the effect of *Cl. oedematiens* toxin on a number of isolated enzyme systems of likely significance, but the results were negative.

The problem of obtaining sufficient capillary endothelium for a direct chemical examination is itself formidable, and the composition of the cement substance is unknown. The possibility that *Cl. oedematiens* toxin may also attack some substance present in muscle is now being explored.

Muscle contains a peculiar protein, tropomyosin, which was isolated from rabbit muscle and characterized by Bailey (1948). Tropomyosin is a cyclic polypeptide which is very viscous in dilute salt solutions owing to linear aggregation. Although water-soluble, it appears to be bound to lipid in the muscle, as it is only readily extracted after treatment of minced muscle with ethanol and ether. The function of tropomyosin is unknown. Bailey suggested that it may be a building unit for myosin, but it seems possible, from its association with lipid and other properties, that tropomyosin may be concerned in some permeability phenomenon in muscle. It has been found recently in this laboratory that a sample of *Cl. oedematiens* toxin decomposes this protein. For example, with a concentration of toxin of about 100 LD_{50}/ml. the relative viscosity of a 0·5 % (w/v) solution of tropomyosin was reduced from 2·5 to 1·25 in 1 hr. at pH 7·0 and 25°; further action resulted in the production of dialysable and trichloroacetic acid-soluble nitrogen. The action is enzymic in character and requires the presence of sulphydryl compounds. Further investigations of this reaction and its significance are in progress.*

Clostridium septicum *toxin.* It appears probable that the lethal factor in *Cl. septicum* toxin is a haemolysin. After much contradictory work, Bernheimer (1944) showed that the lethal and haemolytic activities of the toxins examined were parallel and, more important as identification, that the antihaemolytic and antilethal titres of antitoxic sera from various sources were also parallel. *Cl. septicum* toxins contain a hyaluronidase, and a deoxyribonuclease, but it is considered that the latter is distinct from the lethal toxin (Warrack, Bidwell & Oakley, 1951).

The action of *Cl. septicum* is enzymic in character. The haemolysis is remarkable for an induction period during which the cells swell and become translucent through the action of the toxin; lysis is secondary to this action and can be prevented by the addition of sucrose (Bernheimer, 1947). Apart from its haemolytic action nothing is known of the biochemical mechanism of action of the toxin. Possibly electronmicroscope studies might indicate the site of attack and give a clue to its nature. This toxin does not apparently attack lecithin, kephalin or the cerebrosides. The possibility that it attacks other lipids or proteins does not seem to have been examined.

---

* Neutralization tests with selective antisera have proved that this enzyme is not identical with the lethal α-toxin of *Cl. oedematiens*.

REFERENCES

AUB, J. C., ZAMECNIK, P. C. & NATHANSON, I. T. (1947). Physiologic action of *Cl. oedematiens* (Novyi) toxin in dogs. *J. Clin. Invest.* 26, 404.

BAILEY, K. (1948). Tropomyosin: a new asymmetric protein component of the muscle fibril. *Biochem. J.* 43, 271.

BERNHEIMER, A. W. (1944). Parallelism in the lethal and haemolytic activity of the toxin of *Clostridium septicum*. *J. exp. Med.* 80, 309.

BERNHEIMER, A. W. (1947). Comparative kinetics of haemolysis induced by bacterial and other haemolysins. *J. gen. Physiol.* 30, 337.

BERTHET, J., BERTHET, L., APPELMANS, F. & DUVE, C. DE (1952). Tissue fractionation studies. 2. The nature of the linkage between acid phosphatase and mitochondria in rat-liver tissue. *Biochem. J.* 50, 182.

BULL, C. G. & PRITCHETT, I. W. (1917). Toxin and antitoxin of and protective inoculation against *Bacillus welchii*. *J. exp. Med.* 26, 119.

CINADER, B. (1953). Antigen-antibody interaction using enzymes as antigens. *Biochem. Soc. Symp.* 10, 16.

CROOK, E. M. (1942). The Nagler reaction: the breakdown of lipoprotein complexes by bacterial toxins. *Brit. J. exp. Path.* 23, 37.

EVANS, D. G. (1943 a). The protective properties of the alpha antitoxin and theta antihaemolysin occurring in *Cl. welchii* type A antiserum. *Brit. J. exp. Path.* 24, 81.

EVANS, D. G. (1943 b). The protective properties of the alpha antitoxin and anti-hyaluronidase occurring in *Cl. welchii* type A antiserum. *J. Path. Bact.* 55, 427.

EVANS, D. G. (1945). The *in vitro* production of α-toxin, θ-haemolysin and hyaluronidase by strains of *Cl. welchii* type A, and the relationship of *in vitro* properties to virulence for guinea pigs. *J. Path. Bact.* 57, 75.

EVANS, D. G. (1947). Anticollagenase in immunity to *Cl. welchii* type A infection. *Brit. J. exp. Path.* 28, 24.

HARTLEY, P. (1951). The effect of peptic digestion on the properties of diphtheria antitoxin. *Proc. Roy. Soc.* B, 138, 499.

HAYWARD, N. (1943). The rapid identification of *Cl. welchii* by Nagler tests in plate culture. *J. Path. Bact.* 55, 285.

HILLIER, J. & HOFFMAN, J. F. (1953). On the ultrastructure of the plasma membrane as determined by the electron microscope. *J. cell. comp. Physiol.* 42, 203.

JASMIN, A. M. (1947). Enzyme activity in *Clostridium haemolyticum* toxin. *Amer. J. vet. Res.* 8, 289.

KIELLEY, W. W. & MEYERHOF, O. (1950). Studies on adenosinetriphosphatase of muscle. III. The lipoprotein nature of the magnesium-activated adenosinetriphosphatase. *J. biol. Chem.* 183, 391.

KRAYER, O., AUB, J. C., NATHANSON, I. T. & ZAMECNIK, P. C. (1947). The influence of antitoxin upon the action of *Cl. oedematiens* toxin in the heart-lung preparations of the dog. *J. clin. Invest.* 26, 411.

LEWIS, G. M. & MACFARLANE, M. G. (1953). The lecithinase of *Clostridium bifermentans* toxin. *Biochem. J.* 54, 138.

LEWIS, G. M. & MACFARLANE, M. G. (1954). Examination of the effect of *Clostridium oedematiens* toxin on certain enzyme systems. *Biochem. J.* 56, v.

MACFARLANE, M. G. (1942). The lecithinase activity of *Cl. oedematiens* toxins. *Biochem. J.* 36, iii.

MACFARLANE, M. G. (1948). The biochemistry of bacterial toxins. 3. The identification and immunological relations of lecithinases present in *Clostridium oedematiens* and *Clostridium sordellii* toxins. *Biochem. J.* 42, 590.

MACFARLANE, M. G. (1950a). The biochemistry of bacterial toxins. 4. The lecithinase activity of *Clostridium haemolyticum* toxin. *Biochem. J.* **47**, 267.

MACFARLANE, M. G. (1950b). The biochemistry of bacterial toxins. 5. Variation in haemolytic activity of immunologically distinct lecithinases towards erythrocytes from different species. *Biochem. J.* **47**, 270.

MACFARLANE, M. G. (1950c). Inhibition of succinoxidase activity of mitochondria by *Clostridium welchii* toxin. *Biochem. J.* **47**, xxix.

MACFARLANE, M. G. & DATTA, N. (1954). Observations on the immunological and biochemical properties of liver mitochondria with reference to the action of *Clostridium welchii* toxin. *Brit. J. exp. Path.* **35**, 191.

MACFARLANE, M. G. & KNIGHT, B. C. J. G. (1941). The biochemistry of bacterial toxins. 1. The lecithinase activity of *Cl. welchii* toxins. *Biochem. J.* **35**, 884.

MACFARLANE, R. G., OAKLEY, C. L. & ANDERSON, C. G. (1941). Haemolysis and the production of opalescence in serum and lecitho vitellin by the α-toxin of *Clostridium welchii*. *J. Path. Bact.* **52**, 99.

MACLENNAN, J. D. (1943). Anaerobic infections of war wounds in the Middle East. *Lancet*, ii, 63.

MILES, E. M. & MILES, A. A. (1947). The lecithinase of *Clostridium bifermentans* and its relation to the α-toxin of *Clostridium welchii*. *J. gen. Microbiol.* **1**, 385.

MILES, E. M. & MILES, A. A. (1950). The relation of toxicity and enzyme activity in the lecithinases of *Clostridium bifermentans* and *Clostridium welchii*. *J. gen. Microbiol.* **4**, 22.

MILES, A. A. & MILES, E. M. (1952). Vascular reactions to histamine, histamine-liberator and leucotaxine in the skin of guinea-pigs. *J. Physiol.* **118**, 228.

NAGLER, F. P. O. (1939). Observations on a reaction between the lethal toxin of *Clostridium welchii* (type A) and human serum. *Brit. J. exp. Path.* **20**, 473.

NICOLLE, M., CESARI, E. & RAPHAEL, A. (1915). Études sur le vibrion septique et le Bacterium chauvei. *Ann. Inst. Pasteur*, **29**, 165.

NYGAARD, A. P. & SUMNER, J. B. (1953). The effect of lecithinase A on the succinoxidase system. *J. biol. Chem.* **200**, 723.

OAKLEY, C. L. (1943). The toxins of *Clostridium welchii*. A critical review. *Bull. Hyg., Lond.*, **18**, 781.

OAKLEY, C. L. (1954). Gas gangrene. *Brit. med. Bull.* **10**, 52.

OAKLEY, C. L. & WARRACK, G. H. (1941). Factors affecting the activity of the α-toxin of *Clostridium welchii*. *J. Path. Bact.* **53**, 355.

OAKLEY, C. L., WARRACK, G. H. & CLARKE, P. H. (1947). The toxins of *Clostridium oedematiens* (*Cl. novyi*). *J. gen. Microbiol.* **1**, 91.

PAPPENHEIMER, A. M. (1947). Bacterial toxins. *Fed. Proc.* **6**, 479.

RECORDS, E. & VAWTER, L. R. (1926). Recent studies on icterohaemoglobinuria of cattle. *J. Amer. vet. med. Ass.* **68**, 1.

Report to Medical Research Committee (1919). *Anaerobic Infections of Wounds and the Bacteriological and Serological Problems arising therefrom.* London: H.M. Stationery Office.

ROUX, E. & YERSIN, A. (1888). Contribution à l'étude de la diphthérie. *Ann. Inst. Pasteur*, **2**, 629.

ROUX, E. & YERSIN, A. (1889). Contribution à l'étude de la diphthérie (2e Mémoire). *Ann. Inst. Pasteur*, **3**, 273.

ROUX, E. & YERSIN, A. (1890). Contribution à l'étude de la diphthérie (3e Mémoire). *Ann. Inst. Pasteur*, **4**, 385.

SEIFFERT, G. (1939). Eine Reaktion menschlicher Sera mit Perfringenstoxin. *Z. ImmunForsch.* **96**, 515.

SLATER, E. C. (1950). The components of the dihydrocozymase oxidase system. *Biochem. J.* **46**, 484.

SMITH, T. (1934). *Parasitism and Disease*. Princeton University Press.

TOPLEY, W. W. C. & WILSON, G. S. (1946). *The Principles of Bacteriology and Immunology*, 3rd ed. 2, 1004. London: Edward Arnold and Co.

VAN HEYNINGEN, W. E. (1941). The biochemistry of the gas gangrene toxins. II. Partial purification of the toxins of *Cl. welchii*, type A. Separation of α and θ toxins. *Biochem. J.* **35**, 1257.

VAN HEYNINGEN, W. E. (1950). *Bacterial Toxins*. Oxford: Blackwell Scientific Publications.

VAN HEYNINGEN, W. E. (1954a). In Neurath, H. & Bailey, K. *The Proteins*, **2**, part A, p. 345. New York: Academic Press Inc.

VAN HEYNINGEN, W. E. (1954b). In Florey, H. *Lectures on General Pathology*. London: Lloyd-Luke (Medical Books) Ltd.

WARRACK, G. H., BIDWELL, E. & OAKLEY, C. L. (1951). The beta-toxin (deoxyribonuclease) of *Cl. septicum*. *J. Path. Bact.* **63**, 293.

WEINBERG, M. & SÉGUIN, P. (1915). Le *B. oedematiens* et la gangrène gazeuse. *C.R. Soc. Biol., Paris*, **78**, 507.

WEINBERG, M. & SÉGUIN, P. (1918). *La gangrène gazeuse*. Paris: Masson et Cie.

WOOLDRIDGE, W. R. & HIGGINBOTTOM, C. (1938). The effect of certain bacterial toxins upon some respiratory mechanisms of animal tissues. *Biochem. J.* **32**, 1718.

WRIGHT, G. P. & HOPKINS, S. J. (1946). The fixation of *Clostridium welchii* toxin by skin cells. *J. Path. Bact.* **58**, 573.

ZAMECNIK, P. C. & LIPMANN, F. (1947). A study of the competition of lecithin and antitoxin for *Cl. welchii* lecithinase. *J. exp. Med.* **85**, 395.

ZAMECNIK, P. C., NATHANSON, I. T. & AUB, J. C. (1947). Physiologic action of *Cl. welchii* toxin in dogs. *J. clin. Invest.* **26**, 394.

BOTULINUM AND TETANUS TOXINS

G. PAYLING WRIGHT

Department of Pathology, Guy's Hospital Medical School, London

For a variety of reasons, the neurotoxins of *Clostridium botulinum* and *Cl. tetani* have long attracted the attention of both experimental pathologists and pharmacologists. The exceptional lethality of these substances places them in a wholly separate category amongst noxious bacterial products—the purest preparations of these toxins yet produced contain about ten million mouse-lethal-doses in each milligram of the crystallized protein. Perhaps as a natural accompaniment of this remarkable potency, they are exceptionally specific in their tissue affinities—the only known site of action for both toxins is the nervous system, in which they bring about characteristic syndromes of intoxication which can be reproduced with striking constancy over a wide range of homothermic and poikilothermic vertebrates. Finally, the progressive centripetal extension of the clinical manifestations in the 'ascending' form of tetanus has led many pathologists to study this intoxication as a conceivable model for the possible transportation of other noxious agents, amongst them the neurotropic viruses, from the peripheral tissues along the major motor-nerve trunks to the central nervous system (Doerr, 1939).

BOTULISM
General features

Cl. botulinum, whose toxins are responsible for the dangerous and often fatal form of food poisoning known as 'botulism', 'allantiasis', or 'Wurstvergiftung', is a spore-bearing, anaerobic organism which has often been isolated from samples of soil taken from many parts of the world. In England, Haines (1942) found toxigenic strains of this clostridium in five of the 106 specimens that he obtained from the southern and mainly agricultural counties—a proportion which accords well with observations made by several earlier observers. In spite of the wide distribution of the causative organisms, however, outbreaks of botulism in man, although alarming in their severity, occur only sporadically (Meyer, 1928), though, as their pathogenesis might suggest, they are encountered more frequently in veterinary medicine amongst both birds and herbivorous animals. Carnivorous animals generally are less susceptible to botulinum toxins, though epizootics have been recorded on fur farms among mink and ferrets (Moll & Brandly, 1951).

Studies on the many toxigenic strains of *Cl. botulinum* which have been isolated from various epidemics and epizootics have shown that, in spite of the fact that the clinical features in the affected human beings or animals presented a single, common, mainly neurological syndrome, their respective toxins presented immunological differences that enabled them to be separated into several distinct types. As with *Cl. welchii*, the variant types have been classified chiefly according to the neutralizability of their particular toxin by standard antitoxins of an already accepted nomenclature. Even with this criterion, however, the differentiation between the several types is not always readily accomplished, nor has the problem of classification been made easier by the refusal of certain investigators to free their strains for more general examination by bacteriologists elsewhere. Notwithstanding these impediments to taxonomists, however, at least four types (types A–D) have received general recognition as distinctive variants; others, less common or of a less well-defined nature, have been described and tentatively allotted further distinguishing letters.

The four major types of *Cl. botulinum* produce toxins which vary widely in their pathogenicity and lethality for man and the common laboratory animals. In almost all the human outbreaks in which typing has been carried out, types A and B, usually the former, have been incriminated. In the epizootics, other types are generally found: type C in the 'limberneck' of wild ducks and domestic fowls which follows respectively the ingestion of infected marsh weed or of the larvae of the 'greenbottle' and other similar blowflies that have fed upon contaminated carcasses; type D in the 'forage poisoning' of horse and the 'lamziekte' of cattle and sheep. Although progress has been made, the nomenclature of the botulinum toxins must necessarily remain fluid until many more strains of diversified origins have been subjected to toxin-antitoxin neutralization analysis.

Two unique features of naturally occurring botulism radically distinguish this disease from others associated with the toxigenic clostridia: the first, that it is primarily an intoxication and is not initiated by an infection; and the second, that the responsible toxin is ingested and absorbed into the blood stream from the alimentary tract. Instances of botulism that have followed wound infection with *Cl. botulinum* have been recorded, but they are exceptional. In typical outbreaks of botulism, such as the classical one at Ellezelles in Belgium in 1894, which was so fully investigated by van Ermengem (1897), within a few hours of consuming the contaminated food, the affected persons develop a syndrome whose more conspicuous features include disturbances of salivation, internal and external ocular paralyses, dysphagia and constipation, and later a widespread paralysis of the skeletal muscles which in fatal cases usually culminates in those of respiration. The case-fatality rate of many recorded outbreaks has exceeded 50 %, and when death occurs it usually takes place between 2 and 5 days after the consumption of the contaminated food.

The clinical features of human botulism can readily be reproduced experimentally in all the common laboratory animals, though the doses required may vary widely for the different species. This variation in susceptibility is particularly evident when the toxin is given by mouth; it is less if the intoxication is produced by parenteral injection—a mode of administration which requires much smaller doses to elicit fatal paralysis. On account of the better control of dosage possible with this mode of administration, nearly all the more recent investigations on the pathogenesis of botulism have been carried out with the parenteral rather than the oral method of giving the toxin.

Purification of types A and B toxins

Very soon after the original identification of the exotoxin of *Cl. botulinum* by van Ermengem, it became evident that this bacterial metabolite was unmatched for lethal power by any other poisonous substance known. Even with the crude culture filtrates which he had at his disposal, he obtained deaths in rabbits with subcutaneous injections of a fraction of a cubic millimetre. For long no serious efforts were made to concentrate the lethal constituent, but in the past few years two groups of investigators at Camp Detrick in the United States have undertaken the fractionation of actively toxic filtrates of types A and B cultures, and have effected such a high degree of purification that it is now possible to characterize the toxic protein constituents.

By using a series of precipitations at a succession of different acid reactions, Lamanna and his colleagues (Putnam, Lamanna & Sharp, 1946) were able to separate from their initial type A toxic culture filtrate a protein fraction which possessed the typical biological and immunological properties of this toxin. This protein, which they obtained in a crystallizable and electrophoretically homogeneous form, contained nearly forty million mouse LD 50 per milligram (Putnam *et al.* 1948). Enough of this toxic protein was prepared for them to determine not only its elemental and amino-acid composition (Buehler, Schantz & Lamanna, 1947), but also its sedimentation, diffusion and partial specific-volume constants. From these observations, they calculated that it had a molecular weight of about 900,000. Kegeles and his associates (Abrams,

Kegeles & Hottle, 1946) employed a similar culture medium to that of Lamanna, but, with a different sequence of precipitation procedures, most of them with ammonium sulphate, they obtained a rather higher yield of toxin. Their final crystallizable protein possessed a toxicity that was very close to that of Lamanna's toxin, but on the basis of a rather different physico-chemical examination, it appeared to have the slightly higher molecular weight of 1,130,000 (Kegeles, 1946). The high molecular weights found independently by these two groups of investigators is particularly interesting in view of the fact that in the naturally occurring botulism of both man and animals, the disease is brought about by the absorption of the toxin from the alimentary tract through whose mucosal lining it must have passed.

Lamanna & Glassman (1947) undertook a similar fractionation of type B culture filtrates, and again separated the toxin as an electrophoretically homogeneous protein. It had different characteristics from those of the type A toxic protein, however, being much smaller—a molecular weight of about 60,000—and rather less toxic for mice. Although none of the final preparations thus far made from either type A or B filtrates satisfies all the criteria for the purity of a protein, they represent a long step forward in the concentration and physico-chemical characterizations of these two exceedingly powerful toxins.

Site of action of the toxin

The many recorded observations on the structural changes in the cells of the central nervous system in patients dying from botulism long misdirected pathologists as to the site of action of the toxin. In 1923, however, experimental studies by three independent groups of investigators were published, all of which concurred in focusing attention on functional disturbances in the peripheral nervous system. Much the most important of these papers were those of Dickson & Shevky (1923 a, b), who drew attention, *inter alia*, to the parallelism between the sites of action of acetylcholine, as disclosed by Dale's observations, and those affected by botulinum toxin in their own intoxicated animals. In a series of systematically conducted experiments on cats, dogs and rabbits, they showed that in botulism there was gross impairment in the power: (i) of the vagus nerve to bring about inhibition of the heart; (ii) of the chorda tympani to evoke salivary secretion; (iii) of the nervus erigens to cause contraction of the bladder and erection of the penis; and (iv) of the third cranial nerve to effect constriction of the pupil. They concluded that botulinum toxin affects specifically those portions of the autonomic nervous system termed by Gaskell the bulbo-sacral and prosomatic outflows, and that impulses conveyed along these fibres are blocked at some point at the periphery. On the other hand, they found no evidence of any similar intoxication in the terminal ramifications of the fibres of the thoracico-lumbar outflow.

In their second paper, they turned their attention to the skeletal muscular system, whose progressive weakening is a conspicuous feature of clinical botulism in man. It became clear at once that the disability did not arise from any incapacity of the muscle fibres themselves to respond to stimulation, for they reacted promptly and forcibly to the application of direct electrical and chemical stimuli. Nor was there any evidence that the conducting power of the motor nerves was impaired. But when the motor nerve supplying a limb muscle was excited at frequent intervals, it was found that fatigue soon developed in an intoxicated animal. Whereas in a normal animal the threshold stimulation needed for the continued maximal contraction underwent little change over a period of 2 hr., that needed for the botulinum muscle, though initially the same as for the normal, soon rose sharply and progressively. Moreover, the promptitude with which this fatigue set in became steadily more apparent as the intoxication advanced. From these observations they again concluded that in botulism the skeletal muscular paralysis is dependent upon some peripheral intoxication and not upon any lesion in the central nervous system.

Contemporary with the investigations of Dickson & Shevky were those of Edmunds and his collaborators (Edmunds & Long, 1923; Edmunds & Keiper, 1924) and of Schübel (1923). From carefully conducted experimental analyses of the widely diversified functional disturbances typical of botulism, both reached the conclusion that the paralytic syndrome was primarily dependent upon an impairment of the transmission of impulses across the terminations of both the parasympathetic nerve fibres and the motoneurones to their respective effector organs. Like Dickson & Shevky, they were able to show that the muscle fibres themselves remained responsive to direct stimulation even at the height of the intoxication—indeed, Schübel, who worked mainly with frogs, found that the skeletal muscles of an animal which had been paralysed for nearly 4 months still retained their normal reaction to direct excitation. Though he recognized the essentially peripheral nature of the intoxication, however, Schübel considered that in fatal instances changes developed in the spinal cord that could be recognized morphologically. He believed that he could recognize these lesions by the neurohistological methods of Nissl, and he was led to the hypothesis that the toxin possessed an additional central action.

Although many of the earlier pathologists who recorded their observations in fatal cases of botulism in man described lesions in the spinal cord comparable with those of Schübel, there now seems little doubt that these are due not to any primary action of the toxin, but arise from such secondary causes as the terminal asphyxia characteristic of the respiratory paralysis of the agonal period (Cowdry & Nicholson, 1924). Apart from this last questionable suggestion of some central action, these three experimental studies on the sites of action of botulinum toxin provided firm support for the belief that it acted at two points: the first at the myoneural junctions in skeletal muscle much in the same way as curare; and the second at the nerve terminations of the parasympathetic system in the manner of atropine.

During the decade before the 1939–45 war, the physiological importance of acetylcholine was becoming widely recognized, and the sites of its action upon various neuro-effector systems were increasingly explored. The resulting clarification in the pharmacology of the autonomic nervous system culminated in the concept, first expressed by Dale (1933, 1935), that certain nerves—to which he applied the name 'cholinergic'—operated through the release of acetylcholine at their terminations, while others—the 'adrenergic' nerves—acted through the liberation of adrenalin. This division of the nervous system on a functional chemical basis rather than on one derived from its anatomical arrangement has strongly influenced all the subsequent studies on the site of action of botulinum toxin, and has served to emphasize the parallelism between the sites of action of this toxin and those of acetylcholine to which Dickson & Shevky first directed attention.

The resuscitation of interest in the toxicology of botulism which has taken place since the end of the 1939–45 war has led to the more careful analysis of the nature of the interference with conduction at the myoneural junction in skeletal muscles. The paralysis had been regarded by the earlier observers as similar to that which follows the injection of curare, and the first to draw attention to a significant difference in the character of the disturbance produced by the two agents were Guyton & Macdonald (1947). They showed that, in botulinum-intoxicated muscles, an immediate contraction succeeded the close intra-arterial injection of acetylcholine—a response which cannot be evoked by similar injections of this substance in animals rendered paralytic with curare (Brown, Dale & Feldberg, 1936). This distinction between the modes of action of the toxin and of curare was soon confirmed by other investigators (Masland & Gammon, 1949; Ambache, 1949; Burgen, Dickens & Zatman, 1949), who pointed out that the failure of trans-

6-2

mission at the myoneural junction might result from the incapacity of the nerve endings in the intoxicated muscles to liberate acetylcholine in amounts sufficient to evoke the contraction of the muscle fibres. This possibility was first put to the test by Burgen and his colleagues, who estimated the quantity of acetylcholine that was released by the rat's phrenic nerve-diaphragm preparation on repeated indirect stimulation *in vitro* both before and after exposure to botulinum toxin under conditions in which its destruction by cholinesterase was prevented by the addition of eserine. They recorded a marked fall in recoverable acetylcholine after intoxication; the amount liberated was about one-tenth of that obtained before the toxin had acted.

This diminution in the amount of acetylcholine recoverable from affected muscles may conceivably have been occasioned in one of two ways. First, the toxin may have injured the terminal portion of the nerve fibril—perhaps in the final unmyelinated part of its course—and so led to a blockage of conduction just proximal to its motor end-plate. Secondly, the motor end-plate itself may be damaged in such a way as to lessen its capacity to liberate acetylcholine. The former hypothesis receives some support from Guyton & Macdonald and from Burgen *et al.*, who point out that the administration of anticholinesterase drugs does little to lessen the paralysis, a mitigation that would be expected were even small amounts of acetylcholine to be released from the end-plates.

More direct, though unfortunately conflicting, evidence has been brought to bear on this difficult problem in neuromuscular pathology by the application of methods for the recording of end-plate potentials— the electrical responses which follow from the reception of the nervous impulse at the end-plate but which are ordinarily obscured by the much greater action potential of the contracting muscle which succeeds it. If this latter be suppressed, as by the administration of curare, the end-plate potential can be recognized and recorded. Stover and his colleagues (Stover, Fingerman & Forester, 1953) sought to apply this technique to botulinum-intoxicated muscles, and observed that when two impulses in quick succession were propagated down the nerve, they were able to record two distinct end-plate potentials though only the second was followed by the muscle complex. They interpreted their success with dual stimuli as showing that, in an intoxicated preparation, impulses always get through to the end-plate, but that only if two reach it in rapid succession is sufficient acetylcholine released to effect muscular contraction. Brooks (1953, 1954), on the other hand, was unable to record any end-plate potentials attributable to the first impulse; the second of his impulses, however, reached the end-plate and excited a muscular contraction. He supposed that the terminal nerve fibrils were injured by the toxin in such a way that their power of conducting impulses was impaired, but that the reception of the first impulse made possible by facilitation the passage of the second which promptly followed it. In favour of his belief that the acetylcholine release mechanism in such intoxicated muscles was not itself damaged, he brought the additional evidence that when intoxicated muscles were stimulated directly as much acetylcholine was liberated as from a normal muscle excited indirectly by way of its motor nerves. The discrepant conclusions reached in these two studies may perhaps have arisen, as Brooks has pointed out, from the fact that his observations were made on cats, whereas Stover and his colleagues worked upon frogs; until the conflict between these two views has been settled by further work, the manner in which the intoxication interferes with acetylcholine release at the myoneural junction will remain obscure.

The observations of Dickson & Shevky made it clear that, in addition to its action on skeletal muscles, botulinum toxin had far-reaching paralytic effects on certain parts of the autonomic nervous system. In recent years, many aspects of the intoxication of the parasympathetic nervous system have been re-examined by Ambache. His work has greatly extended knowledge of the distribution of post-intoxication paralyses in structures innervated by this system and has confirmed the belief in the vulnerability of its cholinergic division.

In the eye, the intrinsic muscles of the iris are innervated by both cholinergic and adrenergic fibres—the former supplying the more powerful sphincter pupillae and the latter the dilator pupillae. Ambache (1948, 1949, 1951 a) found that an intra-ocular injection of botulinum toxin was followed a day or so later by a great enlargement of the pupil and a failure of the iris to react to light. By the electrical stimulation of the oculomotor and cervical sympathetic nerves, he could show that this disturbance arose from the paralysis of the cholinergic neuromuscular apparatus and that the adrenergic dilator muscle fibres remained normally responsive. Any suggestion that this botulinum paralysis of the cholinergic sphincter pupillae muscle depends upon an atropine-like action of the toxin, however, is no more correct than the earlier belief that its action on striated muscle is curariform, for an injection of acetylcholine into the anterior chamber of such an intoxicated eye brings about an immediate reduction in the size of the pupil. Ambache (1951 b, 1954) further supplemented these observations on the eye by finding evidence for a similar paralysis, after a local injection of botulinum toxin,

of the cholinergic mechanism in the wall of the small intestine. Again
the adrenergic mechanism is spared and the smooth muscle itself
retains its normal responsiveness to direct applications of acetylcholine.

Through his studies on the effects of local injections of botulinum
toxin on sweat secretion on the one hand, and on the transmission of
impulses through the ciliary and superior cervical ganglia on the other,
Ambache has provided two further pieces of evidence in favour of the
view that this toxin injures specifically the cholinergic nervous system.
For many years the post-ganglionic sudomotor nerves in cats appeared
to occupy an exceptional position in the autonomic nervous system in
that, although they arise from the part which is connected with the
thoracic outflow, the sweat glands which they innervate respond to
acetylcholine and not to adrenalin. It was only in 1934 that Dale &
Feldberg showed that the post-ganglionic fibres which supply these
glands are cholinergic in character; Ambache (1951 a) has since shown
that they can also be paralysed by the local injection of botulinum toxin
into the pads of the feet, the portion of skin from which this animal
normally sweats.

All the earlier studies on the paralytic action of botulinum toxin on
the cholinergic portion of the nervous system have disclosed only its
effect upon the post-ganglionic component fibres; in his work on the
ciliary and superior cervical sympathetic ganglia, Ambache has shown
that the toxin acts also on the pre-ganglionic fibres. The ciliary ganglion
in the orbit is the site of the synapses between the pre-ganglionic fibres
that reach it from the oculomotor nerve and the post-ganglionic fibres
that pass to the sphincter pupillae. Feldberg & Gaddum (1934) had
shown that the pre-ganglionic fibres that enter the superior cervical
sympathetic ganglion are cholinergic, and the observations of Macintosh
(1941) make it likely that this is true also for the ciliary ganglion. By
injecting botulinum toxin locally round the ciliary ganglion, Ambache
(1951 a) was able to produce paralysis of all the structures innervated
by the post-ganglionic fibres which emerged from it, an effect most
readily explicable on the basis of injury to the synaptic endings of the
pre-ganglionic nerves. Later (Ambache, 1952), by infiltrating the
vicinity of the superior cervical sympathetic ganglion with the toxin,
he was able to produce a complete pre-ganglionic paralysis in the
neural pathway to the dilator pupillae muscle in the eye.

A large body of evidence has now been brought together to show that
botulinum toxin acts very widely on all the parts of the peripheral
nervous system that are cholinergic in character irrespective of whether

they form pre- or post-ganglionic components of the autonomic system or are motor nerves to the skeletal muscles. In spite of some evidence that acetylcholine may act as the transmitter substance at certain synapses in the central nervous system, however, there is no indication either from clinical or experimental sources that the toxin has any direct injurious effects upon the brain or spinal cord. Many years ago, van Ermengem (1897) and Forssman (1901) observed that the toxin was no more rapidly lethal when injected intracerebrally than when inoculated parenterally by some other route. The absence of any special suscepti-bility of the brain was confirmed by Davies, Morgan, Wright & Payling Wright (1953) in a comparative study on the modes of action of tetanus and botulinum toxins when very small, but lethal doses of both were inoculated directly into the medulla oblongata of rabbits. Nor does the exposure of botulinum toxin to macerated brain lessen its toxicity, as happens with tetanus toxin in the well-known Wassermann–Takaki reaction (Coleman, 1924). This invulnerability of putatively cholinergic structures in the central nervous system to botulinum toxin thus con-trasts strikingly with the widespread susceptibility of the peripheral cholinergic innervation.

TETANUS

General features

In contrast to botulism, which is almost invariably a form of food poisoning in which the already formed toxin is absorbed from the alimentary canal during digestion, tetanus is always the sequel to the contamination of a wound with spores of *Cl. tetani*, and the subsequent germination, multiplication and formation of toxin by these organisms within the immediate locality of the infected tissues. Both diseases are thus essentially intoxications, but in botulism the toxin is formed outside, whereas in tetanus it is produced within the body.

Among the clostridia generally, *Cl. tetani* has long been notable for its inability to proliferate in cultures under any except strictly anaerobic conditions, but the circumstances attending the establishment of an infection were obscure until they were clarified by Fildes (Fildes, 1927, 1929 *a, b*). He and his colleagues applied the physico-chemical concepts of oxidation-reduction potentials to the problems, first of the germina-tion of the spores (Knight & Fildes, 1930) and second of the multiplica-tion of the vegetative bacteria. Conditions permissive of both germina-tion and growth often develop in the depths of severely damaged tissues, where, as Smith (1949) and Oakley (1954) have pointed out, a number of mutually related changes—among them ischaemia from vascular disturbances, progressively increasing local acidity, anoxia, autolysis of dead cells, and the possible concomitant proliferation of accompanying less-strictly anaerobic bacteria—all produce local conditions which favour the clostridia generally. Little is known of some of these favouring factors, but from a few observations made by Hanke & Bailey (1945) it would seem that the growth requirements of *Cl. tetani* are not unlike those of *Cl. histolyticum*, and that at pH 6·5, a degree of acidity readily produced in injured muscle, both will multiply when the Eh is 85 mV. or less.

In the light of these biochemical findings on the conditions requisite for the growth of these bacteria, it seems surprising to find that clinical tetanus often follows comparatively trivial injuries. Cole & Spooner (1935) have drawn attention to the frequently trifling nature of the preceding lesion, and many authors have found difficulty in accepting the idea that such superficial injuries as abrasions may afford suitable conditions for the growth of so fastidiously anaerobic an organism. It must be realized in this connexion, however, that the diffusibility of oxygen is too low to permit its penetration from the surrounding air for more than a millimetre and often for much less, so that even a thin scab may suffice to establish an anaerobic focus (Goddard, 1945).

Because the signs of tetanus intoxication appear within 2 or 3 days of infection in experimental animals, and occasionally equally soon after contaminated wounds in man, it is evident that the multiplication of the bacteria in the tissues is followed promptly by the release of their toxic metabolites. Unfortunately, few quantitative studies have yet been made upon the rate of formation of toxin at such infected foci. Many years ago, in conjunction with his study on post-vaccinal tetanus, Francis (1914) carried out some experiments which indicated that at the time of death of the animal, the proliferating organisms may be surrounded by a very large depot of their toxin. In dying guinea-pigs, which had been inoculated with spores under conditions conducive to their germination, he was often able to recover with simple saline extraction of scrapings of the infected tissues, more than a thousand guinea-pig lethal doses of the toxin. It is apparent, therefore, that the quantity of antitoxin required to neutralize the accumulated reservoir of toxin and ensure the protection of the animal must be the immunological equivalent of many lethal doses of the toxin. Such considerations have led certain surgeons and immunologists to advocate local as well as general prophylactic injections of antitoxin.

Purification of tetanus toxin

Two methods have been used in recent years with almost equal success for the concentration of the lethal constituent—tetanospasmin—from filtrates of cultures of toxigenic strains of *Cl. tetani*. In the first of these methods, Pickett, Hoeprich & Germain (1945) effected a primary precipitation with cadmium chloride and followed it by a further one with ammonium sulphate. The most active preparation which they obtained had a lethal dose for mice of about $0.14 \times 10^{-3} \mu g$. In the second of these methods, Pillemer, Wittler, Burrell & Grossberg (1948), employing cold methanol in buffered solutions of specified acidity and ionic strength, prepared a toxin with a lethal dose for mice of about $0.09 \times 10^{-3} \mu g$. This material is an electrophoretically homogeneous protein with a minimum molecular weight of 67,000, and its amino-acid residues on hydrolysis have, like those of botulinum type A toxin, a notably high content of isoleucine and aspartic acid. Such highly purified tetanus toxins, however, are unstable in solution and rapidly become converted into toxoid—a change which Pillemer & Moore (1948) suggest may result from the formation of a dimer in which the toxic determinant groupings of the molecule become blocked, but whose antigenicity and ability to flocculate with specific antibody is still retained.

Although the signs of tetanus that appear in experimentally inoculated animals follow a classical pattern that closely resembles that of the human disease, a wide range of variation is found in the relative lethalities of the toxic filtrates of different strains of *Cl. tetani* when these are assayed upon more than one mammalian species. This variation first became apparent as an incidental finding in a study made by Friedemann, Zuger & Hollander (1939) on the permeability of cerebral capillaries to antitoxin. In the course of this work, they employed four different preparations of the toxin and two different species of animal—rabbits and guinea-pigs—on which to assay them. When the toxins were inoculated intracerebrally, it was found that the ratios of the lethal doses of the four preparations ranged between the limits of 100:1 and 6:1. In a later paper, Friedemann & Hollander (1943) extended their observations with similar results by comparing seven toxin preparations on three species—rabbits, guinea-pigs and mice—and using two routes of inoculation—intracerebral and intramuscular. Again the same wide range of relative lethalities was disclosed in a comparative study by Llewellyn Smith (1942–3) when she tested the relative potencies of five different preparations of toxin on rabbits, guinea-pigs and mice.

Whereas their proportionate lethalities for mice and guinea-pigs were roughly the same for all, those for rabbits and guinea-pigs might again differ by a factor of a hundred. The meaning of this species peculiarity remains obscure, but it would seem that some strains of *Cl. tetani* produce culture filtrates which contain some agent which can potentiate the lethal action of tetanospasmin for rabbits, possibly by promoting its readier access to vulnerable centres in the central nervous system.

Site of action of the toxin

Clinically in man, tetanus may present itself in one of several forms, but two of them are so commonly encountered that they have come to dominate discussions on the pathogenesis of the disease: the first, the 'general' form, in which rigidity begins in the muscles of the jaw and neck and spreads thence, often with the accompaniment of intermittent convulsions, to those of the trunk and limbs; and the second, the 'local' form, in which the initial manifestation is spasticity in the muscles near the site of the precursory wound. No visceral symptoms or signs comparable with those met with in botulism are known in clinical tetanus, except those of dysphagia and urinary retention, both of which can be accounted for by the involvement of nearby skeletal muscles.

These two forms of human tetanus can be duplicated in experimental animals by varying the route of inoculation of the toxin: an injection into the muscles of a limb causes first a 'local' tetanus, which is succeeded, if a sufficient dose is introduced, by 'ascending' tetanus with an ultimate intoxication of the brain stem; whereas, if the toxin is injected directly into the blood stream, the 'general' or 'descending' form develops *ab initio*. Naturally, investigators have sought assiduously to bring together all these manifestations of the intoxication into some common scheme of pathogenesis. But in spite of a very large volume of experimental work no single theory has yet emerged, and discussions on the mode of action of the toxin still revolve round whether it operates centrally in the spinal cord and brain stem, or peripherally in the motor-nerve endings of the skeletal muscles, or even at both sites simultaneously or successively. The literature on this question is now extensive and controversial, and records many ingenious experiments designed to throw light on this antithesis. Most of them have been mainly concerned with the phenomena of local tetanus in the belief that if this problem could be made to yield to attack, an explanation of the pathogenesis of general tetanus would more readily follow. The general position will now be briefly reviewed.

(i) *Peripheral site*

(a) *The myoneural junction.* Since the pioneer experiments of Vaillard & Vincent (1891) on the effect of nerve section on local tetanus, there has been no serious dispute about the necessity of an intact motor innervation for its appearance and maintenance. Several authors have believed that the spasticity results from some toxic injury to the motor end-plates which keeps the muscle fibres in a state of unremitting activity. In recent years, this view has been espoused by Abel and his school (Abel, Evans, Hampil & Lee, 1935; Abel & Hampil, 1935; Abel, Hampil & Jonas, 1935; Abel, Firor & Chalian, 1938). Their belief is chiefly based upon two observations recorded by Harvey (1939): the first, that the spasticity persists in intoxicated muscles for several days after the section of their motor-nerve trunks and disappears with the degeneration of the nerve endings; and the second, that a single nerve volley excited by electrical stimulation of the motor-nerve trunk, which gives rise to a muscle action potential in a normal muscle, leads to a repetitive discharge in an intoxicated muscle and inferentially to a prolongation in the contraction of its fibres.

There are serious doubts whether Harvey's findings adequately support the interpretations that he placed on them. In his denervation experiments, he divided the sciatic nerve high in the thigh. Several authors (Courmont & Doyon, 1899; Pochhammer, 1909; Permin, 1913–14) have pointed out that the complete motor denervation of the hind limb requires the section of more than the sciatic nerve. After describing in detail his surgical procedure for ensuring the denervation of the hind limb, Pochhammer states: 'The type and completeness of the denervation of the muscles is by no means immaterial in the employment of such experimental researches on the action of tetanus toxin. Incomplete denervation gives rise to the misconception of a local, apparently purely muscular, tetanus. The assumption of a myogenic origin for the spasms is disproved by the foregoing experiments.' Harvey's observations on the electromyograms of intoxicated muscles in which he recorded repetitive action potentials after a single nerve volley have similarly come under criticism from the later investigators who have attempted to repeat them. Göpfert & Schaefer (1940), Acheson, Ratnoff & Schoenbach (1942) and Perdrup (1946) have all failed to confirm his findings; Göpfert & Schaefer thought that Harvey's multiple-action potentials were probably artefacts which might have been brought about by a spread of electrotonus from the exciting electrodes on the nerve to the end-plates in the muscle.

(b) *Proprioceptive sensory nerve endings.* The many points of similarity between the character and distribution of the spasticity in tetanus
and in decerebrate rigidity, to which Sherrington (1906) originally drew
attention, have suggested in recent years to Schaefer (1944) and to
Perdrup the idea that the spasticity in tetanus might depend upon an
exaggeration of the proprioceptive reflexes on which normal postural
tonus mainly depends. Over-activity of such a kind might result, they
believed, from the intoxication of the sensory nerve endings in muscle
from which the reflex originates.

Schaefer supported his suggestion with experimental observations of
two kinds. In the first, he noted that in guinea-pigs the centripetal
action potentials that could be recorded in the distal divided stump of
the motor-nerve trunk to one of the heads of gastrocnemius after a
sudden stretch had been applied to the tendo achillis became markedly
augmented after tetanus toxin had been injected into the muscle and
sufficient time had elapsed for the development of local tetanus. In
the second, he found that the electromyograms obtainable after crossed
stretch reflexes in control and in intoxicated limbs showed greater
frequency and amplitude when the tension was applied to the tetanus
side and the recordings made from the control one than vice versa.
Both these observations are susceptible of alternative explanations. The
former abnormality probably depends upon changes in the elastic
properties of a muscle that has been in continuous spasm for several
days and the consequently augmented stimulation that any sudden
stretch would impose on the sensory receptor end-organs. The latter
can be readily accounted for by the asymmetry of the intoxication of
the spinal cord which follows from the unilateral inoculation of the
muscles.

Perdrup based his conclusions solely on the observation that an
injection of a dilute solution of procaine into a spastic muscle in local
tetanus abolished its characteristic electromyogram without affecting
its normal voluntary or reflex activity. This finding, too, is inconclusive,
for it fails to distinguish between an augmentation of the proprioceptive
reflex activity of the affected muscles that depends on an increase in the
number of centripetal impulses originating in the supposedly intoxicated
sensory nerve endings, and one in which the number of such afferent
impulses is normal but becomes multiplied through after-discharge at
diseased spinal cord synapses.

Recently Davies, Morgan, Wright & Payling Wright (1954) have
produced evidence that the proprioceptive reflexes from muscles in
local tetanus take no essential part in the genesis of their spasticity.

In rabbits, during the early or neurogenic phase of tetanus, the spasticity and its accompanying continuous electromyographic activity can be promptly suppressed by moderate doses of Nembutal (Pentobarbitone Sodium (B.P.) of Abbot Laboratories Ltd, Greenford, Middlesex). At this level of anaesthesia, however, the patella reflex can be elicited as easily from a limb whose quadriceps extensor muscle has been injected with toxin as from one that is normal. Moreover, the electromyographic record of the tendon jerk remains unchanged in form after the spasticity has been abolished by the Nembutal. It seems, therefore, that the monosynaptic reflex arc which is concerned with such tendon jerks is unaffected by the intoxication and that the 'spontaneous' spinal-cord discharges which are responsible for the initiation and maintenance of the tetanus must have their origins in other neurones.

(ii) *Central site*

So large a mass of experimental observations of very diverse origins has now accumulated which is wholly incompatible with a belief in the peripheral action of tetanus toxin, that it will be impossible here to do more than summarize it briefly. One of the first, and still one of the most forcible, pieces of evidence was brought forward by Meyer & Ransom (1903) when they found that if a very small inoculum of toxin is injected high in the sciatic nerve of a rabbit, the muscles of that limb —including those of the lower leg—develop a characteristic tetanus. Sometimes those of the opposite hind limb later become rigid also. These observations have been confirmed by many investigators subsequently; Abel, Hampil & Jonas alone have disputed the otherwise unanimous testimony. Their supposed failure to produce local tetanus in this way, however, is not borne out by the protocols of their own experiments and has been critically examined by Payling Wright (1953).

The application of intraneural inoculations of toxin to produce local tetanus has been carried a step further by Wright, Morgan & Payling Wright (1950), who injected tetanus toxin into some of the cranial motor-nerve trunks of rabbits. As Abel frequently pointed out, one of the chief difficulties attending the interpretation of experiments carried out on the hind limb has been that even if central intoxication were the sole feature of local tetanus, it could only manifest itself through the spasticity of muscles which lay close to the site of the intraneural injection and consequently would be liable to accidental contamination by toxin or antitoxin used. The transference of the region of experimentation from the lumbar cord to the brain stem with its diversified motor activities circumvents much of this objection. For within a length of brain stem comparable with that of the spinal cord from which the sciatic nerve fibres arise are to be found in close proximity to one another a series of motor nuclei ranging from those subserving the abducent nerve supplying an important extrinsic ocular muscle in the orbit to that of the vagus nerve with its many ramifications in the thoracic and abdominal viscera. With such a widely radiating system of emergent motor nerves, any leakage of toxin from a single site of inoculation in a cranial nerve trunk cannot contaminate more than a small fraction of the effector organs that would be potentially at risk if the intoxication were a central one. Consequently, by removing the experimental area from the lumbar cord to the brain stem it became possible to apply a crucial test of validity to the theory of local contamination. The results of these experiments showed that Abel's criticism was groundless. The injection of toxin into the facial, vagus and hypoglossal nerves was always followed by the same syndrome of strabismus, immobility of vibrissae, salivation, bradycardia and torticollis.

Further support for the belief in central intoxication comes from a series of experiments (Wright et al. 1952) in which the spasticity of local tetanus was suppressed by an intravenous injection of Nembutal. By the application of an inflated rubber cuff round the thigh, it was possible to isolate the lower part of the leg for a short time from the general circulation. Even when thus protected from the access of the Nembutal, the muscles of a tetanus limb lost their spasticity, thus showing that the seat of the intoxication must be proximal to the cuff and cannot be peripherally at the myoneural junctions.

The ascent of toxin to the central nervous system

For long, local tetanus has provided a classical example of hodogenesis (segmental localization), yet the physiological analysis of its centripetal carriage is only just beginning to become clearer. Since the nerve fibres themselves provide the most obvious and complete pathway from the peripheral muscles to the central nervous system, it is natural that they should quickly come under suspicion. This interpretation was first made by Meyer & Ransom and has been accepted with little question by the later investigators who supported the concept of a central site for the intoxication. There now seem to be insuperable objections to the view that the axon itself should provide the necessary conduit (see Payling Wright, 1953). The relatively rapid rate of travel (often less than 24 hr.) from a peripheral muscle to the lumbar cord is quite incompatible with the diffusion of such large protein molecules. Even the much smaller radioactive potassium ion cannot diffuse in the axoplasm at the rate postulated for the toxin (Hodgkin & Keynes, 1953). Nor is there any central translational movement of the axoplasm known which might transport the toxin in a moving current; what knowledge is available of the structure of the mammalian axoplasm suggests that it is very viscous and even semi-solid in consistence. On the other hand, it is apparent from Causey's (1948) observations on motor-nerve trunks in rabbits that a large proportion of the space inside the epineurium is occupied by interstitial fluid, and it seems likely that it is in currents of this fluid, generated by the high intramuscular pressures created during contraction, that the centripetal spread of the toxin is brought about.

Evidence in favour of this extra-axonal pathway has been provided by experiments in which sclerosing solutions have been introduced into the sciatic nerve of rabbits (Baylis, Macintosh, Morgan & Payling Wright, 1952). If a relatively bland sclerosing solution is injected into a large motor-nerve trunk, a fibrous annulus is created at the site. Such a portion of nerve remains capable of transmitting impulses so that no functional disturbance in the lower part of the leg ensues. If tetanus toxin is inoculated into muscles distal to this site, no local tetanus develops. But if subsequently these same rabbits receive an intraneural injection of the toxin *above* the site of sclerosis and near to the point of emergence of the roots from the spinal cord, the lower limb develops spasticity at the expected time. Since the sclerosis prevented local tetanus after the peripheral intramuscular injection of the toxin, although the neural pathway for efferent impulses to the muscles remained functional through the area fibrosed, it seems unlikely that the toxin ordinarily passes up the axons and much more probable that it moves in the interneuronal tissue spaces, from which, at the site of emergence of the trunks from the spinal cord, it enters directly into interstitial tissue fluid of the central nervous system.

THE MODES OF ACTION OF BOTULINUM AND TETANUS TOXINS

It may be stated at once that there is very little material evidence on which to base any conception of the ways in which these toxins bring about their lethal effects. But in spite of our ignorance of the essential biochemical lesion that they inflict, some speculation is permissible if only to direct ideas towards the design of future more fruitful experiments.

The clostridia in general, and *Cl. welchii* in particular, have proved a generous source of material for enzyme chemists, and a number of such bacterial enzymes with defined substrates have been described. Among them, the α-toxin of *Cl. welchii* is of particular interest, because with no other bacterial product have biochemical and lethal properties been so well correlated (see Oakley, 1943, 1954). Lecithin, which is the chief substrate for this phospholipase, is so extensively distributed in the body in the outer membranes and internal organelles of cells, that it is not surprising that the range of the necrotizing action of this toxin should embrace tissues of many types. It seems justifiable to draw two inferences from this wide distribution of the substrate of this α-toxin which may well have a general bearing on the phenomena of bacterial intoxications. First, the very large amount of lecithin present in the body, and the presumably comparably large resources that the tissues possess for the synthesis of this substance, may account for the comparatively large quantity of this toxin that is required for a minimum lethal dose. Secondly, the ready accessibility of much of the lecithin in the cell membranes may be responsible for the rapidity of its fixation and action (Payling Wright & Hopkins, 1946). As a corollary, the small size of the minimum lethal doses of botulinum and tetanus toxins, together with their relatively slow rate of intoxication, might imply a highly restricted substrate in a much less approachable situation; both of these concepts are consistent with the fact that neither toxin is known to injure any other cells than neurones. Whether these two neurotoxins actually operate in virtue of an enzymic property is purely conjectural, but there are several pieces of evidence which are not incompatible with this belief.

One of the remarkable features of these two toxins—and this applies equally to the powerful neurotoxin recently described by van Heyningen & Gladstone (1953)—is the minute size of their minimum lethal doses; all of them are incomparably smaller than those of the most powerful alkaloidal poisons known. Moreover, when the dosages of toxins and alkaloids are expressed in molecular numbers instead of in weights, the discrepancies between the two classes of poison become even more striking. If Wentzel, Sterne & Polson's (1950) estimates of the molecular weight and minimum lethal dose of their preparation of *Cl. botulinum* type D toxin are correct, a fatal intoxication of a mouse could be effected with only about 1000 molecules; even if these molecules are polymers of the actual toxic moiety, the number of molecules must still be incomparably smaller than for any other known poison (see Clark, 1937). In the ordinary concepts of pathogenesis, numbers of this order are more commonly associated with the idea of some replicating particle.

The high-temperature coefficient for the injurious action of both these neurotoxins on poikilothermic animals is again compatible with their behaving in the tissues of such animals like an enzyme from a micro-organism which has become adapted to a habitat at the upper end of this temperature scale. Whether such coefficients are equally consistent with the concept of the toxin interfering with the operation of some essential host enzyme, perhaps by competition for some co-enzyme, is more conjectural. For in intoxications of poikilothermic animals of temperate climates it seems difficult to suppose that any natural process which depends upon enzyme action normally operates to greater ad- vantage, and consequently is more readily impeded by some interfering agent, at temperatures that are well above those to which such animals are naturally exposed.

The only indication of any distinctive metabolic disturbance brought about by botulinum and tetanus toxins are the findings that in the eye in local tetanus intoxication (Ambache, Morgan & Payling Wright, 1948 a, b) and in skeletal muscle in botulism (Burgen et al. 1949; Brooks, 1954), the formation of acetylcholine is much reduced. Such an impair- ment of the liberation of this humoral agent, however, might result from an injury to the nerve terminals of cholinergic fibres of a much more comprehensive kind than one merely affecting the synthesis of acetyl- choline. The only consideration, and it may be a significant one, which might seem to implicate the cholinacetylase system as a specific site for attack by these toxins is the indirect evidence that the nerve terminals of the adrenergic system in the eye are much less, if at all, vulnerable to these neurotoxins. It must be noted, however, that attempts to inhibit the cholinacetylase mechanism in vitro both by Bergen and his colleagues and by ourselves have proved unsuccessful.

The failure of specific antitoxin to halt the progress of an already established intoxication, even supposing that it can reach the site of action of the toxin, does not necessarily exclude the possibility that the toxin is operating enzymatically. It is well known—the literature has recently been reviewed by Marrack (1950) and by Cinader (1953)—that some enzymes are, and some are not, inhibited by their specific anti- body, and that in general the smaller the molecular size of the substrate, the less the likelihood of inhibition. Moreover, even in the instances, such as urease and phospholipase, in which an impairment in their action can be demonstrated, it requires a considerable excess of anti- body to render the inhibition very striking quantitatively, even when there are no tissue barriers to interfere with the free intermingling of antigen and antibody molecules.

More difficult to reconcile with the idea that the intoxication is the result of any simple enzyme action is the far from linear relationship between the dose of toxin and the death time of the animal. This relationship has been evaluated with great care by Ipsen (1941) upon mice for tetanus and some other toxins, and by Legroux, Levaditi & Jéramec (1945) on a less statistical scale upon rabbits for botulism. If a period of 8 hr. is deducted from Ipsen's observed death times—and some latent period must elapse before sufficient toxin can reach the susceptible structures—the abbreviated death time was roughly proportional to the square root of the toxin dose. Such a concentration-action curve is not typical of the ordinary enzyme-substrate catalyses studied *in vitro*.

CONCLUSION

The large volume of physiological work carried out during the last few years with botulinum and tetanus toxins has covered an unusually wide range of animal species and has directed attention to an increasing number of features which the two intoxications have in common. In conclusion, therefore, it seems appropriate to recapitulate very briefly some of these points of resemblance, as well as an important point of difference, in the characters the two present.

Both botulinum and tetanus toxins are neurotoxins in the stricter sense of that term, for they both act directly, and, as far as is known, solely, upon neuronal elements in the nervous system and exert none of their neurological disturbances secondarily through the injury of its vascular, glial, or other supporting structures. The main feature which distinguishes the two intoxications, and determines their characteristic clinical manifestations, is the site of action of the toxins. Botulinum toxin acts exclusively upon the cholinergic nerve endings in the peripheral somatic and autonomic fibres, whereas tetanus toxin operates only upon nerve cells in the cerebrospinal axis itself. There is one structure, the cholinergically innervated sphincter pupillae of the eye, which is known to be similarly affected by both these toxins.

This common ability to paralyse the cholinergic motor fibres to the iris may possibly provide a significant link between the two toxins that may lead to a better understanding of the biochemical disturbances they bring about. In following up their study on the paralysis of the constrictor muscle of the iris, by tetanus toxin injected directly into the anterior chamber of the eye, Ambache *et al.* (1948*b*) found that during the ensuing intoxication there was a marked reduction in the amount of acetylcholine that could be recovered from both the iris and the aqueous humour, and suggested that the main action of the toxin might be to impair the formation and release of this transmitting agent. The close similarity of the effects of botulinum toxin on the rabbit's iris, later described by Ambache, encourages the belief that the main action of this toxin, too, is on the synthesis and liberation of acetylcholine. Stronger direct support, however, has come from the finding by Burgen *et al.* that the poisoning of the rat's phrenic nerve-diaphragm preparation with botulinum toxin *in vitro* is followed by a paralysis in which the output of acetylcholine, that ordinarily results from stimulation of the nerve, is greatly reduced. In spite of the dissimilarities in their sites of action, therefore, there is some evidence that both these clostridial toxins inflict a similar biochemical lesion on the vulnerable nervous elements. What form such an injury might take is, of course, quite unknown, though the insusceptibility of the adrenergic fibres of the autonomic nervous system to both toxins suggests the possibility that the disturbance may be closely related to the metabolism of choline in nerve cells.

REFERENCES

ABEL, J. J., EVANS, E. A., HAMPIL, B. & LEE, F. C. (1935). Researches on tetanus. II. The toxin of the *Bacillus tetani* is not transported to the central nervous system by any component of the peripheral nerve trunks. *Johns Hopk. Hosp. Bull.* **56**, 84–114.

ABEL, J. J., FIROR, W. M. & CHALIAN, W. (1938). Researches on tetanus. IX. Further evidence to show that tetanus toxin is not carried to the central neurones by way of the axis cylinders of motor nerves. *Johns Hopk. Hosp. Bull.* **63**, 373–403.

ABEL, J. J. & HAMPIL, B. (1935). Researches on tetanus. IV. Some historical notes on tetanus and commentaries thereon. *Johns Hopk. Hosp. Bull.* **57**, 343–76.

ABEL, J. J., HAMPIL, B. & JONAS, A. F., JR. (1935). Researches on tetanus. III. Further experiments to prove that tetanus toxin is not carried in peripheral nerves to the central nervous system. *Johns Hopk. Hosp. Bull.* **56**, 317–36.

ABRAMS, A., KEGELES, G. & HOTTLE, G. A. (1946). The purification of toxin from *Clostridium botulinum* type A. *J. biol. Chem.* **164**, 63–79.

ACHESON, G. H., RATNOFF, O. D. & SCHOENBACH, E. B. (1942). The localized action on the spinal cord of intramuscularly injected tetanus toxin. *J. exp. Med.* **75**, 465–80.

AMBACHE, N. (1948). Peripheral action of botulinum toxin. *Nature, Lond.,* **161**, 482.

AMBACHE, N. (1949). The peripheral action of *Clostridium botulinum* toxin. *J. Physiol.* **108**, 127–41.

AMBACHE, N. (1951a). A further survey of the action of *Clostridium botulinum* toxin upon different types of autonomic nerve fibre. *J. Physiol.* **113**, 1–17.

AMBACHE, N. (1951b). Unmasking, after cholinergic paralysis by botulinum toxin, of a reversed action of nicotine on the mammalian intestine, revealing the probable presence of local inhibitory ganglion cells in the enteric plexuses. *Brit. J. Pharmacol.* **6**, 51–67.

AMBACHE, N. (1952). Effect of botulinum toxin upon the superior cervical ganglion. *J. Physiol.* **116**, 9P.

AMBACHE, N. (1954). Autonomic ganglion stimulants. *Arch. int. Pharmacodyn.* **97**, 427–46.

AMBACHE, N., MORGAN, R. S. & WRIGHT, G. PAYLING (1948a). The action of tetanus toxin on the rabbit's iris. *J. Physiol.* **107**, 45–53.

AMBACHE, N., MORGAN, R. S. & WRIGHT, G. PAYLING (1948b). The action of tetanus toxin on the acetylcholine and cholinesterase contents of the rabbit's iris. *Brit. J. exp. Path.* **29**, 408–18.

BAYLIS, J. H., MACINTOSH, J., MORGAN, R. S. WRIGHT, G. & PAYLING (1952). The effect of sclerosis of the nerve trunk on the ascent of tetanus toxin in the sciatic nerve of rabbits and the development of local tetanus. *J. Path. Bact.* **64**, 33–45.

BROOKS, V. B. (1953). Motor nerve filament block produced by botulinum toxin. *Science*, **117**, 334–5.

BROOKS, V. B. (1954). The action of botulinum toxin on motor-nerve filaments. *J. Physiol.* **123**, 501–15.

BROWN, G. L., DALE, H. H. & FELDBERG, W. (1936). Reactions of the normal mammalian muscle to acetylcholine and to eserine. *J. Physiol.* **87**, 394–424.

BUEHLER, H. J., SCHANTZ, E. J. & LAMANNA, C. (1947). The elemental and amino acid composition of crystalline *Clostridium botulinum* type A toxin. *J. biol. Chem.* **169**, 295–302.

BURGEN, A. S. V., DICKENS, F. & ZATMAN, L. J. (1949). The action of botulinum toxin on the neuromuscular junction. *J. Physiol.* **109**, 10–24.

CAUSEY, G. (1948). The effect of pressure on nerve fibres. *J. Anat., Lond.*, **82**, 262–70.

CINADER, B. (1953). Antigen-antibody interaction using enzymes as antigens. *Biochem. Soc. Symp.* No. 10, *Immunochemistry*, p. 16.

CLARK, A. J. (1937). Heffter: *Handbuch der experimentellen Pharmakologie*, **4**, Berlin.

COLE, L. & SPOONER, E. T. C. (1935). The treatment of tetanus. *Quart. J. Med.* **28**, 295–319.

COLEMAN, G. E. (1924). Action of leucocytes and brain tissue on toxin of *B. botulinus* type A. *J. infect. Dis.* **34**, 613–20.

COURMONT, J. & DOYON, M. (1899). *Le Tétanos*, p. 53. Paris.

COWDRY, E. V. & NICHOLSON, F. M. (1924). A histological study of the central nervous system in experimental botulinus poisoning. *J. exp. Med.* **39**, 827–36.

DALE, H. H. (1933). Nomenclature of fibres in the autonomic nervous system. *J. Physiol.* **80**, 10–11 P.

DALE, H. H. (1935). Walter Ernest Dixon Memorial Lecture: Pharmacology and Nerve Endings. *Proc. R. Soc. Med.* **28**, 329–32.

DALE, H. H. & FELDBERG, W. (1934). The chemical transmission of secretory impulses to the sweat glands of the cat. *J. Physiol.* **82**, 121–8.

DAVIES, J. R., MORGAN, R. S., WRIGHT, E. A. & WRIGHT, G. PAYLING (1953). The results of direct injections of botulinum toxin into the central nervous system of rabbits. *J. Physiol.* **120**, 618–23.

DAVIES, J. R., MORGAN, R. S., WRIGHT, E. A. & WRIGHT, G. PAYLING (1954). The effect of local tetanus intoxication on the hind-limb reflexes of the rabbit. *Arch. int. Physiol.* **62**, 248–63.

DICKSON, E. C. & SHEVKY, E. (1923a). Botulism: studies on the manner in which the toxin of *Clostridium botulinum* acts on the body. I. The effect on the autonomic nervous system. *J. exp. Med.* **37**, 711–31.

DICKSON, E. C. & SHEVKY, E. (1923b). Botulism: studies on the manner in which the toxin of *Clostridium botulinum* acts on the body. II. The effect on the voluntary nervous system. *J. exp. Med.* **38**, 327–46.

DOERR, R. (1939). Doerr und Hallauer: *Handbuch der Virusforschung*, **2**, 721 et seq. Wien.

EDMUNDS, C. W. & KEIPER, G. F. (1924). Further studies on the action of botulinus toxin. *J. Amer. med. Ass.* **83**, 495–501.

EDMUNDS, C. W. & LONG, P. H. (1923). Contribution to the pathologic physiology of botulism. *J. Amer. med. Ass.* **81**, 542–7.

FELDBERG, W. & GADDUM, J. H. (1934). The chemical transmitter at synapses in a sympathetic ganglion. *J. Physiol.* **81**, 305–19.

FILDES, P. (1927). Tetanus. VI. Conditions under which tetanus spores germinate *in vivo*. *Brit. J. exp. Path.* **8**, 387–93.

FILDES, P. (1929 a). Tetanus. VIII. The positive limit of oxidation-reduction potential required for the germination of spores of B. tetani in vitro. Brit. J. exp. Path. 10, 151–75.

FILDES, P. (1929 b). Tetanus. IX. The oxidation-reduction potential of subcutaneous tissue fluids of the guineapig: its effect on infection. Brit. J. exp. Path. 10, 197–204.

FORSSMAN, J. (1901). Beiträge zur Kenntnis der Bakteriologie des Botulismus. Zbl. Bakt. (1 Abt. Orig.), 29, 541–5.

FRANCIS, E. (1914). Laboratory studies on tetanus. Bull. U.S. Hyg. Lab. no. 95, p. 72.

FRIEDEMANN, U. & HOLLANDER, A. (1943). Studies on tetanal toxin. I. Quantitative differences amongst various toxins revealed by bioassays in different species and by different routes of injection. J. Immunol. 47, 23–8.

FRIEDEMANN, U., ZUGER, B. & HOLLANDER, A. (1939). Investigations on the pathogenesis of tetanus. I. The permeability of the central nervous system barrier to tetanal toxin. Passive immunity against toxin introduced by various routes. J. Immunol. 36, 473–84.

GODDARD, D. R. (1945). Hoeber: Physical Chemistry of Cells and Tissues, p. 379. Philadelphia.

GÖPFERT, H. & SCHAEFER, H. (1940). Ueber die Mechanik des Wundstarrkrampfes. Arch. exp. Path. Pharmak. 197, 93–122.

GUYTON, A. C. & MACDONALD, M. A. (1947). Physiology of botulinus toxin. Arch. Neurol. Psychiat., Chicago, 57, 578–92.

HAINES, R. B. (1942). The occurrence of toxigenic anaerobes, especially Clostridium botulinum, in some English soils. J. Hyg., Camb., 42, 323–7.

HANKE, M. E. & BAILEY, J. H. (1945). Oxidation-reduction potential requirements of Clostridium welchii and other clostridia. Proc. Soc. exp. Biol., N.Y., 59, 163–6.

HARVEY, A. M. (1939). The peripheral action of tetanus toxin. J. Physiol. 96, 348–65.

HODGKIN, A. L. & KEYNES, R. D. (1953). The mobility and diffusion coefficient of potassium in giant axons from Sepia. J. Physiol. 119, 513–28.

IPSEN, J. (1941). Contributions to the Theory of Biological Standardization, Part III. Copenhagen.

KEGELES, G. (1946). The molecular size and shape of botulinus toxin. J. Amer. chem. Soc. 68, 1670.

KNIGHT, B. C. J. G. & FILDES, P. (1930). Oxidation-reduction studies in relation to bacterial growth. III. The positive limit of oxidation-reduction potential required for the germination of B. tetani spores in vitro. Biochem. J. 24, 1496–1502.

LAMANNA, C. & GLASSMAN, H. N. (1947). The isolation of type B botulinum toxin. J. Bact. 54, 575–84.

LEGROUX, R., LEVADITI, J.-C. & JÉRAMEC, C. (1945). Influence des Voies d'Introduction de la Toxine sur le Botulisme expérimental du Lapin. Ann. Inst. Pasteur, 71, 490–3.

MACINTOSH, F. C. (1941). The distribution of acetylcholine in the peripheral and the central nervous system. J. Physiol. 99, 436–42.

MARRACK, J. R. (1950). Sumner and Myrbäch: The Enzymes, 1, 343–389. New York.

MASLAND, R. L. & GAMMON, G. D. (1949). The effect of botulinum toxin on the electromyogram. J. Pharmacol. 97, 499–506.

MEYER, K. F. (1928). Kolle und Wassermann: Handbuch der pathogenen Mikroorganismen, 3rd ed. 4, 1269.

MEYER, H. & RANSOM, F. (1903). Untersuchungen über den Tetanus. Arch. exp. Path. Pharmak. 49, 369–416.

102   G. PAYLING WRIGHT

MOLL, T. & BRANDLY, C. A. (1951). Botulism in the mouse, mink and ferret with special reference to their susceptibility and pathological alterations. *Amer. J. vet. Res.* **12**, 355–63.

OAKLEY, C. L. (1943). The toxins of *Clostridium welchii*: a critical review. *Bull. Hyg., Lond.*, **18**, 781–806.

OAKLEY, C. L. (1954). Gas gangrene. *Brit. med. Bull.* **10**, 52–8.

PERDRUP, A. (1946). Electromyographic investigations on the mode of action of tetanus toxin. *Acta pharm. tox., Kbh.*, **2**, 121–37.

PERMIN, C. (1913–14). Experimentelle und Klinische Untersuchungen über die Pathogenese und Therapie des Starrkrampfes. *Mitt. Grenzgeb. Med. Chir.* **27**, 1–21.

PICKETT, M. J., HOEPRICH, P. K. & GERMAIN, R. O. (1945). Purification of high titre tetanus toxin. *J. Bact.* **49**, 515–18.

PILLEMER, L. & MOORE, D. H. (1948). The spontaneous conversion of crystalline tetanal toxin into a flocculating atoxic dimer. *J. biol. Chem.* **173**, 427–8.

PILLEMER, L., WITTLER, R. G., BURRELL, J. I. & GROSSBERG, D. B. (1948). The immunochemistry of toxins and toxoids. VI. The crystallization and characterization of tetanal toxin. *J. exp. Med.* **88**, 205–21.

POCHHAMMER, C. (1909). *Samml. klin. Vortr.* (Chir. no. 149), p. 599.

PUTNAM, F. W., LAMANNA, C. & SHARP, D. G. (1946). Molecular weight and homogeneity of crystalline botulinum A toxin. *J. biol. Chem.* **165**, 735–6.

PUTNAM, F. W., LAMANNA, C. & SHARP, D. G. (1948). Physicochemical properties of crystalline *Clostridium botulinum* type A toxin. *J. biol. Chem.* **176**, 401–12.

SCHAEFER, H. (1944). Weitere Untersuchungen zum Mechanismus und zu Therapie des Wundstarrkrampfes. *Arch. exp. Path. Pharmak.* **203**, 59–84.

SCHÜBEL, K. (1923). Ueber das Botulinus Toxin. *Arch. exp. Path. Pharmak.* **96**, 193–259.

SHERRINGTON, C. S. (1906). *The Integrative Action of the Nervous System*, p. 303. New Haven.

SMITH, L. D. (1949). Clostridia in gas gangrene. *Bact. Rev.* **13**, 233–54.

SMITH, M. LLEWELLYN (1942–3). Note on the complexity of tetanus toxin. *Bull. Hlth Org., L.o.N.* **10**, 104–12.

STOVER, J. H., JR., FINGERMAN, M. & FORESTER, R. H. (1953). Botulinum toxin and the motor endplate. *Proc. Soc. exp. Biol., N.Y.*, **84**, 146–9.

VAILLARD, L. & VINCENT, H. (1891). Contribution à l'Étude du Tétanos. *Ann. Inst. Pasteur*, **5**, 1–39.

VAN ERMENGEM, E. (1897). Contribution à l'Étude des Intoxications Alimentaires *Arch. int. Pharmacodyn.* **3**, 213–350, 499–601.

VAN HEYNINGEN, W. E. & GLADSTONE, G. P. (1953). The neurotoxin of *Shigella shigae*. 1. Production, purification and properties of the toxin. *Brit. J. exp. Path.* **34**, 202–16.

WENTZEL, L. M., STERNE, M. & POLSON, A. (1950). High toxicity of pure botulinum type D toxin. *Nature, Lond.*, **166**, 739–40.

WRIGHT, G. PAYLING (1953). Nerve trunks as pathways in infection. *Proc. R. Soc. Med.* **46**, 319–30.

WRIGHT, G. PAYLING & HOPKINS, S. J. (1946). The fixation of *Clostridium welchii* toxin by skin cells. *J. Path. Bact.* **58**, 573–5.

WRIGHT, E. A., MORGAN, R. S. & WRIGHT, G. PAYLING (1950). Tetanus intoxication of the brain stem in rabbits. *J. Path. Bact.* **62**, 569–83.

WRIGHT, E. A., MORGAN, R. S. & WRIGHT, G. PAYLING (1952). The site of action of the toxin in local tetanus. *Lancet*, ii, 316–19.

PROPERTIES AND STRUCTURES OF TUBERCLE BACILLI CONCERNED IN THEIR PATHOGENICITY

R. J. DUBOS

Rockefeller Institute for Medical Research, New York

TUBERCULOUS INFECTION VERSUS *TUBERCULOUS DISEASE*

The word 'tuberculosis' has been used during the past century with two very different meanings. At first, it referred to a pathological state of unknown etiology, often resulting in death and characterized by lesions designated as tubercles. Since the discovery of the tubercle bacillus, and particularly of bacteriological and immunological techniques permitting its recognition in the tissues even in the absence of overt disease, there has been an increasing tendency to identify tuberculosis with tuberculous infection, whether or not this infection expressed itself in detectable lesions or symptoms.

Both meanings of the word—disease or merely infection—have currency at the present time, although there exist profound differences between the pathological and bacteriological concepts. This looseness in terminology is not only a matter of semantic interest. It has unfortunate consequences by engendering confusion in all practical and theoretical aspects of tuberculosis. The failure to define clearly the relations between infection and disease complicates especially analysis of the factors which determine the fate and the effects of tubercle bacilli *in vivo*. Tuberculous *disease* and tuberculous *infection* do not necessarily have the same determinants.

For a long time, the attention of students of tuberculosis was focused almost exclusively on the study of lesions by the techniques of pathology. This emphasis on tuberculous *disease* markedly influenced the formulation of criteria of virulence for the group of mammalian mycobacteria. To be regarded as virulent, a strain had to be capable of causing extensive lesions and progressive fatal disease in normal animals, and presumably in man. All other strains were classed as avirulent. This was the case for example for R_1R_v and BCG: two strains originally derived, respectively, from virulent human and virulent bovine cultures, but having lost during cultivation *in vitro* the ability to cause a fatal disease in normal guinea-pigs.

It is known, however, that R_1R_v and BCG (as well as most of the strains considered avirulent according to the criteria mentioned above) multiply extensively in the tissues of normal animals and man, and can cause definite although self-limiting lesions. They also multiply within monocytes in tissue cultures as do the virulent strains. Finally, they can cause progressive disease and death in animals exposed to silica dust or placed under certain unfavourable metabolic conditions. It would seem more appropriate, therefore, to refer to these strains as 'attenuated' instead of avirulent. Extensive comparative studies, not to be reviewed here, leave little doubt that there exist mycobacteria exhibiting all degrees of attenuation of virulence, and that even the various substrains of BCG differ profoundly one from the other in their ability to multiply *in vivo*, to elicit lesions in normal animals, or to cause the death of animals in abnormal metabolic states.

In addition to the attenuated strains, there are known a few other forms of tubercle bacilli, also derived from virulent cultures, which can be considered as truly 'avirulent' because they appear unable to multiply *in vivo* or even within monocytes in tissue cultures. They are usually identified by the designations R_a (rough avirulent)—for example, $H_{37}R_a$, $JH_{16}R_a$, R_1R_a and H_4R_a are such strains. It must be emphasized that only very few R_a strains have been recognized, and, moreover, that these mutants are rather unstable, often reverting to forms capable of multiplying to some extent *in vivo*. Practically all the strains described as avirulent in the literature belong in reality to the group described as 'attenuated' in the preceding paragraph.

DETERMINANTS OF VIRULENCE

Many individuals who become infected with virulent tubercle bacilli succeed in arresting the infection so completely and so early that no detectable lesion or symptom ensues. On the other hand, as already mentioned, attenuated bacilli can cause progressive tuberculous disease if the resistance of the infected animal has been decreased by the proper procedures. It is obvious therefore that the word virulence has meaning only in terms of certain highly standardized conditions of test.

The nature of the tissue environment, and the characteristics of the strain, constitute two complementary sets of data, both of which must be considered simultaneously if one wishes to identify the determinants of tuberculosis. In reality, however, most attempts to study host-parasite relationships have been focused on the properties of the micro-organism alone, and it is this aspect of the problem that we shall first consider even though it is not necessarily the more important. In particular, we shall briefly review some of the efforts which have been made to discover whether the various strains of mammalian mycobacteria exhibit *in vitro* differential characteristics correlated with their behaviour *in vivo*.

Cytochemical characteristics and virulence

The virulent strains of mammalian mycobacteria rapidly form on the surface of liquid media a thin veil which spreads uniformly over the entire surface and climbs high on the sides of glass containers; in contrast, the avirulent mutants ($H_{37}R_a$ and its like) have less tendency to spread on the surface but form instead more or less discrete islands which coalesce only late in growth. Studies of microscopic morphology, both in liquid and on agar media, have revealed furthermore that the virulent bacilli grow in an impressively orientated pattern, serpentine in appearance, with the rods arranged in parallel along the long axis of the bacillary chains. On the contrary, the avirulent bacilli grow in clumps in a non-orientated, helter-skelter fashion (Steenken & Gardner, 1946; Middlebrook, Dubos, & Pierce 1947).

It is likely that these morphological characteristics are the expression of the presence on the bacillary surface of certain hydrophobic components. Indeed, addition of sufficient amounts of the appropriate wetting agents to the culture media allows all strains to grow diffusely throughout the liquid phase and renders their colonies on agar dome-shaped and smooth. It is of interest in this respect that in general the concentration of wetting agent required to prevent the bacilli from arranging themselves in a serpentine pattern increases with the virulence of the culture (Dubos & Middlebrook, 1948 *a*; Melvin & MacPherson, 1954). Appreciable differences can be recognized between the various substrains of BCG in direct relation to their invasiveness. These findings suggest that there is a correlation between virulence and the existence of a component of the bacterial cell which determines the morphological characteristics of growth. It must be realized, however, that the evidence for this hypothetical correlation is based on the study of only very few strains, and that some attenuated cultures (like R_1R_v and certain substrains of BCG) cannot be clearly differentiated from the virulent cultures by morphological criteria. According to a recent report, furthermore, cultivation of the avirulent $H_{37}R_a$ in media containing the polyoxyethylene ether detergent Triton A_{20} alters this culture in such a manner that it becomes capable of producing the serpentine pattern of growth while remaining devoid of virulence (Hart & Rees, 1954).

Not only is the relation of morphological characteristics to virulence still obscure, but there is as yet no precise knowledge concerning the chemical nature of the cellular constituent responsible for the serpentine pattern of growth. A recent observation which may have a bearing on this problem is that all virulent strains so far tested are capable of binding the basic dye neutral red in the form of its salt even under extremely alkaline conditions. The binding is reversibly inhibited by lower aliphatic amines, and irreversibly by long-chain fatty amines probably because the long-chain fatty amines become firmly bound to the bacterial bodies by virtue of their lipophilic properties (Dubos & Middlebrook, 1948 b; Dubos & Suter, 1949). Two of the lipid fractions extracted from mycobacteria—namely, free mycolic acid and the slightly acidic D wax (lipopolysaccharide) of the chloroform-soluble fraction— have been found to be capable of binding neutral red, and therefore may be responsible for or play a part in, the reaction to the dye exhibited by the intact bacteria (reviewed by Asselineau, 1952). The avirulent strains ($H_{37}R_a$ and the like) fail to bind neutral red; but, in our experience, all attenuated strains bind it as much as the virulent, provided they are tested under the same conditions. The relation of the neutral-red test to virulence is therefore obscure.

Metabolic characteristics and virulence

It is certain that the various strains of mycobacteria differ in their metabolic characteristics, and there is reason to believe that some of the differences are correlated with virulence.

One of the limiting factors in the metabolism of tubercle bacilli is a deficiency in their terminal oxidative system, that involving the tricarboxylic acid cycle (Geronimus, 1949). Yet metabolic intermediates do not accumulate in high concentrations in media in which the bacilli are growing, as would be expected if the citric acid cycle really failed to keep pace with the preliminary carbon-chain desmolysis. It has been suggested that intermediates do not accumulate extracellularly because the plasma membrane of acid-fast bacilli is poorly permeable and does not permit rapid diffusion from the intracellular into the extracellular environment. If this is true, an inhibitory effect on tubercle bacilli might result either from the accumulation within the cells of toxic products of their intermediate metabolism, or from the saturation of certain of their carrier systems (Geronimus & Birkeland, 1951).

When studied by the conventional metabolic techniques, the respiration of virulent cultures is found to be less stimulated than that of their avirulent or attenuated mutants, or than that of saprophytic acid-fast cultures, by the addition of formate, acetate, propionate, butyrate or lactate, as substrate. In a general way, there seems to be a negative correlation between vigour of oxidative attack and degree of virulence (Geronimus, 1949; Geronimus & Birkeland, 1951). Other studies have also shown that the cells of certain avirulent and attenuated strains have a somewhat higher rate of respiration than the virulent cells when tested in a variety of inorganic or complex organic media, either in air or at 1 % oxygen tension (Heplar, 1953; Heplar, Clifton, Raffel & Futrelle, 1954).

Differences apparently related to virulence also come to light when the metabolism of tubercle bacilli is measured by the Thunberg dehydrogenation tests. In the presence of glucose or glycerine, washed suspensions of saprophytic acid-fast bacilli, avirulent tubercle bacilli, or BCG, reduce methylene blue much more rapidly than do the cells of virulent cultures. Yet the virulent bacilli contain the dehydrogenase because they become capable of reducing methylene blue rapidly after they have been broken up by grinding, or treated with petroleum ether. The failure of virulent bacilli to reduce the dye when they are young and intact has been explained by assuming that they are surrounded by a lipid coating (called cord factor) which prevents or retards contact between substrate and enzyme. This assumption implies the belief that 'the cord factor, present only in virulent strains, covers the entire surface of the cell' (Bloch, 1950a). The nature of the so-called cord factor will be considered later.

It is not easy to relate these metabolic differences to the ability of the bacilli to multiply under ordinary conditions. At neutrality, in the usual synthetic media or on egg slants, and with adequate aeration, most strains of mammalian mycobacteria grow at approximately the same rate in vitro (Fenner & Leach, 1953). Differences observed do not bear any relation to virulence (Dubos, unpublished). There is some indication, however, that metabolic differences may express themselves in certain special types of environment, as shown in the following experiments.

Young cultures in Tween-albumin medium were incubated at 37° in an atmosphere from which oxygen and CO_2 were removed. The numbers of viable cells were determined at different intervals of time by plating graded dilutions on albumin-agar medium. Marked differences were observed in the ability of the various strains to survive under these conditions. As can be seen in Table 1 the two virulent cultures (one of bovine and one of human type) survived the longest, whereas the avirulent culture $H_{37}R_a$ died first. The relative survival time of the attenuated strains R_1R_v, BCG-P and BCG-T was related to their degree of attenuation. As Table 2 shows, similar differences among strains were found when bacilli, washed free of culture medium, were resuspended in a balanced ionic solution and aerated by violent agitation in a shaking machine (Weiss & Dubos, unpublished). In fact it has been a general observation in our laboratory that the more attenuated the strain, the more readily it loses its viability under conditions inimical to growth.

Table 1. *Survival of tubercle bacilli under anaerobic conditions**

(Weiss & Dubos, unpublished.)

		No. of viable bacilli (per ml.) recovered after			
Strain	Virulence	5 days	10 days	15 days	20 days
Vallee	++++	2×10^8	9×10^7	8×10^6	1×10^6
BCG-P	++	2×10^8	3×10^7	5×10^6	4×10^5
BCG-T	+	1×10^8	7×10^4	2×10^1	0
$H_{37}R_v$	++++	6×10^7	2×10^7	4×10^6	8×10^5
R_1R_v	+++	7×10^7	7×10^7	1×10^6	8×10^4
$H_{37}R_a$	−	5×10^6	9×10^4	1×10^1	0

* 6-day cultures in Tween-albumin medium placed in anaerobic jar. Viable cells enumerated at intervals of time by plating dilutions on albumin-agar medium.

Table 2. *The survival of tubercle bacilli in mineral solution under highly aerobic conditions**

(Weiss & Dubos, unpublished.)

Substrate (pH 6·8)	Strain	Virulence	No. of viable bacilli (per ml.)		
			Initial	6 days	30 days
Mineral solution	Vallee	++++	2×10^6	1×10^6	2×10^5
	BCG-P	++	4×10^6	2×10^6	7×10^4
	BCG-T	+	4×10^5	2×10^4	1×10^2
	$H_{37}R_v$	++++	3×10^6	1×10^6	3×10^4
	R_1R_v	+++	3×10^8	4×10^6	1×10^6
	$H_{37}R_a$	−	3×10^5	6×10^3	3×10^1

* Washed bacterial cells resuspended in balanced ionic mineral solution at pH 6·8. Suspension placed in shaking machine at 27°. Samples taken for enumeration of bacilli after 6 and 30 days' shaking.

Since completion of this review, there have been published some findings which suggest that avirulent bacilli are less able than the virulent to utilize low concentrations of oxygen for their multiplication *in vitro* (Guy, Raffel & Clifton, 1954).

We shall discuss later the possible relevance of the metabolic peculiarities exhibited by tubercle bacilli *in vitro* to their fate and pathogenic behaviour *in vivo*. For reasons of convenience in presentation, however, it appears best to consider first some of the factors responsible for the toxic manifestations of tuberculosis.

TOXIC PROPERTIES OF TUBERCLE BACILLI

Ever since the discovery that tubercle bacilli contain large amounts of various types of lipids, there has been a natural tendency to regard these bacillary constituents as responsible for the lesions and toxic manifestations of tuberculosis. There is no doubt indeed that many of the tissue reactions peculiar to this disease can be reproduced by injecting certain tuberculolipids into experimental animals. The histopathological aspects of this problem will not be considered here.

More recently, claims have been published that certain lipid fractions are endowed with toxic properties and are more abundant in virulent than in attenuated and avirulent strains. For this reason specific lipids have been thought to play a dominant role as determinants of virulence. We shall now consider the validity and significance of these claims.

When tubercle bacilli killed by heat are extracted with mineral oil, there goes into solution a lipid constituent (termed PMKO) containing a lipopolysaccharide, which can be separated from the oil phase by precipitation with dioxane. This constituent has been claimed: (i) to be more abundant in virulent than in avirulent cultures, (ii) to exhibit extraordinary toxicity for guinea-pigs, and (iii) to be capable of eliciting a specific antigenic reaction, and some protective immunity (Choucroun, 1940, 1943 a, b, 1947, 1948).

Although the toxicity findings reported in earlier publications for the fraction PMKO were very startling indeed, they have never been confirmed (personal communications from several independent investigators, and results from our own laboratory); their significance is therefore questionable. Furthermore, the experimental results so far published do not demonstrate that PMKO can elicit immunity or that the amount of PMKO present in the bacterial bodies is correlated with the virulence of the tubercle bacilli from which it was extracted. There is consequently no reliable information concerning the possible role played by this lipid fraction in the pathogenesis of tuberculosis.

On the other hand, quantitative extraction and fractionation studies with the various lipids of a few strains of tubercle bacilli have been carried out independently by another group of investigators. Their findings suggest that the amount of chloroform-soluble fraction designated as wax D—which is also a lipopolysaccharide like PMKO—may be related to the virulence of the strain (reviewed in Asselineau, 1952). As can be seen from the results presented in Table 3, however, the relation of the amount of wax D to virulence is not striking. Indeed, its significance is rendered even more doubtful by the fact that the amount of this substance recovered by the ordinary extraction techniques does not necessarily reflect the amount initially present in the bacterial bodies. It has been our experience that, in general, attenuated and avirulent cultures die more rapidly, and undergo autolytic changes sooner, than do virulent cultures. As the quantitative extraction tests reported above (Table 3) were carried out chiefly on cultures 6 weeks old, it can be assumed that there had been time for the bacterial masses to undergo various degrees of autolysis (Asselineau, 1952). This may have resulted in some hydrolytic alteration of the lipopolysaccharide (wax D). It is of interest in this regard to note that only 0·54 % of wax D was recovered from cultures of $H_{37}R_a$, 6 weeks old, whereas the yield reached 2 % in younger cultures.

Table 3. *Content (percentage of dry weight of bacilli) of wax D (lipopoly-saccharide) in mammalian tubercle bacilli of various degrees of virulence*

(Modified from Asselineau, 1952.)

Strain	Virulence	Age of culture (weeks)	Lipopoly-saccharide (% of dry weight of bacilli)
Brevannes (human)	+++	4	6·9
Aeschbacher (human)	+++	6	7·6
$H_{37}R_v$ (human)	+++	6	7·3
Test (human)	++	6	6·2
R_1 (human)	+	6	2·1
L_{25} (human)	±	6	4·5
L_{65} (human)	±	6	1·3
$H_{37}R_a$ (human)	−	6	0·5
$R_{37}R_a$ (human)	−	4	2·0
Vallee (bovine)	+	6	0·6
Marmoreck (bovine)	++	6	2·8
BCG (bovine)	−	6	1·6

It has been found in another study that extraction with petroleum ether releases from certain tubercle bacilli a toxic lipid fraction insoluble in ethanol and free of phosphorus. Great interest has been aroused in this fraction, which has been designated 'cord factor', because of the statement that it possesses several properties having a direct bearing on virulence. According to the initial reports, the active substance is present in large amounts only in virulent bacilli; is responsible for their ability to form serpentine strands (hence the name cord factor); is abundant only in young cultures, thus accounting for their greater virulence; is endowed with great toxicity as manifested by its ability to inhibit the migration of leucocytes in tissue cultures and to cause a lethal effect in certain strains of mice; and is most active against the strains of mice most susceptible to tuberculous infection (Bloch, 1950b, 1950c).

Needless to say, this extraordinary constellation of properties would give to the so-called cord factor a unique place among components of virulent tubercle bacilli and indeed would go far toward accounting for their behaviour *in vivo*. Unfortunately, several of the statements made concerning this material appear invalid in the light of recent publications as well as of critical scrutiny of the early reports (Philpot & Wells, 1952; Bloch, Sorkin & Erlenmeyer, 1953; Noll & Bloch, 1953; Asselineau, Bloch & Lederer, 1953; reviewed in Asselineau, 1952).

The material first described under the name cord factor is not a chemical entity but a mixture of the various bacillary constituents soluble in petroleum ether. The toxic component constitutes at most a minute fraction of it (of the order of 1 %), and there is no indication that it has anything to do with either virulence or serpentine pattern of growth. There is no evidence that the amount of cord factor or of toxic material differs from one strain to the other, or is related to their behaviour *in vivo*. As to the biological tests used, their significance is at best difficult to interpret. Inhibition of migration of leucocytes, and production of haemorrhagic pulmonary lesions in mice, can be brought about by petroleum-ether extracts, not only of virulent bacilli, but also of BCG strains as well as of saprophytic bacilli, and of other unrelated material such as ox lungs (see Table V in Bloch, 1950*b*).

It is disturbing, furthermore, that the toxicity for mice becomes apparent only after several successive injections of the material (which is a lipid and certainly exerts many varied non-specific actions on tissues). The technique of repeated injection of mice leaves open the possibility that the effects observed may not be due altogether to toxicity of the material, but may be produced instead by activation of latent pulmonary viruses, or sensitization, or any number of other artifacts.

Thus, there is at present no proof that virulent strains owe their greater ability to cause disease to special toxic properties. On the other hand, it is certain that tubercle bacilli of all strains are endowed with the ability to cause profound toxic reactions if present in sufficient quantities in the tissues.

It is possible to cause rapid death of mice by injecting into them large amounts of living virulent tubercle bacilli, 12 mg. wet weight (approximately 2–3 mg. dry weight) being required to cause acute death by intravenous injection (Youmans & Youmans, 1951). Interestingly enough, the acute lethal dose is independent of the virulence of the strain, and remains of the same order after the bacilli have been killed by phenol and washed with acetone and ether. The results of intraperitoneal injection of bacilli killed by exposure to 2 % (w/v) phenol and washed with acetone, show, for example, that the cells of the avirulent strain $H_{37}R_a$ have a primary toxicity as high as those of BCG, R_1R_v, or of human and bovine virulent strains (Dubos, unpublished observation). It has been shown also that some of the water-soluble or water-dispersible components of old autolysed cultures can produce chronic intoxication resulting in cachexia and death (Pinner & Voldrich, 1931). Furthermore, experiments in our laboratory have revealed that it is possible to extract from bacilli a fraction soluble in monochlorobenzene and insoluble in cold petroleum ether which produces similar toxic effects (Spitznagel & Dubos, 1955); although the active material behaves as an acidic lipid, its chemical nature has not yet been ascertained.

The most thoroughly studied of the properties of tubercle bacilli concerned in toxaemia has been their extraordinary power to elicit allergic reactions, of both the immediate (anaphylactic) and delayed (tuberculin) type. These studies cannot be reviewed here, but it seems worth recalling that tubercle bacilli, through their wax fraction (probably a lipopolysaccharide), possess the unique property of enhancing the antigenicity of tuberculoproteins as well as of other unrelated substances (Raffel, 1950; Raffel, Lederer & Asselineau, 1954). It is very likely that allergic reactions play the dominant part in the toxic manifestations of tuberculosis.

As already pointed out, there is no indication at the present time that per weight unit, the bacterial bodies of virulent strains are as a group more toxicogenic or more allergenic than those of attenuated or avirulent mycobacteria. It must be recognized, however, that this possibility has not been ruled out, since there has not been any systematic study of the problem. But on the basis of available information, it seems best to assume that the severity of the toxic reactions in tuberculosis is determined by the amount of bacillary material in the tissues. In other words, the virulence of tubercle bacilli appears to be primarily an expression of their ability to multiply *in vivo*, and of the population level which they can reach in the organs of the invaded host.

FATE OF TUBERCLE BACILLI *IN VIVO*

The measurement of virulence. The comparative virulence of the various strains and mutants of mammalian tubercle bacilli is usually estimated by determining the extent of the lesions which they produce in experimental animals or the survival time of the animal following infection. One of the methods most extensively used in our laboratory is to count the number of living bacilli in the organs of mice at weekly intervals after intravenous injection of a small infective dose. Let it be noted in passing that whatever the technique used to measure virulence

—extent of lesions, survival time, or growth of the bacterial population *in vivo*—the strains so far tested fall in the same order and arrange themselves in a continuous spectrum ranging from maximum virulence through all degrees of attenuation (R_1R_v, BCG-P, BCG-T, etc.) down to inability to multiply *in vivo*. The last group (avirulent cultures) can, however, produce lesions if large amounts of bacterial substance are injected.

Although it is not possible to describe here experiments designed to study the trends of the levels of microbial population *in vivo*, their results can be summarized in the form of the five general statements which follow (for documentation see Dubos, 1954).

(1) All virulent and attenuated cultures begin to multiply shortly after their introduction into the animal body. The avirulent cultures ($H_{37}R_a$ and the like) do not multiply at all if small inocula are injected.

(2) The rate of multiplication *in vivo* is characteristic for each strain in a given breed of animal maintained under uniform physiological conditions.

(3) The maximum level of microbial population reached in the spleen is also characteristic for each strain and is to a large extent independent of the size of the inoculum.

(4) After a few weeks, the microbial population in the spleen begins to decrease, but only gradually. It is worth noting that even with strain $H_{37}R_a$ the bacilli may persist in the tissues for some weeks after injection. Clearly, lack of virulence is not the result of susceptibility to the bactericidal power of humours or cells.

(5) With most strains (except $H_{37}R_a$ and perhaps BCG-T) the microbial population continues to increase in other organs at the time that it is decreasing in the spleen. In man, similarly, it is well known that bacilli can disappear almost completely from closed necrotic lesions while multiplying in other parts of the body in the same individual. These facts emphasize the importance of *local* tissue factors in determining the fate of tubercle bacilli *in vivo*.

We shall now consider some aspects of the *in vivo* environment and of bacterial metabolism which may be of significance in explaining these peculiarities of tuberculosis.

The physico-chemical environment of the bacilli in vivo. At first sight, it would appear that the infectious process follows its course in the physiological *milieu intérieur* determined by the homeostatic mechanisms of the body. In reality, however, the bacilli find themselves *in vivo* under conditions far different from those termed physiological. Whatever their virulence they are taken up by phagocytic cells as soon as they are

8

introduced into the body, and the first phase of infection is consequently intracellular. Only in a later phase does tissue necrosis cause the bacilli to be released into the extracellular environment of the lesions. It is certain that the physico-chemical conditions prevailing both within phagocytic cells and extracellularly within the lesions are very different from those of the physiological *milieu intérieur*. Although little is known of these physico-chemical characteristics, some facts appear worth recording because they may have a bearing on the fate of tubercle bacilli *in vivo*.

It has been demonstrated that leucocytes can produce large amounts of lactic acid, and it is probable that their intracellular pH following phagocytosis is rather low (reviewed in Dubos, 1954). Similarly, there is little doubt that the pH of inflammatory exudates is commonly very acid (values as low as pH 5·3 have been reported), in part at least as a result of the local accumulation of lactic acid produced by inflammatory cells and perhaps also by fixed-tissue cells (Frunder, 1951, 1953 and reviewed in Dubos, 1954). In the light of these facts, it is of particular interest that the viability and the multiplication of tubercle bacilli *in vitro* are unfavourably influenced at low pH by concentrations of lactic acid of the order of those that may occur *in vivo* locally at the site of the lesion (Dubos, 1950, 1953a).

It is certain, on the other hand, that the oxygen supply to many lesions or parts of lesions is greatly reduced by vascular thrombosis, the crowding of migratory cells, and other interference with blood flow. These same factors also contribute to a local increase in the CO_2 tension. As far as is known, tubercle bacilli are obligatory aerobes, and their growth is retarded or prevented at high CO_2 tensions (Davies, 1940). It is clear, therefore, that the gaseous environment in the centre of lesions, or in areas of the lungs which have been collapsed, is inimical to multiplication of tubercle bacilli. Moreover, they die rapidly and disintegrate when incubated anaerobically in media containing lactic acid, particularly under high CO_2 tension (Dubos, 1953a).

Because the tuberculous lesion is the site of profound necrotic changes, a great variety of substances resulting from the breakdown of tissue cells must accumulate in it. We shall mention a few which presumably can exert an effect on tubercle bacilli *in vivo*.

Of the lipids, some, like sphingomyelin, facilitate bacillary multiplication under all circumstances tested; others, like long-chain fatty acids, enhance growth or prevent it depending upon their concentration, the pH of the environment, and the presence of proteins capable of binding these lipids (Dubos, 1947).

From lymphoid tissue undergoing autolytic breakdown, a basic peptide rich in arginine can be isolated, and this peptide possesses marked bacteriostatic properties for tubercle bacilli; another type of basic peptide, particularly rich in lysine and also endowed with antimycobacterial activity, has been obtained from a variety of animal tissues (Dubos & Hirsch, 1954; Hirsch, 1954; Hirsch & Dubos, 1954; Watson, Cromartie, Bloom, Heckley, McGhee & Weissman, 1947; Watson & Bloom, 1952). The two types of peptide probably inhibit the growth of tubercle bacilli by different mechanisms because their respective bacteriostatic effects are antagonized by unrelated inhibitors—sulphur compounds being antagonistic to the arginine peptide, and organic acids of high molecular weight to the lysine peptide. It is possible that the antituberculous substance recently separated from infected lymph nodes, spleen and liver may be related to these peptides (Soltys, 1953).

The granulocytes and probably other cells which accumulate around the lesion contain the antibacterial agent lysozyme. It is not known whether this enzyme acts intracellularly within the granulocytes, but there is evidence that it is released in an active state in the external environment after any injury to the cells which contain it (Kerby, 1952). Although tubercle bacilli are not lysed by lysozyme, they rapidly die in the presence of even small concentrations of this enzyme.

Tubercle bacilli are also killed by the polyamines spermine or spermidine in very low concentrations provided the medium contains the enzyme spermine-oxidase. The effective bactericidal agent is a product of oxidative deamination of these amines which has not yet been identified chemically. It does not inhibit bacteria other than tubercle bacilli. Of the micro-organisms which have been tested, the mammalian mycobacteria are by far the most susceptible to its action (Hirsch & Dubos, 1952; Hirsch, 1953 a, b).

Spermine and spermidine occur in many animal and human tissues in concentrations greater than those sufficient to kill tubercle bacilli *in vitro*, but spermine-oxidase is more unevenly distributed. Since the polyamines are inactive *per se*, the presence of the oxidase and the proper environmental conditions for oxidative deamination are the limiting factors of antibacterial activity. One example will be given to illustrate the possible significance of these facts in pathogenesis. In guinea-pig tuberculosis, the kidneys usually remain free of disease, even when virulent bacilli are injected directly into renal tissue. In contrast, the kidneys of the rabbit are extremely susceptible to tuberculous infection. The fact that the enzyme spermine-oxidase is present in guinea-pig kidney, but not in rabbit kidney, suggests that the spermine–

spermine-oxidase system might play a role in natural resistance to tuberculous infection. It must be emphasized, however, that too little is known of the distribution of the enzyme, and of the conditions under which it functions, to justify any conclusion at present.

These few examples must suffice to illustrate the manner in which the tissue environment can be profoundly modified locally by the metabolic activities of inflammatory cells and the breakdown of tissues. Inflammation and necrosis mobilize or release in and around the tuberculous lesion a series of physico-chemical factors many of which affect the multiplication and survival of tubercle bacilli. Some of these factors tend to enhance infection, others to repress it. It is the balance of these conflicting forces which determines in each particular location the course and outcome of the infectious process. We do not completely understand what happens to the bacilli under natural disease conditions; nevertheless, it may be worth while to consider briefly the possible application of the facts presented above to a few specific pathological problems.

The multiplication of bacilli intracellularly and extracellularly

Let us consider first two simplified experimental systems, one in which all the bacilli are within monocytes, the other in which they are all extracellular.

It has been observed that, in tissue cultures, the *intracellular* multiplication of tubercle bacilli is slower when the monocytes are crowded than when they are sparse in the medium (Mackaness, 1954*a*, *b*; Mackaness, Smith & Wells, 1954). This observation might be explained by assuming that the phagocytic cells are compelled to derive energy from a more anaerobic type of metabolism when they are crowded in an area with limited facilities for gas exchange. Partial anoxia, higher CO_2 tension and increased concentration of lactic acid can then be expected to prevail intracellularly and thus interfere with bacterial growth.

The effect of the *extracellular* environment on the fate of tubercle bacilli *in vivo* is not easily observed because phagocytosis takes place rapidly under normal conditions if living tissue cells are present. This experimental difficulty has been overcome by the following ingenious technique (Lurie, 1939). Tubercle bacilli incorporated in an agar gel were placed in silk bags which had been impregnated with collodion in such a manner as to render them impervious to leucocytes, but still permeable to proteins and other soluble constitutents of the plasma. The bags containing the bacilli were introduced into the peritoneal cavity of normal and tuberculous animals. When they were removed 2 weeks later, it was found that the bacilli had multiplied extensively in the bags placed in the normal animals, whereas they had decreased in numbers in most of those in the tuberculous animals. As phagocytic cells had not penetrated the bags, the difference in microbial population in the two groups was obviously due to the antimicrobial activity of some humoral factor present in the tuberculous animals (Lurie, 1939). Although it is possible that this humoral factor was an antibody of a nature as yet undefined, other possibilities appear worth considering.

The bacilli and their metabolic products naturally called forth an inflammatory response around the silk-collodion bags. In the tuberculous animals in particular, the tuberculoproteins and tuberculopolysaccharides, diffusing through the bags, must have elicited immediate allergic reactions of both the tuberculin and the anaphylactic type, resulting in intense production of cellular exudate and in thrombosis of the vascular bed. This sequence of events must have rendered the local environment partially anaerobic and caused a predominantly glycolytic metabolism of the inflammatory cells—a conclusion supported by the low pH of the contents of the bags in the tuberculous animals.

In no case was the pH in the bags sufficiently low to be alone responsible for inhibition of growth. But along with the increase in acidity there were probably other biochemical changes caused by the inflammatory reaction and inimical to tubercle bacilli—for example, increased concentration of lactic acid and CO_2, decreased oxygen tension, the presence of lysozyme and necrotic products, and so on. It appears possible, therefore, that the decrease in microbial population in the tuberculous animals was the result of physico-chemical agents and not of a direct action of antibody on the bacilli. This view is compatible with the fact that the only bags in tuberculous animals which contained large numbers of bacilli at the end of the experiment were those in which the pH was 7·25–7·3—that is, as high as in the control. In brief, one might suppose that whereas the state of allergy, either of anaphylactic or of tuberculin type, caused an early reaction resulting in inhibition of growth in the tuberculous animals, the inflammatory response occurred only later in the normal animals, thus permitting bacillary multiplication to proceed uninhibited for a longer time.

The fact that the infectious process takes place both in the intracellular and extracellular phase under natural conditions, greatly complicates analysis of the factors which influence the multiplication and survival of the bacilli *in vivo*. In all cases studied by quantitative bacteriological techniques, it has been found that the rate of bacillary multiplication in the spleen is at first uniformly rapid and then slows down or stops completely. This course finds an explanation in the facts reported in the preceding pages. It is probable that the bacilli multiply uninhibited intracellularly during the first period following infection. Eventually some of the phagocytic cells are injured by the excessive bacillary proliferation and then release the bacillary components which they contain, thus permitting the development of allergy. Inflammatory cells migrate into the area where the injured phagocytes have settled and the inflammatory response becomes even more intense at the site of the lesion after the allergic state has become established and necrotic phenomena set in. All the physico-chemical factors described earlier, which retard or completely stop bacillary multiplication, are thus brought into play.

The death of bacilli in necrotic lesions

If the tissue reaction is such that the lesion is completely or almost completely enclosed, the environment may become so inimical to the bacilli as to cause their death. Indeed, it is often found in man and in experimental animals that many closed necrotic areas which were at first rich in bacilli eventually become almost sterile.

The disappearance of bacilli under these conditions cannot be attributed to ordinary immunological mechanisms, because phagocytic cells do not function within caseous areas, and because bacillary proliferation begins again when plasma penetrates the lesion during softening of the caseous matter. Probably the bacilli disappear because they progressively exhaust their metabolic reserves when the conditions *in vivo* do not permit them to synthesize new protoplasm. Once energy is no longer available for the maintenance of cell structure, autolytic enzymes begin to function, and morphological and staining characteristics are progressively lost. Observations *in vitro* reveal that the time required for the completion of this destructive process differs enormously from one species of micro-organism to another—a matter of hours or even minutes for pneumococci, probably of weeks or months for tubercle bacilli. But before these irreversible reactions resulting in death and autolytic changes take place, the micro-organisms go through a phase during which they are still potentially capable of reproduction but yet poorly able to start multiplying *in vivo* or in ordinary culture media. Hence arise the present controversies concerning the living or non-living state, of bacilli seen in necrotic lesions as rods which are still acid-fast and yet which appear non-viable by the usual tests *in vitro* and *in vivo*.

Comparative behaviour of virulent and attenuated bacilli in vivo

Under ordinary circumstances, the aggregation of factors at the site where the bacilli have begun to multiply is sufficient eventually to stop their further multiplication if they belong to an attenuated strain—R_1R_v or BCG, for example. In contrast, the more virulent organisms are able to overcome the tissue response and give rise to progressive disease. Although it is not yet possible to explain this difference in behaviour, it may be worth while to list a number of facts which suggest certain lines of investigation.

As already mentioned, there is the possibility, as yet unproven, that the virulent strains are endowed with greater toxicity than the attenuated or avirulent strains. On the other hand, it is known that the virulent strains multiply more rapidly than the attenuated during the initial phase of infection and that they survive for longer periods of time within necrotic lesions. These happenings *in vivo* have their counterpart in certain findings *in vitro*. Although the different cultures of mammalian mycobacteria are potentially capable of multiplying at the same rate *in vitro* in ordinary culture media, there is some evidence that BCG multiplies more slowly than virulent mycobacteria within monocytes in tissue cultures (Mackaness *et al.* 1954), and that it displays a much longer lag period as a result of ageing. We have also noted that attenuated and avirulent cultures die more rapidly than do virulent cultures when incubated under anaerobic conditions at pH 6·5 or aerobically in media devoid of nutrients or sources of energy, and that they seem to be somewhat less able to multiply at low oxygen tensions. It is tempting to postulate that the quantitative differences in behaviour, both *in vitro* and *in vivo*, among virulent, attenuated and avirulent strains are the expression of quantitative differences in some particular aspect of their cellular structure or metabolism. Although there is no evidence for this view, the facts presented in earlier parts of the present report suggest that the degree of virulence is somehow related to peculiarities of the oxidative metabolism of the cultures. It is also possible that this in turn bears a relation to the presence on the bacterial surface of the material responsible for the serpentine pattern of growth. Even if this working hypothesis were correct, the mechanism through which differences in metabolism and morphology affect the ability of the organisms to multiply and survive *in vivo* is still obscure.

TISSUE METABOLISM AND RESISTANCE TO TUBERCULOSIS

Intrinsic differences between strains of mammalian mycobacteria are of obvious importance in determining the course and outcome of the infection to which they give rise, but it is also true that changes in the *in vivo* environment can affect the pathogenic process in a profound manner. It has already been pointed out, for example, that silicosis and metabolic disturbances can permit attenuated bacilli to give rise to disease states undistinguishable from those produced by virulent bacilli. Similarly, clinical experience leaves no doubt that many types of physiological upset can greatly increase the susceptibility of man to tuberculosis.

Patients suffering from uncontrolled diabetes, or in a state of starvation, are known to be highly susceptible to tuberculosis, whereas their resistance returns to normal when the diabetes is controlled or the nutritional state improved. In these cases, therefore, the poor ability to resist infection is linked to a reversible metabolic disturbance. Needless to say, many kinds of biochemical disorder are associated with the wasting of tissues in uncontrolled diabetes or in starvation, and there is little reason to single out any particular one of them as bearing a causal relation to susceptibility to tuberculosis. Nevertheless, it seems worth considering the possibility that ketosis which is a feature both of uncontrolled diabetes and starvation may be the factor which enhances infection in these disease states.

We have mentioned earlier that under normal metabolic circumstances the burst of acidity which occurs after phagocytosis or at the site of inflammation is due almost entirely to the production of lactic acid. It is possible that the concentration of lactic acid is decreased in ketosis, and that there are produced instead other metabolites which exert a protective effect on tubercle bacilli. Irrespective of their virulence, the bacilli can multiply aerobically and survive both aerobically and anaerobically over a very wide range of acid reactions in media containing keto compounds and polycarboxylic acids, whereas they fail to multiply and may die rapidly in the presence of lactic, acetic, propionic or butyric acids (Dubos, 1953b, 1954). These facts might explain in part the greater susceptibility to infection of tissues under conditions where acetone bodies are known to accumulate.

The relation of ketosis to infection is of course only a working hypothesis which could be verified only by observations *in vivo*. In an attempt to approach the problem experimentally, efforts are being made in our laboratory to produce in experimental animals, metabolic disturbances that might affect their susceptibility to tuberculosis. A marked increase in susceptibility of mice has been achieved by feeding these animals diets rich in glycerides of short-chain fatty acids. Cocoa butter was selected as a natural source of these materials, because it contains a large proportion of C_8–C_{12} acids, the oxidation of which commonly leads to the accumulation of acetone bodies *in vivo*. It was found that the infection-enhancing effect of cocoa butter is markedly increased by adding citrate to the diet, and that citrate alone also enhanced susceptibility of mice to tuberculosis. Let it be mentioned in passing that similar results could be obtained by the oral administration of thyroxine of dinitrophenol and by partial starvation. Some of the results are presented in Table 4. (For more recent observations on these problems, see Dubos (1955*a* and *b*)).

Table 4. *Effect of nutritional and metabolic factors on susceptibility of mice to tuberculosis*

(Dubos, unpublished observations.)

Additions to diet	Strain	ml.*	Virulence	0–20	21–40	41–60	61–80	81–100	Survival after 100 days
		Infection		No. of 10 inoculated mice dead at specified times (days)					
Nothing (control)	MV	0·01	++++	—	1	11	111	—	4
Dinitrophenol	MV	0·01	++++	11	11111	111	—	—	0
Thyroid extract	MV	0·01	++++	111	111111	1	—	—	0
Cocoa butter	MV	0·01	++++	11	11	11111	1	—	0
Citrate	MV	0·01	++++	1	111	11	1	1	2
Cocoa butter and citrate	MV	0·01	++++	111	11111	11	—	—	0
Nothing (control)	BCG-P	0·2	++	—	—	1	—	—	9
Dinitrophenol	BCG-P	0·2	++	—	1	11	11	1	4
Cocoa butter and citrate	BCG-P	0·2	++	—	11	1	111	11	2
Nothing (control)	BCG-T	0·2	+	—	—	—	—	—	10
Dinitrophenol	BCG-T	0·2	+	—	—	—	—	111	7
Cocoa butter and citrate	BCG-T	0·2	+	—	111	1	1	1	4

Basic diet; dried milk 20, wheat flour 50, salts.

Dinitrophenol 0·1, thyroid extract 0·05, cocoa butter 20, Na citrate 10: cerelose added to complete 100; dry mixture resuspended in equal weight of 7·5 % (w/v) gelatin in tap water.

Mice infected intravenously 1 day after weaning (3 weeks) and immediately given experimental diets.

* 10-day-old culture in liquid Tween-albumin medium.

It is obvious that the overall effects of metabolic stimulants (dinitrophenol or thyroxine) or of abnormal diets (containing cocoa butter, or citrate, or both) are extremely complex and may express themselves indirectly through hormonal action—involving the adrenal cortex, for example. It would not be profitable therefore to attempt at this stage to analyse in biochemical terms the mechanism of the startling enhancement of susceptibility illustrated in Table 4. But whatever its biochemical mechanism, the fact that attenuated organisms so regularly produce progressive disease and death in animals suffering from metabolic disturbances is of obvious significance in any interpretation of the pathogenic behaviour of tubercle bacilli.

Virulence is not a qualitative, all-or-none characteristic, but an attribute which varies quantitatively from one strain of mycobacterium to another. It exists in many degrees forming a continuous spectrum, and the extent of its manifestations depends upon the physico-chemical characteristics of the *in vivo* environment in which the infectious process follows its course. In final analysis, virulence is an ecological concept which expresses the fitness of the micro-organism to survive and multiply under highly specific conditions. The physico-chemical environments provided by the phagocytic cells and the inflammatory response constitute in all likelihood the factors that determine the ability of mycobacteria to behave as pathogenic agents.

CONCLUSIONS

Mammalian tubercle bacilli exist in a large variety of variant strains. These form a continuous spectrum ranging from maximum virulence to inability to multiply in animal tissues, with all intermediate steps of behaviour *in vivo*.

There is no proof at the present time that the degrees of virulence are the expression of differences in amounts of toxic components produced by bacilli of the various strains.

The more virulent the strain, the more rapidly it multiplies intracellularly during the initial phase of infection, and the longer it survives extracellularly in the necrotic tissues. The differences in multiplication rates and in lengths of survival of the bacilli *in vivo* appear to be related in some obscure manner to peculiarities of the oxidative metabolism of the various strains.

All strains of mammalian tubercle bacilli are inhibited *in vitro* by the addition to the medium of lactic acid, fatty acids and certain autolytic products of tissues, in concentrations of the order found in inflammatory areas and in tuberculous lesions. The bacilli die rapidly in the presence of these metabolites under anaerobic conditions, especially if the CO_2 tension is high. They can multiply over a much wider range of acidity and survive for a longer time anaerobically if keto compounds are added to the medium.

These facts probably explain some aspects of the fate of tubercle bacilli *in vivo*, and may have a bearing on the great susceptibility to tuberculosis of man and experimental animals in certain disturbed metabolic states.

REFERENCES

ASSELINEAU, J. (1952). Lipides du bacille tuberculeux. *Progrès Explor. Tuberc.* **5**, 1–44.

ASSELINEAU, J., BLOCH, H. & LEDERER, E. (1953). A toxic lipid component of the tubercle bacillus ('cord factor'). *Amer. Rev. Tuberc.* **67**, 853–8.

BLOCH, H. (1950a). Enzymatic characteristics of suspensions of different mycobacteria. *Amer. Rev. Tuberc.* **61**, 270–1.

BLOCH, H. (1950b). Studies on the virulence of tubercle bacilli. Isolation and biological properties of a constituent of virulent organisms. *J. exp. Med.* **91**, 197–218.

BLOCH, H. (1950c). Studied on the virulence of tubercle bacilli. The relationship of the physiological state of the organisms to their virulence. *J. exp. Med.* **92**, 507–25.

BLOCH, H., SORKIN, E. & ERLENMEYER, H. (1953). A toxic lipid component of the tubercle bacillus ('cord factor'). I. Isolation from petroleum ether extracts of young bacterial cultures. *Amer. Rev. Tuberc.* **67**, 629–42.

CHOUCROUN, N. (1940). Les lésions de la tuberculose peuvent être engendrées par une substance extraite du bacille. *C.R. Acad. Sci., Paris*, **210**, 511–13.

CHOUCROUN, N. (1943a). Antigenic carbohydrate-lipid isolated from paraffin oil extract of dead tubercle bacilli. *Science*, **98**, 237.

CHOUCROUN, N. (1943b). Biological effects of a toxic and a sensitizing substance isolated from paraffin oil extract of dead tubercle bacilli. *Science*, **98**, 327–9.

CHOUCROUN, N. (1947). Tubercle bacillus antigens. *Amer. Rev. Tuberc.* **56**, 203–26.

CHOUCROUN, N. (1948). Role joué par le lipo-polysaccharide du bacille tuberculeux dans l'hypersensibilité à la tuberculine et dans l'acido-résistance du bacille. *C.R. Acad. Sci., Paris*, **226**, 1477.

DAVIES, R. (1940). The effect of carbon dioxide on the growth of the tubercle bacillus. *Brit. J. exp. Path.* **21**, 243–53.

DUBOS, R. J. (1947). The effect of lipids and serum albumin on bacterial growth. *J. exp. Med.* **85**, 9–22.

DUBOS, R. J. (1950). The effect of organic acids on mammalian tubercle bacilli. *J. exp. Med.* **92**, 319–32.

DUBOS, R. J. (1953a). Effect of the composition of the gaseous and aqueous environment on the survival of tubercle bacilli in vitro. *J. exp. Med.* **97**, 357–66.

DUBOS, R. J. (1953b). Effect of ketone bodies and other metabolities on the survival and multiplication of staphylococci and tubercle bacilli. *J. exp. Med.* **98**, 145–55.

DUBOS, R. J. (1954). *Biochemical Determinants of Microbial Diseases.* Harvard University Press.

DUBOS, R. J. (1955a). Effects of metabolic factors on mouse tuberculosis. *J. exp. Med.* (in the Press).

DUBOS, R. J. (1955b). Metabolic determinants of infection. *Bull. N.Y. Ac. Med.* (in the Press).

DUBOS, R. J. & HIRSCH, J. G. (1954). The antimycobacterial activity of a peptide preparation derived from calf thymus. *J. exp. Med.* **99**, 55–63.

DUBOS, R. J. & MIDDLEBROOK, G. (1948a). The effect of wetting agents on the growth of tubercle bacilli. *J. exp. Med.* **88**, 81–8.

DUBOS, R. J. & MIDDLEBROOK, G. (1948b). Cytochemical reaction of virulent tubercle bacilli. *Amer. Rev. Tuberc.* **58**, 698–9.

DUBOS, R. J. & SUTER, E. (1949). The effect of ammonium ions and aliphatic amines on the ability of virulent mycobacteria to bind neutral red. *Amer. Rev. Tuberc.* **60**, 384.

124 R. J. DUBOS

FENNER, F. & LEACH, R. H. (1953). The growth of mammalian tubercle bacilli in Tween-albumin medium. *Amer. Rev. Tuberc.* **68**, 342–71.

FRUNDER, H. (1951). *Die Wasserstoffionenkonzentration im Gewebe Lebender Tiere —nach messungen mit der Glaselektrode.* Jena: Gustav Fischer.

FRUNDER, H. (1953). *Der Stoffwechsel des entzundeten und geschadigten Gewebes. (The mechanism of inflammation, An international symposium.)* G. Jasmin & A. Robert, eds. Montreal: Acta, Inc. pp. 175–86.

GERONIMUS, L. H. (1949). Studies on the oxidative systems in mycobacteria with special emphasis upon the employment of cell-free extracts. Ph.D. thesis, Ohio State University.

GERONIMUS, L. H. & BIRKELAND, J. M. (1951). The relationship between the virulence of tubercle bacilli and the vigor of their oxidative attack upon certain substrates. *Amer. Rev. Tuberc.* **64**, 520–33.

GUY, R. L., RAFFEL, S. & CLIFTON, C. E. (1954). Virulence of the tubercle bacillus. II. Effect of oxygen tension upon growth of virulent and avirulent bacilli. *J. infect. Dis.* **94**, 99–106.

HART, P. D'A. & REES, R. J. W. (1954). Changes in morphology of an avirulent strain of *mycobacterium tuberculosis* under the influence of non-ionic surface-active agents. *J. gen. Microbiol.* **10**, 150–9.

HEPLAR, J. Q. (1953). Respiratory quotients of tubercle bacilli at low oxygen tension. *Amer. Rev. Tuberc.* **67**, 699–70.

HEPLAR, J. Q., CLIFTON, C. E., RAFFEL, S. & FUTRELLE, C. M. (1954). Virulence of the tubercle bacillus. I. Effect of oxygen tension upon respiration of virulent and avirulent bacilli. *J. infect. Dis.* **94**, 90–8.

HIRSCH, J. G. (1953a). The essential participation of an enzyme in the inhibition of growth of tubercle bacilli by spermine. *J. exp. Med.* **97**, 327–44.

HIRSCH, J. G. (1953b). Spermine oxidase: an amine oxidase with specificity for spermine and spermidine. *J. exp. Med.* **97**, 345–55.

HIRSCH, J. G. (1954). Mechanisms involved in the antimycobacterial activity of certain basic peptides. *J. exp. Med.* **99**, 79–88.

HIRSCH, J. G. & DUBOS, R. J. (1952). The effect of spermine on tubercle bacilli. *J. exp. Med.* **95**, 191–208.

HIRSCH, J. G. & DUBOS, R. J. (1954). Chemical studies on a basic peptide preparation derived from calf thymus. *J. exp. Med.* **99**, 65–78.

KERBY, GRACE P. (1952). Release of enzyme from human leukocytes on damage by bacterial derivatives. *Proc. Soc. exp. Biol., N.Y.*, **81**, 381.

LURIE, M. B. (1939). Studies on the mechanism of immunity in tuberculosis. The role of extracellular factors and local immunity in the fixation and inhibition of growth of bacilli. *J. exp. Med.* **69**, 555–77.

MACKANESS, G. B. (1954a). The growth of tubercle bacilli in monocytes from normal and vaccinated rabbits. *Amer. Rev. Tuberc.* **69**, 495–504.

MACKANESS, G. B. (1954b). The relationship between host-cell and parasite in tuberculosis. *Brit. med. J.* (in the Press).

MACKANESS, G. B., SMITH, N. & WELLS, A. Q. (1954). The growth of intracellular tubercle bacilli in relation to their virulence. *Amer. Rev. Tuberc.* **69**, 479–94.

MELVIN, I. G. & MACPHERSON, D. A. (1954). The relation of cord formation to virulence in mycobacteria. *Bact. Proc.* p. 95.

MIDDLEBROOK, G., DUBOS, R. J. & PIERCE, C. H. (1947). Virulence and morphological characters of mammalian tubercle bacilli. *J. exp. Med.* **86**, 175–84.

NOLL, H. & BLOCH, H. A. (1953). A toxic lipid component of the tubercle bacillus ('cord factor'). II. Occurrence in chloroform extracts by young and older bacterial cultures. *Amer. Rev. Tuberc.* **67**, 828–52.

PHILPOT, F. J. & WELLS, A. Q. (1952). Lipids of living and killed tubercle bacilli. *Amer. Rev. Tuberc.* **66**, 28–35.

PINNER, M. & VOLDRICH, M. (1931). The disease caused by filtrates of tubercle bacillus cultures. Its alleged relation to filterable forms of tubercle bacilli. I. The problem. *Amer. Rev. Tuberc.* **24**, 73–94.

RAFFEL, S. (1950). Chemical factors involved in the induction of infectious allergy. *Experientia*, **6**, 410.

RAFFEL, S., LEDERER, E. & ASSELINEAU, J. (1954). Lipoidal factors in induction of tuberculous hypersensitivity. *Fed. Proc.* **13**, 509.

SOLTYS, M. A. (1953). An anti-tuberculous substance in tuberculous organs. *J. comp. Path.* **63**, 147.

SPITZNAGEL, J. & DUBOS, R. J. (1955). A toxic lipid from tubercle bacilli. *J. exp. Med.* (in the Press).

STEENKEN, W. & GARDNER, L. U. (1946). History of H_{37} strain of tubercle bacilli. *Amer. Rev. Tuberc.* **54**, 62–6.

WATSON, D. W. & BLOOM, W. (1952). Antimicrobial activity of a natural and a synthetic polypeptide. *Proc. Soc. exp. Biol., N.Y.*, **81**, 29–33.

WATSON, D. W., CROMARTIE, W. J., BLOOM, W. L., HECKLEY, R. J., McGHEE, W. J. & WEISSMAN, N. (1947). Studies on infection with *Bacillus anthracis. J. infect. Dis.* **80**, 121–36.

YOUMANS, G. P. & YOUMANS, A. S. (1951). The relation between the size of the infecting dose of tubercle bacilli and the survival time of mice. *Amer. Rev. Tuberc.* **64**, 534.

STUDIES ON THE CHEMICAL BASIS OF THE PATHOGENICITY OF *BACILLUS ANTHRACIS* USING ORGANISMS GROWN *IN VIVO*

H. SMITH AND J. KEPPIE

Microbiological Research Department, Ministry of Supply,
Porton, Wilts

Studies on the purification and chemical identification of bacterial products have been related mostly to their immunizing action and their serological behaviour. Less attention has been given to the part played by these products in the disease process and in causing the death of the host. This is particularly true of the organisms capable of producing bacteraemic conditions in which no potent extracellular toxins seem to play a part. *Bacillus anthracis* is an organism of this kind, and the work described here aims at identifying chemically the substances and processes involved in its pathogenicity.

A pathogenic organism must first establish itself in a host and secondly produce disease, which may be fatal—as anthrax is in the guinea-pig. The chemical substances and processes responsible for pathogenicity can therefore be divided into two classes, which may or may not be connected. First there are the so-called aggressins which combat the defence mechanisms of the host and allow the organism to grow freely in the host's tissues. In anthrax, as in other bacteraemic diseases, a very large number of organisms must grow in the host before it dies. The harmful effect attributable to each organism is therefore low. This emphasizes the importance in any study of the overall pathogenicity of such an organism of the aggressins which help it to grow to such large numbers in the host. The second class of compounds or processes are those which operate to kill the host when the body defences have been overcome. In the work to be described attention has been given to both these aspects of pathogenicity.

When establishing itself in the host, the bacterium will undoubtedly be affected by the particular nutritional conditions in the host's tissues. The possibility that the bacterium reacts in some way to the challenge of the defence mechanisms must also be borne in mind. There is abundant evidence that the complex metabolic activity of a pathogen under the cultural conditions of the host's tissues is different from its metabolism *in vitro*. Evidence for this is seen, for example, in the change in morphology and colony appearance and the decrease in virulence which frequently occurs when recently isolated organisms are sub-cultured. Further, the fact that the pathogenicity of an organism can frequently be increased by animal passage implies that substances and processes connected with pathogenicity are produced *in vivo* (possibly as a result of mutation or selection of virulent types) and not to any significant extent by culture *in vitro*. A similar conclusion can be drawn from the difficulty or impossibility of distinguishing between virulent and avirulent strains of certain species such as *Pasteurella pestis* (Wilson & Miles, 1946, p. 775; Jawetz & Meyer, 1943) by *in vitro* tests. Perhaps, however, the most striking instances of the difference between culture *in vitro* and *in vivo* are those in which the use of living vaccines form the only effective means of preventing the disease.

To be certain therefore that the organism is producing all the com-pounds and processes involved in pathogenicity, the growth conditions which exist *in vivo* are essential, but our limited knowledge of bacterial nutrition makes it impossible for the present to reproduce these *in vitro*. It seemed then that the best way of studying compounds and reactions responsible for pathogenicity was to use organisms and their products isolated from infected animals. This does not necessarily mean that there is an absolute difference between 'animal organisms' and those grown *in vitro*. If the compounds and reactions responsible for patho-genicity in the host could be identified, it might lead to the production in defined media of some of the metabolic processes which occur *in vivo*. The work of Gladstone (1946, 1948) in producing the immunizing anti-gen of *B. anthracis* in artificial culture, which has been extended by Wright, Hedberg & Slein (1954) and Belton & Strange (1954), is en-couraging in this respect.

In our present study on the chemical basis of pathogenicity, bacteria and their products from infected animals have been the starting materials. *B. anthracis* was chosen as the pathogen to be studied for two main reasons: first, anthrax is characterized by the presence in the host of large numbers of organisms which made it probable that the yield of bacteria would be satisfactory; secondly, the majority of chemical studies of *B. anthracis* have been made with organisms grown *in vitro*. Until now, the only progress made has been on the chemical basis of immunity to the disease (Strange & Belton, 1954). Although much was known about the aggressive activity of *B. anthracis*, only very scanty knowledge has accumulated about the chemical compounds responsible for it. Even less was known about the killing power of *B. anthracis*. Neither the general nature of the lethal effect on the host nor even the products or processes of the organism mainly responsible for the characteristic and spectacular symptoms of the disease were known. No study of the chemical basis of this aspect of pathogenicity has therefore been possible. However, sufficient knowledge has been gained in the biological field to indicate the general lines of attack on these problems and to encourage the use of organisms and their products produced *in vivo*.

Reviews of the literature on the pathology and immunochemistry of *B. anthracis* and its infections are available (Sobernheim, 1913, 1931; Cromartie, Bloom & Watson, 1947; Treffers, 1947). These show that attention has been focused mainly on three aspects of the subject, namely, immunity to the disease, invasiveness of the organism, and speculations about the cause of death.

The problem of immunity to anthrax has received much attention, and although we are primarily concerned here with pathogenicity, a discussion of the immunity processes adds to our understanding of the disease. For nearly half a century after the introduction of a vaccine consisting of living attenuated cultures by Pasteur (1881), and sterile oedema fluid from infected animals by Bail (1904), no further progress was made. Dead bacteria and various bacterial extracts (Gladstone, 1946) were ineffective. Gladstone (1946, 1948), however, using *ad hoc* methods, produced an extracellular immunizing antigen by *in vitro* culture. This protective antigen has not yet been shown to react in any of the usual types of *in vitro* serological tests (Watson, Cromartie, Bloom, Kegeles & Heckly, 1947a), or to be associated specifically with the virulence of the organism. Recently Gladstone's work has been extended by Wright *et al.* (1954), who prepared the protective antigen in a purely synthetic medium. Belton & Strange (1954) have modified Wright's medium to give better yields of the antigen.

With regard to the ability of *B. anthracis* to grow in the host tissues, Bail & Weil (1911) found that anthrax lesions contain substances which interfere with host resistance. They called them aggressins, and since other organisms produced similar substances they developed the much discussed 'aggressin theory' of invasion (see Wilson & Miles, 1946, p. 1068). Both phagocytosis (Adami, 1909) and extracellular lysis by an anthracidal substance that appears in the serum of some species and in leucocyte extracts (Bloom, Watson, Cromartie & Freed, 1947a) constitute the main defence mechanisms of the host. Their relative importance no doubt varies from species to species. Bail & Weil (1911) found that a combination of serum and leucocytes had the highest bactericidal activity, and it was this activity that the aggressins inhibited.

Little is known about the chemical nature of these aggressins. Gruber & Futaki (1907) and Preisz (1909) suggested that they were associated with the capsule because crude capsular material protected the organisms from phagocytosis and anthracidal substance. It seems that the capsule is of importance in pathogenicity because all pathogenic strains have capsules (Bail, 1915*a*, *b*, *c*; Sterne, 1937). Clearly, however, other factors are involved because capsulated non-pathogenic strains are known to exist (Sterne, 1937). Furthermore, resistance to phagocytosis is not of unique importance, because in general capsulated attenuated strains are resistant to phagocytosis *in vivo* and *in vitro* (Sterne, 1954, private communication). Bail & Weil (1911) did not think that the aggressin and the capsule were related. Capsulated, phagocytosis-resistant strains and phagocytosis-sensitive uncapsulated organisms are susceptible to anthracidal substance *in vitro*. They observed that extracts from anthrax lesions interfered with this but that extracts of capsulated organisms did not. Watson, Cromartie, Bloom, Heckly, McGhee & Weissman (1947*b*) showed that their crude 'inflammatory factor' isolated from oedema fluid of infected rabbits inhibited anthracidal substance. It seems therefore that at least two factors are involved in invasiveness: one connected with the capsule and the other an extracellular product. Sterne (1937) suggested that this extracellular product might be connected with the immunizing activity of the organism.

The cause of death of the host has received some attention but no definite conclusions have resulted from work in the past. A difficulty in this field has been that no lethal endo- or exotoxin has been found in cultures of the organism (Eurich & Hewlett, 1930; Sobernheim, 1931; King & Stein, 1950). A slight tissue-damaging activity has been found by many workers in extracts of infected tissue (Sobernheim, 1931; Watson *et al.* 1947*b*). These extracts when injected into the skin produced small oedematous lesions which soon healed. Production of oedema is not confined to capsulated virulent strains of *B. anthracis*. Uncapsulated variants also produce oedema (Stamatin & Stamatin, 1936). Enzymes produced by *B. anthracis* which might be connected with this activity are collagenases, gelatinases, proteinases and lecithinases (Evans & Wardlaw, 1953; McGaughey & Chu, 1948; Gladstone, 1946, 1948). Recently Evans & Shoesmith (1954) have described a skin reaction in the rabbit which rapidly follows injection of concentrates of old cultures of *B. anthracis*. However, they did not study the specificity of this reaction or whether the preparation was lethal. Its relationship to the pathogenicity of *B. anthracis* has yet to be established.

In view of the apparent absence of toxin many speculations have been made on possible causes of death. The intense bacteraemia present in the typical death from anthrax prompted the suggestion that deoxygenation of the blood or capillary obstruction might cause death (Vaughan & Novy, 1902; Zinsser & Bayne-Jones, 1939). Reports that a few animals of some species die without a marked bacteraemia (Bloom, McGhee, Cromartie & Watson, 1947b; Stockman, 1911) are evidence against this suggestion. Several different workers agree that a marked hyperglycaemia occurs in anthrax (Singer, 1927; Caifaleanu, Combiesco & Stamatesco, 1930; Bloom et al. 1947b), but no explanation for this has been offered. An interference with calcium metabolism was suggested as a possible cause of death by Bloom et al. (1947b). The symptoms of the disease were compared with those of calcium deficiency, the work of Weinstein (1938) on the protective effect of parathyroid hormone on anthrax was noted, and the protective effect of certain calcium salts was demonstrated. Both the calcium salts and the parathyroid extract were given from the time of challenge onwards, and the effect may have been on the initial invasion rather than on the killing power of the organism. It is relevant to point out that Govaerts (1951) and Renaux (1952) noted the adverse effect on the pathogenicity of B. anthracis when calcium salts were added to cultures. De Moulin (1936) reported lesions in the nervous system and attributed the symptoms of anthrax and the death of the host to damage of this system. The authors are not aware of any confirmation of de Moulin's work.

Purely chemical studies of B. anthracis have mostly been carried out with organisms grown in vitro. Apart from vague mention of 'nucleoproteins' as precipitates formed by the addition of acetic acid (Ivanovics & Erdös, 1937; Grabar & Staub, 1944) the only chemical substances which have been studied in extracts of B. anthracis are D-polyglutamic acid and the somatic polysaccharide.

Following earlier work by Tomcsik & Szongott (1933) and Ivanovics & Erdös (1937), Ivanovics & Bruckner (1937) isolated D-polyglutamic acid and proved its general constitution. The more intimate structure of the compound, mainly the question of whether α links or γ links, or a mixture of both, join the glutamic acid residues is still in dispute (Hanby & Rydon, 1946; Bruckner, Kovacs & Denes, 1953). Previous work suggests, but does not prove, a connexion between the polyglutamic acid of B. anthracis and its invasiveness. The capsule is connected with invasiveness, and polyglutamic acid almost certainly occurs in the capsule since non-capsulated strains do not produce it. On the other hand, there is no evidence that the capsule of B. anthracis is composed entirely of polyglutamic acid. The capsular material of Gruber & Futaki

(1907) and Preisz (1909) undoubtedly contained polyglutamic acid, as did the 'inflammatory factor' of Watson *et al.* (1947*b*), but these preparations were almost certainly impure. We are unaware of purified polyglutamic acid of *B. anthracis* having been tested for aggressin activity, although the behaviour of the polyglutamic acid of *B. subtilis* (Watson *et al.* 1947*b*) suggested that it would have such activity. Because the capsule and polyglutamic acid can be produced by non-pathogenic strains, they are clearly not the only factors involved in pathogenicity. It is possible that different polyglutamic acids are produced by pathogenic and non-pathogenic strains. Thorne, Gomez & Housewright (1952) and Thorne, Gomez, Blind & Housewright (1953) have shown that pathogenic strains of *B. anthracis* need CO_2 for polyglutamic acid production, whereas non-pathogenic strains do not.

The polysaccharide of *B. anthracis* first isolated by Ivanovics (1940) was a polymer of galactose and glucosamine containing acetyl groups. It was not clear whether the 10 % of peptide material that remained was part of the molecule or not. This polysaccharide, although serologically active, has not been shown in any way to be associated with pathogenicity, and capsulated pathogenic strains and uncapsulated non-pathogenic strains produce the same polysaccharide (Ivanovics, 1940). It appears to be part of the cell wall which projects into the capsule (Chu, 1953; Tomcsik, 1951), the polyglutamic acid filling the space between the projections. Ivanovics & Horvath (1953*a*, *b*) dispute this structure of the capsule.

Neither the polyglutamic acid nor the polysaccharide is connected with the protective antigen (Staub & Grabar, 1943; Staub, 1949). Watson *et al.* (1947*a*) found that the immunizing activity was associated with a globulin fraction of rabbit oedema fluid and the activity was destroyed by heat and trypsin. Strange & Belton (1954) in purifying the protective antigen produced *in vitro* have found that it is a protein or closely associated with one.

THE COLLECTION OF *BACILLUS ANTHRACIS* FROM GUINEA-PIGS

As earlier studies had not revealed the compounds or chemical processes responsible for the pathogenicity of *B. anthracis*, the use of organisms grown *in vivo* seemed advisable, and the first question to be decided was whether sufficient material of adequate purity for chemical investigation could be obtained from infected animals. Fractionation of body fluids containing extracellular products of an infecting organism had been done before (e.g. Watson *et al.* 1947*a*), but there had been no studies of bacterial substance so produced. Until now organisms grown *in vivo* had not been obtained in large enough quantity and of sufficient purity for chemical examination and for a study of their metabolism.

Smith, Keppie & Stanley (1953a) have established a method for collecting and separating *B. anthracis* and body fluids containing its extracellular products from infected guinea-pigs. Large guinea-pigs were infected intraperitoneally and intrapulmonarily with *B. anthracis* (strain N.P.). At death, the thoracic and peritoneal exudate (approx. 5 parts) and the plasma (approx. 1 part) were collected and mixed. By differential centrifugation at 0°, the body fluids and the bacteria were separated from the blood cells. It was possible to collect from 100 infected guinea-pigs 1·5–2·0 g. of dry *B. anthracis* and 1·5–2·5 l. of body fluids containing the extracellular products of this organism. These quantities were sufficiently large to allow a chemical study of the factors involved in the pathogenicity of *B. anthracis* in guinea-pigs. A high degree of freedom from blood cells was obtained by a process involving only a small overall loss (10–13 %) of the total bacteria present in the harvested material. Relative counts of blood cells to bacteria, together with a knowledge of their relative size, showed that the bacteria were contaminated with less than 1 % (w/w) of blood-cell substance; for the purposes of this calculation the specific gravity of blood and bacterial cells was considered equal. This contamination with blood-cell substance could be considered negligible and would be diluted out in most extraction procedures.

The guinea-pig was used as the host for this infection and for all further work on pathogenicity. It was a compromise between two requirements. From the point of view of obtaining the maximum yield of products, a large animal such as a sheep would have been the best host for the infection. But if the ultimate products of chemical extraction were to be adequately tested for properties connected with pathogenicity, in a homologous system, a species that could be tested in large numbers had to be used.

Although grossly contaminated with plasma constituents, the sterile extracellular products could be examined directly for biological properties connected with pathogenicity and could undergo chemical extraction for the substances responsible for these biological properties. Before the same procedure was adopted for the bacterial substance two questions had to be answered. First, were these bacteria appreciably different from those obtained by growing the same strain *in vitro*? Secondly, could extracts containing nearly all of the original bacterial substance be made by methods which would result in the minimum alteration of the cell constituents? Smith, Keppie & Stanley (1953*b*) described work which gave an affirmative answer to both questions.

The widely held view that organisms from an infected host differ from those obtained from cultures was substantiated for *B. anthracis* (strain N.P.) from infected guinea-pigs. A study of morphology and susceptibility to phagocytosis sharply differentiated organisms grown *in vivo* from those grown in tryptic meat broth. This same differentiation was not so sharp for those cultured in three other media: sheep serum, guinea-pig plasma and the medium of Belton & Strange (1954). However, organisms from guinea-pigs rapidly lysed in ammonium carbonate solution (0·16 % w/v) at 0°. This rapid lysis was not shown by any of the organisms grown *in vitro*, including those from media containing plasma constituents. The action of ammonium carbonate, the basis of which is unknown, serves to underline the chemical difference between the two types of organism.

A method of removing the capsule without damaging the bacterial cell would have been of great value in investigating the part that the capsule plays in pathogenicity. Many attempts were made to do this but without success. After this failure, two methods were used to dissolve the bacterial substance—namely, the use of ammonium carbonate solution, and shaking with 'ballotini' (small glass beads). The proportion of material dissolved was over 95 %. Of the two methods, extraction with dilute ammonium carbonate solution was the easier, and it is doubtful whether any gross harm was done to constituents by a pH of 8·8–8·3 at 0–3°. However, the second method of extraction at pH 7 rules out any possible detrimental effect of these slightly alkaline conditions.

The technical difficulties of obtaining bacteria and their products from *in vivo* sources had thus been solved. These materials were now used in this study of the chemical basis of the pathogenicity of *B. anthracis*.

THE NATURE OF THE AGGRESSINS

It is proposed first to describe how far work on the invasiveness of this organism has progressed. Plasma/exudate representing the extracellular products and the two bacterial extracts were examined in biological tests for aggressin activity. The crude materials proved active in these tests and therefore they were extracted chemically for the substances responsible. Similar studies on the extracellular products of *B. anthracis* have already been reviewed (Treffers, 1947), but we still lacked information about the intracellular products, whose behaviour was therefore of special interest.

Three types of test were used to demonstrate aggressin activity (Keppie, Smith & Harris-Smith, 1953): (1) Enhancement of the effect of a sublethal dose of *B. anthracis* (strain N.P.) given intraperitoneally to guinea-pigs. (2) Reduction of the phagocytic index in a normal *in vitro* phagocytosis test involving whole guinea-pig blood and broth-grown *B. anthracis* (strain N.P.). (3) Reduction of the bactericidal effect of whole guinea-pig blood—an effect which was proved to be due to phagocytosis and not to extracellular lysis because no anthracidal substance was demonstrable in guinea-pig serum.

Plasma/exudate (2 % w/v, citrate free), ammonium-carbonate bacterial extract (1·25 % w/v), and 'ballotini' bacterial extract (1·25 % w/v) caused a 200-fold enhancement of virulence. In the second form of test, final concentrations of about 1·25 % w/v of each preparation caused significant reductions in the phagocytic index. Similarly, the three products at a final concentration of approximately 0·6 % w/v reduced the bactericidal activity of guinea-pig whole blood in the third type of experiment. This bactericidal test proved the most convenient of the three tests and has been used for following the fractionation of the crude aggressins. The concentrations of the fractions quoted in Table 1 are the lowest final concentration in the mixture (Keppie *et al.* 1953) which produced a significant inhibition of the bactericidal activity. A modified virulence-enhancing test has also been used at intervals to check the aggressin content of fractions. For this purpose an attenuated strain, 'Pasteur II', was kindly provided by Miss R. Jordan of the Sir William Dunn School of Pathology, Oxford. In the absence of added aggressin, the intradermal injection (0·2 ml.) of doses of $0·2 \times 10^8$, 10^6 and 10^5 spores killed 15/16, 2/16 and 0/16 guinea-pigs (350 g.) respectively. The addition of fractions with aggressin activity enhanced the killing power of the lower doses. For the sake of brevity in the succeeding section of this paper concentrations of fractions have been described as active if they gave death-rates in adequate batches of guinea-pigs of 75 and 25 % or over, when injected with $0·2 \times 10^6$ and 10^5 spores respectively. Tests with fractions described as inactive gave results indistinguishable from control groups.

Smith & Zwartouw (1954; and unpublished work), have fractionated the intracellular material of *B. anthracis* grown *in vivo*. The ammonium carbonate extract was used because it was easier to prepare than the ballotini extract and because no significant difference in aggressin activity of the two types of extract could be detected.

In summary the method of fractionation was as follows. After preliminary dialysis, a barium acetate/ethanol fractionation gave four main fractions thus: 1 % w/v barium acetate at pH 7, protein; ethanol added to 5 % v/v, crude polyglutamic acid; ethanol added to 33 % v/v, protein; supernatant, polysaccharide. The polyglutamic acid and the polysaccharide were purified and satisfied electrophoretic, ultracentrifugal and other tests for homogeneity. This is the first time that the polysaccharide of *B. anthracis* has been subjected to such studies. The analyses of the sample differed somewhat from that quoted by Ivanovics (1940). Two special points of interest emerge. According to the proportion of hexosamine (37 %), the acetyl figure (14·7 %) was about 1½ times that required for *N*-acetyl hexosamine, and approximately 4 % of amino-acid residues appear to be combined in the polysaccharide. After removing some insoluble material from a solution of the first freeze-dried fraction, the addition of 1 % w/v barium acetate precipitated an active essentially protein fraction (N 12–13 %, carbohydrate residues 1–3 %, P 0·2 %) which was free of polyglutamic acid. The aggressin activity of these defined fractions are given in Table 1.

Table 1. *Fractionation of the intracellular and extracellular aggressins of* Bacillus anthracis *grown* in vivo

Fraction	Antibactericidal* activity	Virulence enhancing† activity
A. Intracellular material:		
Diffusate	Inactive 2·5 %	Inactive 2 %
Polyglutamic acid	Active 2–1 %	Active 1 %
Polysaccharide	Inactive 2·5 %	Inactive 1 %
Protein ppt. by 1 % barium acetate	Active 0·05 %	Active 0·2 %
B. Extracellular products:		
Diffusate	Inactive 1·6 %	—
Polyglutamic acid	Active 2–1 %	Active 1–0·5 %
2 % barium acetate/10 % ethanol fraction	Active 0·03 %	Active 0·08 %
2 % barium acetate/20 % ethanol fraction	Active 0·2–0·1 %	—
Soluble	Inactive 2 %	Inactive 2 %

* The concentrations (% w/v) quoted are those in the final mixture of guinea-pig blood and aggressin in the bactericidal test described by Keppie *et al.* (1953).

† Details of the test are given in the text; the concentrations (% w/v) quoted as active are those 0·2 ml. of which substantially enhance the virulence of an intradermal sublethal dose of *B. anthracis* (Pasteur II) in guinea-pigs.

Smith & Gallop (Smith, Zwartouw & Gallop, 1954c; Smith & Gallop, unpublished work) have fractionated the plasma/exudate (i.e. the body fluids of infected guinea-pigs) for the extracellular aggressins of *B. anthracis*. The essential details of this fractionation have been described. After dialysis, barium acetate (2 % w/v) and ethanol added to 5 % v/v precipitated a fraction (1 % yield) composed largely of polyglutamic acid. This was purified and satisfied ultracentrifugal, electrophoretic and other tests for homogeneity. Raising the ethanol concentration to 10 % v/v produced a small highly active essentially protein fraction (yield 1 %, N 13·2 %, carbohydrate residues 1·5 %, P less than 0·1 %). The addition of 20 % ethanol removed practically all the remaining activity and the bulk of the plasma protein (yield 35 %) remained in solution. The aggressin activity of these fractions is given in Table 1.

Chemical fractionation of both intracellular and extracellular products has been made difficult by the fact that the freeze-drying of solutions of active fractions produced solids which were incompletely soluble. Furthermore, insoluble material produced by this treatment was usually intensely active in the antibactericidal test (often at concentrations of less than 0·01 % w/v) and also, if obtained from the extracellular material, in the protective antigenicity test. This was a relatively specific phenomenon, since other insoluble materials did not have such activity. All the activities quoted in Table 1 are of soluble materials; any slight amount of insoluble material had been removed by centrifugation. This behaviour of the active fractions is probably due to the presence of lipid which has been found in both intra- and extra-cellular products and which to some extent explains their N contents which were low for true proteins. Recently, freeze-drying has been dispensed with throughout the work, and this has largely prevented the appearance of these insoluble materials. The fractionations described above have been further improved through the introduction by Zwartouw of an ion-exchange resin to remove barium ions from precipitates.

From the results summarized in Table 1 it is apparent that *B. anthracis* produces at least three aggressins when growing *in vivo*. Of the three, polyglutamic acid shows activity only in high concentration (1 % w/v). However, in view of its concentration in the capsule around the organism it probably exerts a considerable effect in preventing phagocytosis. The two other aggressins produced by the organism are more powerful on a weight basis than polyglutamic acid, and are both present in essentially lipoprotein fractions. Their behaviour in two biological tests suggests, however, that they are different compounds. First, the well-known protective antigen of *B. anthracis* is directly connected with the extracellular aggressin but not with the intracellular material. Secondly, the intracellular material is connected with anticomplementary activity, which is not found in the fraction containing the extracellular aggressin.

By active-immunity test in guinea-pigs Keppie *et al.* (1953) demonstrated the well-known antigen of *B. anthracis* in the plasma/exudate. Fractionation of the plasma/exudate showed a parallelism between the aggressin and the protective antigen (Smith *et al.* 1954c), the important fraction showing activity at a concentration of 0·025 % w/v in the test for protective antigen. The existence of this parallelism was supported by the fact that the purified antigen of Strange & Belton (1954), produced *in vitro*, had aggressin activity. In contrast, both the crude intracellular material and the purified aggressin (0·8 % w/v) therefrom were inactive in the protective antigen test. In addition, Keppie, Smith & Harris-Smith (unpublished) have shown that, whereas plasma/exudate (1 % w/v) had no anticomplementary activity in a test for such activity involving sheep cells, guinea-pig complement and anti-serum, the bacterial extracts (1 % w/v) were active. The extracellular aggressin (1 % w/v) was not anticomplementary in this test, but the intracellular aggressin (0·4 and 0·1 % w/v) was highly active. No other fraction of the intracellular material showed anticomplementary activity at concentrations of 1 % w/v or above. Polyglutamic acid (1 %) showed no activity in both anticomplementary and protective-antigen tests.

It should be emphasized that ultracentrifugal and electrophoretic evidence shows that both aggressin fractions are impure. It is not known whether the lipid or any other moiety is essential for activity. Investigations into the mode of action of these aggressins have been started, and preliminary observations suggest that the extracellular aggressin causes damage to the phagocytes which persists after washing the cells. Polyglutamic acid must be present with the phagocytes and organisms to prevent phagocytosis. The possibility that the intracellular material increases the growth or resistance to phagocytosis of the test organism in the aggressin assays is being investigated.

The results of these fractionations support the views expressed earlier in the examination of the literature—namely, that invasiveness and virulence are connected with capsular substance and an extracellular factor, both of which must be present for full effectiveness. To these a further cellular aggressin may now have to be added.

THE CAUSE OF DEATH IN ANTHRAX

The body of biological information available on the invasiveness of *B. anthracis* allowed an immediate approach to the chemical fractionation and identification of aggressins. Unfortunately, the literature upon the cause of death in anthrax had little to offer other than speculation. Our main effort, therefore, in this connexion was directed to establishing the nature of the fatal syndrome and in recognizing the substance causing it. This was essential before chemical work could begin.

Our first attempt to demonstrate a lethal factor in the products of *B. anthracis* growing *in vivo* was unsuccessful. Large quantities of a mixture of 5 parts thoracic exudate and 1 part plasma from guinea-pigs dying of anthrax were not lethal when injected intraperitoneally into guinea-pigs. The result was the same when bacterial extracts were injected equivalent to an amount of bacteria twice that estimated to be present in a guinea-pig when it dies of anthrax (Keppie *et al.* 1953). These preparations, although non-lethal, produced the weak oedematous skin reaction already associated with such materials.

This lack of toxicity led to consideration of the hypotheses propounded in the literature that a massive bacteraemia blocked the capillaries or produced a deficiency of oxygen or essential nutrients (e.g. glucose). To assess the importance of such hypotheses it was essential to know whether the bacteraemia had to reach its possible maximum before death from anthrax followed. It is generally agreed that a pronounced bacteraemia is a usual feature in death from anthrax in many species, and we have found it invariably so in our work with guinea-pigs. However, a few reports state that partly immune guinea-pigs (Sterne, 1953, private communication) and some animals of other species (Bloom *et al.* 1947*b*; Stockman, 1911) die of anthrax with only a slight bacteraemia. Such reports were the exception to the general rule and were in the main incidental to other studies. A thorough investigation of the significance of the final bacteraemia in the death of guinea-pigs seemed necessary (Keppie, Smith & Harris-Smith, 1955).

Guinea-pigs (700 g.) were infected intradermally with *B. anthracis* (strain N.P.). On the third day and in the 12 hr. preceding death, the number of organisms in the blood rose from approximately 3×10^5 to 1×10^9 chains/ml. The progress of this final bacteraemia could be followed quickly and conveniently by microscopic examination of stained blood films from the ear. These films were prepared in a standard manner (one loopful over 1 sq.cm.) and the average number of organisms in one field was counted (magnification $\times 600$). In fifteen comparisons with haemocytometer counts of the bacteria the relationship with the absolute count was obtained and the error of the maximum scatter was within $\pm 50\%$. In Table 2 the results given in the two left-hand columns show that the degree of bacteraemia is closely related to the period of survival; each survival time is the average of observations on 10–15 animals in six experiments.

The next step was to use antibiotic therapy in an attempt to terminate the bacteraemia abruptly at progressive stages in its development, in order to detect the earliest stage at which damage to the host was such as to cause eventual death. Streptomycin in the dosage described in Table 2 proved effective for this purposes and non-toxic to guinea-pigs. It rapidly terminated the infection. Multiplication of the organisms ceased within 1–1$\frac{1}{2}$ hr., and the organisms were then disintegrating; after 5–7 hr. no bacilli remained free in the blood. This applied even in animals treated approximately 4 hr. before they would otherwise have died. At times later than this only 50–75 % of the animals could be freed from infection.

Table 2. *The relationship between the degree of anthrax bacteraemia in guinea-pigs and the time interval to death. The results of streptomycin treatment*

Infected animals				Streptomycin-treated animals†		
Organisms in blood		Hours until death		Number dead/ Number treated	Hour until death	
No. per field*	No. per ml. × 10⁶ (±50 %)	Average	Standard deviation		Average	Standard deviation
1/80	0·2	12·7	0·6	0/2	—	—
1/40	0·4	11·5	0·7	0/6	—	—
1/20	0·8	9·5	1·2	2/12	—	—
1/10	1·5	8·5	1·7	1/12	—	—
1/5	3·0	8·1	1·3	11/20	—	—
1/2	7·5	6·9	1·0	36/37	43	15
1	15	6·1	0·8	19/19	39	12
2	30	4·9	1·1	16/16	36	12
4	60	4·4	0·7	9/9	24	8
8	120	3·6	1·0	14/14	17	6
16	240	2·4	0·5	12/12	10	4
32	480	1·5	0·5	7/7	6	2
64	960	death	—	—	—	—

* Films stained with methylene blue, magnification × 600.

† Streptomycin 40 mg. i/p, and 40 mg. s/c: followed 6–8 hr. later by 40 mg. s/c. together with 25 mg. streptomycin cerate i/m every 24 hr.

The right-hand columns of Table 2 show that removal of the infection by streptomycin would save guinea-pigs, provided the bacteraemia had not increased beyond *c.* 3×10^6 chains/ml. of blood. All guinea-pigs having a bacteraemia greater than this critical value died 1–3 days later although free from infection. Such experiments showed conclusively that in guinea-pigs a bacteraemia was intimately associated with death from anthrax, but in fact the death of the guinea-pig was determined when the bacterial invasion was still only about $\frac{1}{300}$th of its possible maximum. This finding seems to render untenable the hypothesis that death from anthrax is due to the bacteria blocking the capillaries or producing a deficiency in the host of O_2 or essential nutrients (e.g. glucose).

At this stage in the work short investigations were made into the validity of earlier recorded hypotheses on the cause of death from anthrax. First, it is recalled that the objection we offered to the suggestion that the bacteraemia produced a fatal disturbance in calcium metabolism (Bloom *et al.* 1947*b*) was the fact that the protective action of calcium and parathyroid injections might be ascribed to their effect on the initial invasion. In our experiments, administration of large quantities of calcium borogluconate and of parathyroid extract separately or together did not save or prolong the survival time of guinea-pigs given streptomycin at a time immediately beyond the level of bacteraemia which predetermined death of the animals 1–3 days later. It seems therefore that the action of the calcium and parathryoid injections was not on the killing mechanism of the organism. Secondly, we have failed to find support for de Moulin's hypothesis that fatal damage occurs in the central nervous system. Our colleague Dr Joan M. Ross has made histological examinations of the central nervous system, the liver, the spleen, the lungs, the suprarenals, the pancreas, the bone-marrow and the kidneys of guinea-pigs dying of untreated anthrax, and of those in which active infection has been stopped by streptomycin injection after the critical point in the bacteraemia. The only significant changes occurred in the kidneys of these animals, and these will be described later. The changes described by de Moulin in the central nervous system were not detected.

The discovery that an early stage of bacteraemia predetermined death in the guinea-pig suggested a renewed search for the toxic substance produced by *B. anthracis in vivo*. An insight into the probable biological nature of this factor was provided by the identification of the hitherto unknown pathological syndrome leading to death. This was achieved by carrying out extensive chemical analyses of the blood, and by histological examinations and clinical observations on infected guinea-pigs.

The phase of the disease selected for these observations was the final 10 hr. of the infection. The major pathological changes were expected to occur during this time because the studies on the bacteraemia had shown that the fate of infected animals was not decided until some 8 hr. before beath. Previous workers in this field (Singer, 1927; Caifaleanu *et al.* 1930; Bloom *et al.* 1947*b*) made observations throughout the duration of the disease commencing at the time of the initial infection. The inconclusive results they recorded may be due, in part at least, to their having paid insufficient attention to this important final phase in the disease.

Guinea-pigs were examined at the following progressive stages in the final bacteraemia: (1) Immediately before the critical point of the bacteraemia when the blood had $0.2–1 \times 10^6$ chains/ml. and where, in the absence of treatment, death would ensue in approximately 9 hr. (2) Shortly after the critical point when there were 4–30×10^6 chains/ml. and death would occur in approximately 6 hr. (3) At an advanced stage when the blood contained $2 \cdot 5$–6×10^8 chains/ml. and death would occur in about $1\frac{1}{2}$ hr. (4) A few observations were made on animals within $\frac{1}{2}$ hr. from death or immediately after this had occurred. Supplementary studies were made on guinea-pigs treated with streptomycin at stage (2) above; as recorded earlier such animals would die about 2 days later free from active infection. Normal animals treated with streptomycin were also examined. In addition, animals treated with streptomycin at stage (1) were killed and examined 2 days later. In retrospect, it is evident to us that it was the chemical analysis of the organism-free plasma of these streptomycin-treated animals that first materially assisted the diagnosis of the pathological state. They were of special importance in the demonstration of renal failure which is discussed below.

The data which accumulated (Smith, Keppie, Ross & Stanley, 1954a; Smith, Keppie & Stanley, 1954b) from diverse assays carried out on 5–20 animals at each of these stages of the disease fitted together to establish that secondary shock (Sodeman, 1950; Cappell, 1951; Lovatt Evans, 1952) plays a major role in the death of guinea-pigs from anthrax. It is only possible here to give a brief summary of these observations under headings associated with shock. The reader must consult references appended to each heading for information on their significance.

In the analysis of whole blood, corrections were made for the bacteria present (Smith *et al.* 1953a). Samples of plasma for analysis were filtered through 'Millipore filters' (Lovell Chemical Company, Massachusetts) which left normal plasma unaltered in composition. Details of experimental methods will be found elsewhere (Smith *et al.* 1954b). They gave results with control animals which were within the normal range of each analysis.

(1) *Reduced blood volume and reduced bleeding volume* (Sodeman, 1950; Cappell, 1951; Lovatt Evans, 1952; Tabor & Rosenthal, 1947). Estimates of the blood volume by means of red corpuscles labelled with radioactive phosphorus indicated a 25–40 % reduction of the circulating blood volume in guinea-pigs within $1\frac{1}{2}$ hr. of death from untreated anthrax. The maximum amount of blood obtainable from similar animals by cardiac puncture was 33 % of that obtainable from normal control animals.

(2) *Reduced blood pressure* (Sodeman, 1950; Cappell, 1951; Lovatt Evans, 1952). Direct cannulation of the carotid artery under local anaesthesia showed the blood pressure to be 85, 56, 39 and 18 % of the

normal value at approximately 9, 6, $1\frac{1}{2}$ and $\frac{1}{2}$ hr. respectively before death from untreated anthrax.

(3) *Haemo-concentration.* In secondary shock, loss of plasma from the circulation leads to haemo-concentration, whereas haemorrhage results in haemodilution. In conditions where haemorrhage accompanies loss of plasma, the results obtained from examination of the blood reflect the summation of the two effects (Sodeman, 1950; Cappell, 1951; Lovatt Evans, 1952; Scott, 1954; Bull, 1954). Results derived from determinations of haemoglobin, haematocrit and blood nitrogen on untreated guinea-pigs showed that haemoconcentration was 10, 15–20 and 15–20 %, at approximately 9, 6 and $1\frac{1}{2}$ hr. respectively before death. This haemoconcentration persisted in the guinea-pigs whose death was delayed for 1–3 days by streptomycin therapy.

(4) *Presence of oedema and haemorrhage.* Oedema and haemorrhage occur in anthrax infection in guinea-pigs as in other species (Sobernheim, 1931). Plasma protein nitrogen was reduced 25, 30 and 30% in guinea-pigs approximately 9, 6, and $1\frac{1}{2}$ hr. respectively before death from untreated anthrax and a 45 % reduction occurred in animals dying 1–3 days after treatment with streptomycin.

(5) *Fall in body temperature* (Sodeman, 1950; Tabor & Rosenthal, 1947; Stoner, Threlfall & Green, 1952). The rectal temperatures of guinea-pigs dropped from 99 to 88° F. during the final 6 hr. of infection and from 90 to 80° F. in streptomycin-treated animals in the 10 hr. preceding death.

(6) *Interference with phosphate metabolism* (Magee & Spector, 1951–2; Allison, Cole, Holmes & Root, 1947; Root, Allison, Cole, Holmes, Walcott & Gregerson, 1947). Plasma inorganic phosphate increased to 170, 175 and 250 % of the normal value in guinea-pigs at 9, 6 and $1\frac{1}{2}$ hr. respectively before death from untreated anthrax. The value in animals saved by streptomycin treatment did not significantly change in the following 2 days, but in those treated later in the infection and which eventually died the plasma inorganic phosphate had increased to 300 % of the normal value.

(7) *Disturbance in electrolyte balance.* There is agreement in the literature that a disturbance in electrolyte balance occurs in shock. The pH of the plasma falls as does its content of Na^+ and HCO_3^-. The plasma K^+ and Mg^{++} content rise, but changes in Ca^{++} and Cl^- concentrations are somewhat inconsistent (Sodeman, 1950; Magee & Spector, 1951–2; Root *et al.* 1947; Rosenthal, 1943). Determinations on the plasma of guinea-pigs approximately 9 and 6 hr. before death from untreated anthrax showed that the Na^+ content was reduced by

4 % at the terminal stage, the scatter of the plasma Na$^+$ values was wide but many determinations indicated that a slight rise to normal values occurred. Plasma bicarbonate showed a 10, 20 and 40 % reduction, and plasma chloride a 3, 4 and 7 % reduction at the respective stages. The pH of the plasma dropped towards the end of the bacteraemia. No significant change was detected in the plasma Mg^{++} and Ca^{++} before the critical point of the infection, but these elements increased as the bacteraemia progressed and were 220 and 170 % respectively of the normal values about 1½ hr. before death. About 1½ hr. before death, a 70 % increase in K$^+$ was shown, but a slight haemolysis (approximately 1·5 % of the red cells) might have accounted for some of this increase.

(8) *Sludged blood and increased clotting time* (Sodeman, 1950; Kniseley, Block, Eliot & Warner, 1947). In untreated infected guinea-pigs sludging of the blood began 3–4 hr. before death and was marked in the last hour. The well-known delay in the clotting of the blood of animals infected with *B. anthracis* (Bloom *et al.* 1947 *b*) was also noted.

(9) *Interference with carbohydrate metabolism* (Stoner *et al.* 1952; Green & Stoner, 1954). There was a rise of 30 % in the plasma glucose in the early part of the bacteraemia and a reduction of 65 % in animals at death. This confirms previous work (Bloom *et al.* 1947 *b*), which showed interference with carbohydrate metabolism in anthrax, for which no explanation could then be found.

(10) *Evidence of acute renal failure.* It is well known that secondary shock leads to damage of kidney tissue and renal failure (for references see Green, Stoner, Whiteley & Elgin, 1951). The gradual development of uraemia was shown by analyses of plasma non-protein nitrogen (N.P.N.) and urea on guinea-pigs at all the various stages of anthrax described above. At 9 and 6 hr. before death from untreated anthrax the guinea-pigs showed a little evidence of uraemia. Their plasma N.P.N. and urea values were 30–50 % above the normal values (36 (S.D. 3·6) and 54 (S.D. 7·1) mg./100 ml.) respectively. At about 1½ hr. before death these values had risen to 92 (S.D. 10) and 115 (S.D. 12) mg./100 ml. respectively. This indication of renal damage was more pronounced in animals which were treated with streptomycin but which died 2 days later free from infection. In these animals anuria developed. Thus, the daily urine (5 ml. per animal) was low during the 2 days before death, even if a daily injection of saline (30 ml.) was given. Control animals produced 30 ml. of urine daily. Plasma N.P.N. and urea values for the dying animals were 185 (S.D. 15) and 284 (S.D. 43) mg./100 ml. respectively. The animals which were given early treatment with streptomycin and were recovering when they were killed 2 days later, had

plasma N.P.N. and urea values of 68 (S.D. 23) and 98 (S.D. 37) mg./100 ml. respectively. Similarly treated animals which were allowed to recover developed some degree of anuria but within 5–7 days could again excrete normal quantities of urine.

The histopathology of the kidneys of these streptomycin-treated and untreated animals has been described (Smith *et al.* 1954*a*). Tubular damage was found similar to that characterizing a number of conditions (e.g. 'traumatic uraemia', 'crush syndrome') which give rise to anuria and have as a common feature a disturbance of the general circulation (Hadfield, 1953). The tubular damage was most marked in the guinea-pigs which died either from untreated anthrax or after delayed treatment with streptomycin. It was relatively slight at approximately 9 and 6 hr. before death in untreated animals and had not significantly increased in the guinea-pigs that would have been saved by streptomycin but were killed 2 days later.

(11) *Loss of alkaline phosphatase from the kidney.* Abnormally high alkaline phosphatase values in the blood and urine of guinea-pigs within $1\frac{1}{2}$ hr. from death in untreated anthrax led to the histological demonstration of a loss of this enzyme from the kidney (Smith *et al.* 1954*a*). This finding has not been generally recognized as being a feature of shock. However, a similar loss of alkaline phosphatase from the kidney has been described by McManus (1952) in traumatic anuria and by Berg, Levinson & Wang (1951), and Berg & Levinson (1952) in the shock produced in dogs by the toxin of *Clostridium welchii*.

It was this accumulated evidence that led to the diagnosis of severe secondary shock in the terminal phase of anthrax. Shock could play an important role in a number of other infections in which the cause of death remains obscure. Some of the symptoms of shock have been shown to follow the injection of certain bacterial toxins such as those of the gas-gangrene group (Berg *et al.* 1951; Berg & Levinson, 1952; Miles & Niven, 1950), staphylococcal toxin (Miles & Niven, 1950) and the endotoxins of the Gram-negative bacilli (Miles & Niven, 1950; Thomas, 1954). Detailed study of the chemico-pathology of these and other diseases by the methods used here for anthrax might be fruitful.

THE SPECIFIC LETHAL FACTOR PRODUCED *IN VIVO* BY *BACILLUS ANTHRACIS*

Since secondary shock plays an important role in the death of guinea-pigs from anthrax, an oedema-producing factor responsible for the oligaemia of the host should be found in the products of the pathogen.

There were signs that such a factor was present. Crude plasma/exudate (Keppie *et al.* 1953) produced a small, transient, oedematous plaque in the skin of guinea-pigs as had many similar preparations in the past (Sobernheim, 1931; Watson *et al.* 1947*b*). The distribution and activity of this factor in the tissues of guinea-pigs dying of anthrax was re-examined and it was found to occur mainly in the plasma.

The intradermal injection of filtered heparinized plasma (0·2 ml.) from guinea-pigs dying of anthrax produced an extensive area of oedema and congestion in the skin of normal guinea-pigs. The average diameter of this lesion was 40–45 mm., and a positive skin reaction still resulted from a dilution of 1 in 81 of the material. Filtered urine from the same guinea-pigs produced no skin reaction and peritoneal exudate only a slight reaction. Thoracic exudate which contained about 20 % of blood gave only a moderate reaction which disappeared at a dilution of 1 in 27. The plasma/exudate used in our earlier work was composed largely of exudate, and the reason for its low activity was therefore obvious. Extracts of the spleens from dying guinea-pigs were also tested because an analysis had shown that at the critical point of the bacteraemia half the total organisms in the body were to be found in this organ. Therefore the possibility of selective action of a lethal factor at this site had to be considered. However, only a trace of oedema-producing activity was found in concentrated extracts which also were non-lethal for mice.

Skin tests on samples of plasma taken at intervals during the final bacteraemia showed that the tissue-damaging activity increased regularly with the increase in the number of organisms in the blood. The oedema-producing activity of this guinea-pig plasma was not affected by mixing with half its volume of normal horse serum but was completely neutralized by anthrax antiserum prepared in the horse (Smith & Keppie, 1954; Smith *et al.* 1954*a*). The specificity of the reaction was therefore established.

The possibility of there being a specific lethal factor in the plasma undiluted with exudate was investigated. These experiments have been reported briefly (Smith & Keppie, 1954; Smith *et al.* 1954*a*). The plasma killed mice and guinea-pigs when injected intravenously and intraperitoneally. The specificity of the lethal effect was established when it was completely neutralized by horse anthrax-antiserum but was unaffected by normal horse serum. The approximate LD 50 of the toxic plasma for mice (22 g.) and guinea-pigs (250 g.) was 0·4 and 5 ml. respectively by the intravenous route. A higher death-rate and a shorter survival time indicated that the plasma was more lethal when given intravenously than by the intraperitoneal route. Animals dying in these

experiments showed collapse with subnormal temperatures together
with oedema and nephrosis similar to the infected animals. It is hoped
to carry out a more detailed investigation of the pathology of these
animals in the near future.

Much effort was directed towards demonstrating the oedema-producing activity and the lethal factor in the bacteria grown *in vivo* (Smith
et al. 1953*a*). A suspension of organisms from large quantities of toxic
plasma was (1) mixed with streptomycin, (2) shaken with 'ballotini' and
streptomycin, and (3) shaken with 'ballotini' and the extract sterilized
by filtration. A negligible skin reaction and no lethal effect on mice was
shown by these preparations; the activity of toxic plasma was unchanged
by any of these treatments. It seems therefore that the specific lethal
factor is essentially extracellular.

These findings now laid open the possibility of examining the chemical
basis of the killing power of *B. anthracis* because the product of the
organism responsible for it had been demonstrated and was available
for chemical fractionation. Only preliminary investigations of the lethal
factor were made before the preparation of this paper, but certain facts
have emerged.

So far our studies indicate that the oedema-producing substance and
the lethal factor in the toxic plasma are identical. In addition, it appears
to be connected with the protective antigen of *B. anthracis* and therefore
with the extracellular aggressin. The evidence for these relationships
has been reported (Smith *et al.* 1954*a*) and is briefly as follows. The
protective antigen produced *in vitro* by Belton & Strange (1954) was
not toxic or oedema-producing. However, the lethal and oedema-
producing properties of the toxic guinea-pig plasma were completely
neutralized by an antiserum to this material produced *in vitro*. Finally,
fractionation of the toxic plasma by the method already described for
plasma/exudate gave the oedema-producing activity in the fraction
which contained the aggressin and protective antigen; it was present in
no other fraction.

As with the protective antigen and the extracellular aggressin, the
lethal factor does not appear to be connected either with the capsule of
the organism or with polyglutamic acid. First, two types of horse
anthrax-antiserum neutralized the lethal factor (Smith & Keppie, 1954;
Smith *et al.* 1954*a*), and both of these sera were derived from the 'Sterne'
uncapsulated strain of *B. anthracis*. Secondly, both pure and crude
polyglutamic acid produced by *B. anthracis in vivo* were non-toxic to
guinea-pigs and mice and did not give a skin reaction (Smith *et al.* 1954*a*).

A possible explanation of these results is that the protective antigen is a 'toxoid' form of the lethal factor. The toxic and skin-reacting properties of the lethal factor are unstable. They survive freeze-drying but are destroyed by standing at 0° for 12 weeks, heating to 60° for half an hour, or incubation at 37° for 8 hr. The activity largely disappears when the pH is adjusted to 5 or 10 and in the barium acetate/ethanol fractionation already described.

CONCLUSIONS

The overall pathogenicity of *Bacillus anthracis* is the result of the production within the host of an armoury of different substances which may be interconnected. The present work has demonstrated at least three important substances, all with aggressive activity, and one of them responsible for the death of the host. Some progress has been made towards identifying them, but their exact effect in the aggressin assays has yet to be investigated. Two of the aggressins are intracellular, and one of these, polyglutamic acid, occurs in the capsule whose connexion with pathogenicity is recognized; the other occurs in an impure lipoprotein fraction and its relation to the capsule is unknown. The third aggressin is produced extracellularly and is connected with the specific lethal factor, which in anthrax leads to the death of the host in secondary shock. The successful demonstration of a lethal product of *B. anthracis*, following the many failures from the use of *in vitro* cultures, is the direct result of using the products of the organism growing *in vivo* for the study of its pathogenicity. Now that the biological nature of the lethal factor has been established, the production of it *in vitro* may become possible. As the factors responsible for the development of classical secondary shock are a matter of conjecture, the isolation of this specific lethal factor of *B. anthracis* may prove of value in the general study of shock. It is more easily defined than are the substances already thought to be implicated, since its lethal activity can be neutralized with specific antiserum.

It seems that a strain is only fully pathogenic when all the substances of the anthrax armoury are produced. The absence of one may result in a strain becoming relatively non-pathogenic, although its capacity to produce the others is unimpaired. The metabolism of the pathogen within the host which enables it to produce these substances is therefore a subject of interest. Consequently Smith and Tempest have begun a study of the nutrition of *B. anthracis* when growing in the blood of guinea pigs during the final bacteraemia of the disease.

These observations have been made solely with one strain (N.P.) of *B. anthracis* in the guinea-pig. It is hoped to extend this work to test other strains and animal species.

We are indebted to Dr D. W. Henderson and Prof. W. T. J. Morgan for encouragement when this approach to the problem of pathogenicity was first suggested and for their continued interest. Our thanks are also due to Prof. G. R. Cameron, Prof. E. J. King, Dr H. B. Stoner and Dr W. G. Spector for their help on the subject of 'shock', and to our colleagues, at The Microbiological Research Department, H. T. Zwartouw, J. L. Stanley, Mrs P. W. Harris-Smith and R. C. Gallop, for their contributions to this work.

Acknowledgement is made to the Chief Scientist, Ministry of Supply, for permission to publish this communication.

REFERENCES

ADAMI, G. F. (1909). *Inflammation*. London: Macmillan and Co.

ALLISON, J. B., COLE, W. H., HOLMES, J. H. & ROOT, W. S. (1947). The effect of haemorrhage and muscle trauma upon the blood-phosphate of dogs. *Amer. J. Physiol.* **149**, 422.

BAIL, O. (1904). Untersuchungen über natürliche und künstliche Milzbrandimmunität. XI. Erster Bericht über Milzbrandschutzimpfungen an Schafen. *Zbl. Bakt.* **37**, 270.

BAIL, O. (1915a). Veränderungen der Bakterien im Tierkorper. IX. Über die Korrelation zwischen Kapselbildung, Sporenbildung, und Infektiosität des Milzbrandbacillus. *Zbl. Bakt.* **75**, 159.

BAIL, O. (1915b). Veränder ungenvon Bakterien im Tierkorper. XI. Untersuchungen über kapsellosen Milzbrand. *Zbl. Bakt.* **76**, 38.

BAIL, O. (1915c). Veränderungen von Bakterien im Tierkorper. XII. Abschwächungsversuche am Milzbrandbacillus bei 42°. *Zbl. Bakt.* **76**, 330.

BAIL, O. & WEIL, E. (1911). Beiträge zum Studium der Milzbrandinfektion. *Arch. Hyg., Berl.,* **73**, 218.

BELTON, F. & STRANGE, R. E. (1954). Studies on a protective antigen produced *in vitro* from *Bacillus anthracis*: medium and methods of production. *Brit. J. exp. Path.* **35**, 144.

BERG, M., LEVINSON, S. A. (1952). Alkaline phosphatase activity of the kidney. *Arch. Path.* **53**, 179.

BERG, M., LEVINSON, S. A. & WANG, K. J. (1951). Effect of experimental shock induced by *Clostridium perfringens* toxin on the kidneys of dogs. *Arch. Path.* **51**, 137.

BLOOM, W. L., WATSON, D. W., CROMARTIE, W. J. & FREED, M. (1947a). Studies on infection with *Bacillus anthracis*. IV. Preparation and characterization of an anthracidal substance from various animal tissues. *J. infect. Dis.* **80**, 41.

BLOOM, W. L., McGHEE, W. J., CROMARTIE, W. J. & WATSON, D. W. (1947b). Studies on infection with *Bacillus anthracis*. VI. Physiological changes in experimental animals during the course of infection with *B. anthracis*. *J. infect. Dis.* **80**, 137.

BULL, J. P. (1954). Shock caused by burns and its treatment. *Brit. med. Bull.* **10**, 9.

BRUCKNER, V., KOVACS, J. & DENES, G. (1953). Structure of poly-D-glutamic acid isolated from capsulated strains of *B. anthracis*. *Nature, Lond.,* **172**, 508.

CAIFALEANU, A., COMBIESCO, D. & STAMATESCO, S. (1930). Les valeurs du sucre sanguin et du glycogène hépatique au cours de l'infection charbonneuse expérimentale. *C.R. Soc. Biol., Paris,* **104**, 1151.

CAPPELL, D. F. (1951). Muir's *Textbook of Pathology*, p. 42. London: Edmund Arnold and Co.

CHU, H. P. (1953). Cytochemical structure of *Bacillus anthracis* with special reference to its cell wall. *Proc. 6th Congr. int. Microbiol.,* Rome.

CROMARTIE, W. J., BLOOM, W. L. & WATSON, D. W. (1947). Studies on infection with *Bacillus anthracis*. A histopathological study of skin lesions produced by *B. anthracis* in susceptible and resistant animal species. *J. infect. Dis.* **80**, 1.

EURICH, F. W. & HEWLETT, R. T. (1930). *A System of Bacteriology*, **5**, chap. 10. London: Medical Research Council.

EVANS, D. G. & SHOESMITH, V. G. (1954). Production of toxin by *Bacillus anthracis*. *Lancet*, no. 266, p. 136.

EVANS, D. G. & WARDLAW, A. C. (1953). Gelatinase and collagenase production by certain species of *Bacillus*. *J. gen. Microbiol.* **8**, 481.

GLADSTONE, G. P. (1946). Immunity to anthrax. Protective antigen present in cell-free culture filtrates. *Brit. J. exp. Path.* **27**, 394.

GLADSTONE, G. P. (1948). Immunity to anthrax. Production of the cell-free protective antigen in cellophane sacs. *Brit. J. exp. Path.* **29**, 379.

GOVAERTS, A (1951). Influence du calcium sur l'attenuation du bacille du charbon par la méthode de Pasteur. *Ann. Inst. Pasteur*, **81**, 424.

GRABAR, P. & STAUB, A. M. (1944). Recherches immunochimiques sur la bactéridie charbonneuse. II. Les fractions protéidiques du liquide d'œdème charbonneux et des extraits de *B. Anthracis*. *Ann. Inst. Pasteur*, **70**, 129.

GREEN, H. N. & STONER, H. B. (1954). Effects of injury on carbohydrate metabolism and energy transformation. *Brit. med. Bull.* **10**, 38.

GREEN, H. N., STONER, H. B., WHITELY, H. J. & ELGIN, D. (1951). A case of traumatic uraemia. *Brit. J. Surg.* **39**, 80.

GRUBER, M. & FUTAKI, K. (1907). Über die Resistenz gegen Milzbrand und über die Herkunft der milzbrandfeindlichen Stoffe. *Med. Wschr.* **54**, 249.

HADFIELD, G. (1953). *Recent Advances in Pathology*, 6th ed., p. 281. London: J. and A. Churchill Ltd.

HANBY, W. E. & RYDON, H. N. (1946). The capsular substance of *Bacillus anthracis*. *Biochem. J.* **40**, 297.

IVANOVICS, G. (1940). Untersuchungen über das Polysaccharid der Milzbrandbazillen. *Z. ImmunForsch.* **97**, 402.

IVANOVICS, G. & BRUCKNER, V. (1937). Die chemische Struktur der Kapselsubstanz des Milzbrandbazillus und der serologisch identischen spezifischen Substanz des *Bazillus mesentericus*. *Z. ImmunForsch.* **90**, 304.

IVANOVICS, G. & ERDÖS, L. (1937). Ein Beitrag zum Wesen der Kapselsubstanz des Milzbrandbazillus. *Z. ImmunForsch.* **90**, 5.

IVANOVICS, G. & HORVATH, S. (1953a). The structure of the capsule of *B. megatherium*. *Acta physiol. hung.* **4**, 175.

IVANOVICS, G. & HORVATH, S. (1953b). On the chemical structure of the capsule of *B. anthracis* and *B. megatherium*. *Acta physiol. hung.* **4**, 401.

JAWETZ, E. & MEYER, K. F. (1943). Avirulent strains of *Pasteurella pestis*. *J. infect. Dis.* **73**, 124.

KEPPIE, J., SMITH, H. & HARRIS-SMITH, PATRICIA W. (1953). The chemical basis of the virulence of *Bacillus anthracis*. II. Some biological properties of bacterial products. *Brit. J. exp. Path.* **34**, 486.

KEPPIE, J., SMITH, H. & HARRIS-SMITH, PATRICIA W. (1955). The chemical basis of the virulence of *Bacillus anthracis*. III. The role of the terminal bacteraemia in death of guinea-pigs from anthrax. *Brit. J. exp. Path.* (in the Press).

KING, H. K. & STEIN, J. H. (1950). The non-toxicity of *Bacillus anthracis* cell material *J. gen. Microbiol.* **4**, 48.

KNISELY, M. H., BLOCK, E. H., ELIOT, T. S. & WARNER, L. (1947). Sludged blood. *Science*, **106**, 431.

LOVATT EVANS, C. (1952). *Principles of Human Physiology*, p. 669. London: J. and A. Churchill Ltd.

McGAUGHEY, C. A. & CHU, H. P. (1948). The egg-yolk reaction of aerobic sporing bacilli. *J. gen. Microbiol.* **2**, 334.

McMANUS, J. F. A. (1952). *Medical Diseases of the Kidney.* London.

MAGEE, P. N. & SPECTOR, W. G. (1951–2). Body water and electrolytes in acute anhydraemia. *Proc. Roy. Soc.* B, **139**, 584.

MILES, A. A. & NIVEN, J. S. F. (1950). The enhancement of infection during shock produced by bacterial toxins and other agents. *Brit. J. exp. Path.* **31**, 73.

DE MOULIN, F. W. K. (1936). An investigation on the cause of death by apoplexy in cases of anthrax. *Ned-ind. blad. Diergeneesk*, **48**, 126.

PASTEUR, L. (1881). De l'atténuation des virus et de leur retour à la virulence. *C.R. Acad. Sci., Paris*, **92**, 429.

PREISZ, H. (1909). Experimentelle Studien über Virulenz, Empfänglichkeit und Immunität beim Milzbrand. *Zbl. Bakt.* **49**, 341.

RENAUX, E. (1952). Culture de *Bacillus Anthracis* en milieu calcique et en milieu oxalate. *Ann. Inst. Pasteur*, **83**, 38.

ROOT, W. S., ALLISON, J. B., COLE, W. H., HOLMES, J. H., WALCOTT, W. V. & GREGERSON, M. I. (1947). Disturbances in the chemistry and in the acid-base balance of the blood of dogs in haemorrhagic and traumatic shock. *Amer. J. Physiol.* **149**, 52.

ROSENTHAL, S. M. (1943). Experimental chemotherapy of burns and shock. III. Effects of systemic therapy on early mortality. *Rep. Pub. Hlth U.S.A.* **58**, 513.

SCOTT, R. B. (1954). Blood transfusion and the effects on injury. *Brit. med. Bull.* **10**, 22.

SINGER, E. (1927). Milzbrandstudien. *Z. ImmunForsch.* **54**, 144.

SMITH, H. & KEPPIE, J. (1954). Observations on experimental anthrax: demonstration of a specific lethal factor produced *in vivo* by *Bacillus anthracis. Nature, Lond.*, **173**, 869.

SMITH, H., KEPPIE, J. & STANLEY, J. L. (1953a). A method for collecting bacteria and their products from infections in experimental animals, with special reference to *Bacillus anthracis. Brit. J. exp. Path.* **34**, 471.

SMITH, H., KEPPIE, J., & STANLEY, J. L. (1953b). The chemical basis of the virulence of *Bacillus anthracis.* I. Properties of bacteria grown *in vivo* and preparation of extracts. *Brit. J. exp. Path.* **34**, 477.

SMITH, H. & ZWARTOUW, H. T. (1954). Fractionation of the intracellular material of *Bacillus anthracis* grown *in vivo*; the polysaccharide and polyglutamic acid. *Biochem. J.* **56**, viii.

SMITH, H., KEPPIE, J., ROSS, JOAN M. & STANLEY, J. L. (1954a). Observations on the cause of death in experimental anthrax. *Lancet*, ii, 474.

SMITH, H., KEPPIE, J. & STANLEY, J. L. (1954b). The chemical basis of the virulence of *Bacillus anthracis.* IV. Secondary shock as the major factor in death of guinea-pigs from anthrax. *Brit. J. exp. Path.* (in the Press).

SMITH, H., ZWARTOUW, H. T. & GALLOP, R. C. (1954c). The nature of the aggressins produced by *Bacillus anthracis* growing *in vivo. Biochem. J.* **56**, ix.

SOBERNHEIM, G. (1913). *Handbuch der Pathogenen Mikroorganismen*, 2nd ed. p. 583. Jena: Gustav Fischer.

SOBERNHEIM, G. (1931). *Handbuch der Pathogenen Mikroorganismen*, 3, part 2, p. 1041. Jena: Gustav Fischer, Urban and Schwarzenberg.

SODEMAN, W. A. (1950). *Pathologic Physiology*, p. 36. London: W. G. Saunders and Co.

STAMATIN, N. & STAMATIN, L. (1936). Le pouvoir immunisant des souches acapsulogènes de *Bacillus anthracis. C.R. Soc. Biol., Paris*, **122**, 491.

STAUB, A. M. (1949). Recherches immunochimiques sur la bactéridie charbonneuse. VIII. Action de divers serums normaux ou anticharbonneux sur le pouvoir vaccinant des filtrats de culture (plasma culture filtrate) de Gladstone. *Ann. Inst. Pasteur*, **76**, 331.

STAUB, A. M. & GRABAR, P. (1943). Recherches immunochimiques sur la bactéridie charbonneuse. Rôle de la capsule dans l'immunisation anticharbonneuse. *C.R. Soc. Biol., Paris*, **137**, 623.

STERNE, M. (1937). Variation in *Bacillus anthracis*. *Onderstepoort J. vet. Sci.* **8**, 271.

STOCKMAN, S. (1911). The epizootology of anthrax. *J. comp. Path.* **24**, 97.

STONER, H. B., THRELFALL, C. T. & GREEN, H. N. (1952). Studies on the mechanism of shock. Carbohydrate metabolism in nucleotide and ischaemic shock. *Brit. J. exp. Path.* **33**, 131.

STRANGE, R. E. & BELTON, F. C. (1954). Studies on a protective antigen produced *in vitro* from *Bacillus anthracis*: purification and chemistry of the antigen. *Brit. J. exp. Path.* **35**, 153.

TABOR, H. & ROSENTHAL, S. M. (1947). Body temperature and oxygen consumption in traumatic shock and haemorrhage in mice. *Amer. J. Physiol.* **149**, 449.

THOMAS, L. (1954). The physiological disturbances produced by endotoxins. *Ann. Rev. Physiol.* **16**, 467.

THORNE, C. B., GOMEZ, C. G., BLIND, G. R. & HOUSEWRIGHT, R. D. (1953). Synthesis of glutamic acid and glutamyl polypeptide by *Bacillus anthracis*. III. Factors affecting peptide production in synthetic liquid media. *J. Bact.* **65**, 472.

THORNE, C. B., GOMEZ, C. G. & HOUSEWRIGHT, R. D. (1952). Synthesis of glutamic acid and glutamyl polypeptide by *Bacillus anthracis*. II. The effect of carbon dioxide on peptide production on solid media. *J. Bact.* **63**, 363.

TOMCSIK, J. (1951). Complex structure of the bacterial capsule in the genus *Bacillus*. *Experientia*, **7**, 460.

TOMCSIK, J. & SZONGOTT (1933). Über ein spezifisches Protein der Kapsel des Milzbrandbazillus. *Z. ImmunForsch.* **78**, 86.

TREFFERS, H. P. (1947). Immunochemistry. *Ann. Rev. Microbiol.* **1**, 263.

VAUGHAN, V. C. & NOVY, F. G. (1902). *Cellular Toxins*, 4th ed. New York: Lea Brothers and Co.

WATSON, D. W., CROMARTIE, W. J., BLOOM, W. L., KEGELES, G. & HECKLY, R. J. (1947a). Studies on infection with *Bacillus anthracis*. III. Chemical and immunological properties of the protective antigen in crude extracts of skin lesions of *B. anthracis*. *J. infect. Dis.* **80**, 28.

WATSON, D. W., CROMARTIE, W. J., BLOOM, W. L., HECKLY, R. J., McGHEE, W. J. & WEISSMAN, N. (1947b). Studies on infection with *Bacillus anthracis*. V. The isolation of an inflammatory factor from crude extracts of lesions of *B. anthracis* infection and its biological and chemical relationship to glutamyl polypeptide. *J. infect. Dis.* **80**, 121.

WEINSTEIN, L. (1938). The prophylaxis of experimental anthrax infection with various hormone preparations. *Yale J. Biol. Med.* **11**, 369.

WILSON, G. S. & MILES, A. A. (1946). Topley & Wilson's *Principles of Bacteriology and Immunity*, 3rd ed. London: Edward Arnold and Co.

WRIGHT, G. C., HEDBERG, M. A. & SLEIN, J. B. (1954). Studies on immunity in anthrax. III. Elaboration of protective antigen in a chemically defined, non-protein medium. *J. Immunol.* **72**, 263.

ZINSSER, H. & BAYNE-JONES, S. (1939). *A Textbook of Bacteriology*. New York: D. Appleton Century Co. Inc.

THE BASIS OF VIRULENCE FOR MICE
OF *PASTEURELLA PESTIS*

T. W. BURROWS

*Microbiological Research Department, Ministry of Supply,
Porton, Wilts.*

Our knowledge of the means by which infecting bacteria produce changes in the host recognizable as disease is incomplete in many cases and quite scanty in others. It is improbable that whole bacterial bodies would of themselves cause any inconvenience to a host except when present in enormous numbers capable of interfering with body function in a purely mechanical manner. In the final analysis, disease results from interference with vital host systems by products of the bacterial cells excreted during their life or liberated by lysis after their death. In particular diseases, no examples of which so far have been described, it is possible that this interference could result not from the liberation of toxic products by the invading organism but from competition between it and vital host systems for essential factors of limited availability. It must be a rare occurrence in nature for bacteria to gain access to a host in such numbers that without further multiplication they are capable of causing recognizable disease. It follows that an essential preliminary to the establishment of a disease process is the multiplication of the infecting cells. The study of the mechanisms whereby infecting cells are able to increase in numbers despite the antagonistic systems of the host is therefore fundamental to the larger study of the pathogenicity of a particular organism for a particular host. The fact that these mechanisms are poorly understood in the case of plague in rodents and in man justifies the inclusion of this paper in a symposium on the mechanisms of bacterial pathogenicity.

In describing an experimental investigation of a particular disease the terms virulent or avirulent are convenient for expressing the variable ability of different strains of the causative organism to initiate the disease under investigation. As it is probable that any organism administered in a sufficiently large dose will produce disease in any host, it is considered that the adjectival phrases 'of high virulence' or 'of low virulence' would be strictly more correct for expressing this variable ability. However, purely for ease of composition, in this paper the terms virulent and avirulent will be used to denote strains of *Pasteurella pestis* having an average lethal dose (A.L.D.) for mice of less than 100 or more than 100 millions respectively, when the organisms are injected intraperitoneally suspended in 0·2 ml. phosphate buffer pH 7·4 and the animals are observed over 7 days.

Strains of many pathogenic genera can be classified as virulent for a particular host on their ability to produce certain well-defined reactions *in vitro*—reactions which are performed poorly or not at all by those classified as avirulent. With *P. pestis* this is not the case. Certain strains of this pathogen can readily be differentiated from typical virulent strains by their inability to elaborate important surface antigens and, in consequence, to evoke mouse protective antisera in rabbits; but other avirulent strains exist which appear identical with fully virulent strains in all *in vitro* tests applied to them. These avirulent strains are actively immunogenic in mice and yield protective antisera in rabbits qualitatively and quantitatively similar to those obtained with killed virulent organisms. Serological studies with whole organisms or extracted fractions have not so far revealed antigenic differences between this type of protective avirulent strain and fully virulent organisms (Wats, Wagle & Puduval, 1939; Schütze, 1939; Jawetz & Meyer, 1943; Baker, Sommer, Foster, Meyer & Meyer, 1947; Amies, 1951).

A few words on the nature and properties of these antigenic components may not be out of place in this introductory section. Three main antigens are readily recognizable, although evidence from antigen-antibody precipitation zones in agar diffusion plates and columns suggests that this number is too low and that up to eight antigenic components are present in both virulent and avirulent strains (Burrows, unpublished; Davies, personal communication). This number is quoted on the assumption that each zone represents a distinct antigen, an assumption which is open to question in view of recent work by Jennings (1954). Of major importance, with respect to virulence and immunogenicity, is the surface antigen designated fraction 1 by Baker *et al.* (1947), synonymous with the 'envelope' of Rowland (1914) and Schütze (1932*a*), antigen A of Seal (1951), and the capsular antigen of Amies. Although Amies (1951) considered his material to be a simple protein the more exhaustive studies by Meyer's school (see Baker *et al.* 1947) indicate fraction 1 to consist of a carbohydrate protein (fraction 1 A) and a serologically indistinguishable protein (fraction 1 B), which has been obtained in crystalline form. This antigen complex is not formed at temperatures below 28° but accumulates maximally at 37° in those strains capable of its production (Schütze, 1932*a*); when it becomes visible as a capsule or envelope best seen in India-ink preparations (Rowland,

1914). As mentioned above, certain avirulent strains are unable to produce this material at all. Fraction 1 is of low toxicity for all animal species tested, is heat-labile and is of major importance for the protec- tion by active immunization of rats and mice (and probably man) against virulent infection. It is, however, without marked protective value for the guinea-pig (Schütze, 1934; Baker *et al.* 1947, 1952).

Somatic antigenic components of *P. pestis* have received little atten- tion but appear not to differ in the strains examined and to have features in common with those of the causative organism of pseudotuberculosis (Schütze, 1932*b*; Fadeeva, 1939). These components are poorly pro- tective for rats and mice but are of high protective value for the guinea- pig (Baker *et al.* 1947). Some interesting observations of Bhatnaghar & Shrivastava (1946) indicate that antibody against 'somatic antigen' not only fails to protect mice against virulent challenge but increases their susceptibility. Plague toxin is the third of the better-known antigenic components. Formerly believed to be a true endotoxin liberated only after the death and lysis of the containing cells, it has recently been shown by Engelsberg & Levy (1954) to accumulate in the medium during logarithmic growth under their conditions. Toxin is synthesized abundantly by all virulent strains examined and in similar amounts by several avirulent strains. Mice and rats are highly susceptible to micro- gram amounts of toxin; guinea-pigs are highly resistant to several thousand mouse lethal doses. It is relatively heat-stable and rapidly converted to toxoid by formalin.

With regard to the physical conditions for growth of *P. pestis in vitro*, Sohkey & Habbu (1943*a*, *b*) record growth occurring in nutrient broth over a temperature range of -2 to $45°$, optimum $28°$, and within a pH range of 5·0–9·6, optimum between 7·2 and 7·4. For the initiation of growth from single cells isolated on agar surfaces additions such as blood, haemin, or bisulphite to the medium are necessary under aerobic, but not under anaerobic, conditions of incubation (Herbert, 1949).

To display a high degree of virulence it is obvious that a pathogen must find the environment of the host physically and nutritionally acceptable. Unless these requirements are fulfilled the possession of a particular complement of antigens will be insufficient to permit the manifestation of virulence. In the case of avirulent strains of *P. pestis*, antigenically indistinguishable from fully virulent strains, their avirulent state appears not to result from a nutritional impediment, as judged by *in vitro* studies by Rao (1939), Doudoroff (1943), Hills & Spurr (1952), Ross (personal communication) and myself (unpublished). However, failure to demonstrate a nutritional difference between strains when determining the minimal supplements of pure compounds required to permit growth *in vitro* does not necessarily exclude the possibility that avirulent strains are nutritionally handicapped *in vivo*, where particular essential factors may be rendered available only to organisms enzymically equipped to derive these factors from higher compounds.

Jawetz & Meyer (1944), comparing the survival and distribution of virulent and avirulent organisms introduced by various routes into normal and immune guinea-pigs, concluded that the behaviour of the two strains differed in degree rather than in kind. Virulent cells in immune animals behaved similarly to avirulent cells in non-immune. They emphasized that it was characteristic of avirulent cells that they did not multiply even in a severely intoxicated host. Later reports from this group, however, indicate that certain avirulent strains, even when introduced in non-toxic doses, are able to persist and proliferate in both guinea-pigs and mice (Walker, Foster, Chen, Larson & Meyer, 1953).

Previous work has thus failed to disclose the basic factors which permit one strain of *P. pestis* to display high virulence while another apparently identical strain cannot. This led us to believe that, as commonly cultured and examined *in vitro*, the two types were in fact indistinguishable, and that to reveal the important differences which must exist, comparison should be made *in vivo*, in which environment their behaviour is strikingly different. This article records work based on such considerations.

As a preliminary to our study it was desirable to obtain virulent and avirulent representatives as genotypically identical as possible. Attempts were made therefore to induce mutation from avirulence to virulence, relying on the mouse as an efficient selective medium capable of selecting for rare virulent mutants arising in an irradiated avirulent suspension. The strain Twijidej Smooth (referred to as TS throughout), originally described by Otten (1936) and extensively used as a living vaccine for the prophylaxis of plague in many areas, was chosen as a suitable parent strain possessing *in vitro* properties indistinguishable from those of existing virulent laboratory strains. The induction of mutation in this direction was preferred to the reverse mutation, to avoid the difficulty of selecting avirulent forms with unchanged colony form and antigenic composition from predominantly virulent populations, and because of the evolutionary and epidemiological interest of mutation from avirulence to virulence. These attempts, which have been described elsewhere (Burrows & Bacon, 1954), resulted in the isolation of a single virulent strain from over 200 trials. In the absence of any marker characters this strain cannot conclusively be proved to have arisen by mutation of strain TS. It has, however, a characteristic infra-red absorption spectrum distinguishing it from TS and from the other virulent laboratory strains examined. We have designated this strain MP6. Using parent strains bearing nutritional markers for tryptophan, arginine, or nicotinamide dependence respectively, no virulent mutants were recovered in over 100 trials.

The two strains TS and its (provisionally) virulent mutant MP6 behaved in a remarkably similar manner when compared *in vitro*. For growth at 28° both required cystine, methionine, and phenylalanine as essential factors and were stimulated in minimal medium by the addition of glycine + valine + isoleucine. Both yielded mutants independent of the stimulatory effect of this group of amino-acids. Spontaneous mutation rates to methionine independence were similar in both strains. Reliable growth at 37° occurred with both only in media containing those factors required for growth at 28° and further supplemented with leucine, threonine, biotin and pantothenate. On prolonged incubation on synthetic agar containing haemin both strains produced brown pigmented colonies. Antigenic analysis by the agar-diffusion technique (Oudin, 1948; Oakley & Fulthorpe, 1953) gave no indication of any differences between them. In contrast to virulent and avirulent strains of *P. tularensis* described by Yaniv & Avi-dor (1953), and by Avi-dor & Yaniv (1953), the two plague strains grown under identical conditions showed no differential salt sensitivity and no evidence of any inhibitory effects of one towards the other, as judged by a comparison of the lethal effects of suspensions of 10^7 TS + 10^2 MP6 grown separately and mixed in these proportions just before injection with those of suspensions resulting from 18 hr. growths using mixed inocula of the two strains in these proportions. Despite the great similarity of behaviour of TS and MP6 *in vitro*, the A.L.D. for mice of TS was *c.* 150 millions, whereas that of MP6 was between 5 and 100 cells. These two strains therefore appeared eminently suitable for the comparative studies which we wished to undertake.

COMPARATIVE BEHAVIOUR *IN VIVO*

Into two series of mice, 500 million virulent or avirulent cells were injected intraperitoneally. At intervals over a period of 5 hr. pairs from each series were killed; smears of the peritoneal exudate were prepared, and the number of ingested organisms per 100 polymorphonuclear cells, together with the percentage of polymorphs containing ingested organisms, was determined. At the time of injection the total number of white cells free in the peritoneal cavity was *c.* 15 millions (70 % polymorphs) and was increased by the fifth hour to *c*. 18 millions (95 % polymorphs) in both series. Both strains, harvested from 18 hr. growths on tryptic meat agar (TMA) at 37°, were observed to be ingested equally rapidly and abundantly by polymorphs during the first 30 min. after injection. This high rate of ingestion was maintained with the avirulent strain until the number of free organisms had been reduced to a low level, after which it consequently declined. With the virulent strain phagocytosis declined very rapidly after 30 min. to become negligible within 5 hr. despite the presence of large numbers of uningested organisms throughout the whole period. In both series the cells which had been ingested became swollen, poorly stainable, and eventually unrecognizable as plague organisms. An appearance suggesting multiplication of ingested virulent cells within mouse polymorphs was not seen.

Evidently virulent cells differ from avirulent in that, after a short period *in vivo*, they acquire the power to resist phagocytosis by the polymorphs of the host. Virulent cells recovered from mice 5 hr. after injection (*i.e.* at a time when their phagocytosis had ceased) and injected into normal mice, either suspended in the recovered fluid or sedimented and resuspended in buffer, were found not to be ingested by normal mouse polymorphs even during the initial 30 min. after injection. They also were resistant to phagocytosis in *in vitro* phagocytic systems. Avirulent organisms harvested from moribund animals were readily taken up by polymorphs of normal mice either when injected suspended in buffer or when suspended in the cell-free fluid derived from mice moribund from virulent infection. In peritoneal smears derived from mice moribund from virulent infection it is rare to see a single bacterial cell, of the immense numbers present, ingested by a polymorph, whereas in similar smears from animals moribund from avirulent infection practically every polymorph is seen to be crowded to capacity with ingested organisms.

The failure of polymorphs to ingest virulent organisms grown *in vivo* could be due to inactivation of essential opsonic factors, to impairment of the function of the polymorphs by products of the organisms, or to some alteration in structure of the virulent organisms which makes them phagocytosis-resistant. These mechanisms could operate singly or in any combination. *In vitro* phagocytosis experiments, referred to later, clearly demonstrate that the presence of mouse serum or peritoneal fluid is not essential for the phagocytosis of plague cells. Normal mouse polymorphs five times washed with heparinized gelatin-Locke solution and resuspended therein are just as capable of ingesting agar-grown virulent or avirulent organisms as are polymorphs either unwashed or washed and resuspended in heparinized normal mouse serum. Inactivation of hypothetical opsonins can therefore be excluded as contributing to the failure of polymorphs to ingest virulent organisms grown *in vivo*.

The cell-free fluid derived from the peritoneal cavities of mice 5 hr. after virulent infection (by rinsing each cavity with 1 ml. buffer and centrifuging) had no demonstrable adverse effect on normal mouse polymorphs *in vitro* when compared with cell-free fluids derived in a similar manner from normal mice. Avirulent cells suspended in the former fluid were not protected from phagocytosis on injection into normal mice, which suggests the absence of any free antiphagocytic principle active at the dilution of peritoneal fluid employed. Although no antiphagocytic principle is demonstrable in these peritoneal washings, the large numbers of polymorphs in the peritoneal cavity of mice 5 hr. after virulent infection are functionally inefficient. They are unable to ingest, to any appreciable extent, a second dose of agar-grown virulent or avirulent plague cells or staphylococci. This functional inefficiency does not result from previous ingestion and lysis of virulent organisms during the early stages of infection, because the same inability to ingest avirulent organisms is observed within 5 hr. of the injection of virulent organisms grown *in vivo*, which are not ingested even during the initial 30 min. after injection. Intraperitoneal injection of normal mouse serum 5 hr. after virulent infection does not result in phagocytosis of the abundant virulent organisms, and polymorphs harvested at this stage are unable to ingest avirulent organisms when suspended in normal mouse serum *in vitro*. It is unlikely therefore that the loss of phagocytic function is due to inactivation of a normal host component essential for phagocytosis. We must conclude that polymorphs at this stage are in fact inactivated.

The failure of the polymorphs of normal mice to ingest virulent organisms grown *in vivo* indicates that the organisms either are in a phagocytosis-resistant state or experience no lag in the production of an antiphagocytic factor. If the second explanation held, one would expect that avirulent organisms injected into normal mice together with virulent organisms grown *in vivo* would be ingested to a lower extent than if injected by themselves. The presence of large numbers of virulent organisms derived from mice was found, however, not to affect the rate of ingestion of accompanying avirulent organisms over a 30 min. period, from which it was concluded that the resistance to ingestion shown by virulent organisms grown *in vivo* resulted primarily from their change to a resistant state, and that inactivation of polymorphonuclear cells occurred later as a secondary process. This conclusion was supported by the observation that normal mouse polymorphs injected into mice 5 hr. after virulent infection did not ingest the organisms present in the peritoneal cavity. As no free antiphagocytic factor can be demonstrated in the cell-free fluid from such animals it is unlikely that the injected normal polymorphs became instantaneously inactivated.

Concurrently with the investigation of the response of the polymorphonuclear defence mechanism towards the virulent and avirulent representative strains MP6 and TS, the rate of increase or decrease in numbers of free (*i.e.* uningested) organisms in the peritoneal cavity was observed with each type after intraperitoneal injection of known numbers of each strain. The results supported the deductions drawn from observations of phagocytosis. A high rate of reduction in numbers of virulent organisms occurred during the initial 30 min. Within 1 hr. this rate had been reduced to zero, resulting in little change in numbers of free virulent organisms in the next 2–3 hr.; after this time the number of free organisms increased. The initial high rate of reduction observed with avirulent organisms was maintained with little change during a 4 hr. period, by which time the number of free cells remaining had been reduced to *c.* 1/10,000th of the injected dose. During a further 2 hr. little change was detected in the small number remaining.

Why are virulent organisms grown *in vivo* resistant to phagocytosis? This question is as yet unanswered. For phagocytosis of a particle to occur physical contact between it and the phagocyte is a first necessity. As polymorphonuclear cells are selective in their phagocytic activities and normally do not ingest small normal host components, e.g. platelets and erythrocytes, with which they must frequently come into contact, it must be presumed that contact with these bodies fails to initiate the mechanism which would lead to their ingestion. That is, these components do not provide the stimulus which presumably is given by a foreign ingestible particle on being brought into physical contact with the polymorph cell. The absence of this stimulus would probably result if the surface properties of both polymorph and particle was physically and chemically identical—as, for example, if a coating of serum protein were adsorbed to each. One could visualize then that if virulent organisms had surface properties permitting such adsorption, whereas avirulent organisms had not, the differential phagocytosis of the two types *in vivo* could be explained. However, we were unable to demonstrate the presence of adsorbed mouse serum on the surface of virulent organisms grown *in vivo*, either with the aid of a rabbit antiserum prepared against mouse serum or by the ability of organisms grown *in vitro* to absorb mouse serum from solution.

More direct evidence for the rejection of this hypothesis was obtained from observations of the behaviour *in vivo* of a purine-dependent mutant M 1 of the virulent strain MP 6. As with purine-dependent mutants of virulent strains of *Salmonella typhi* (Bacon, Burrows & Yates, 1951) of *S. typhimurium* (Burrows, unpublished), and of *Klebsiella pneumoniae* (Garber, Hackett & Franklin, 1952) mutant M 1 is avirulent for mice. Loss of virulence in mutants of this type is attributable to the fact that limited availability of purines in the host prevents multiplication of dependent organisms to a fatal level (Bacon *et al.*, 1951). From growths on agar, purine-dependent M 1, which apart from its mutation to purine-dependence is genotypically a virulent strain, was found to follow the avirulent pattern of phagocytosis and reduction in viable numbers on intraperitoneal injection into mice. A short period of incubation *in vivo* did not permit this mutant to develop resistance to phagocytosis, in contrast to the behaviour of its virulent parent. When injected together with small amounts of hypoxanthine, which satisfies its purine requirement, M 1 follows the virulent pattern of phagocytosis and becomes resistant to ingestion. Evidently active metabolism of virulent organisms *in vivo* is essential to permit them to become phagocytosis-resistant, and prolonged incubation in the absence of active metabolism is ineffective.

For growth in a synthetic medium capable of supporting strains MP 6 and TS, mutant M 1 requires the addition of hypoxanthine, guanine or xanthine. It does not respond to the addition of adenine. A mutant T 3, which responds in synthetic medium to the addition of adenine, but not to that of guanine, xanthine or hypoxanthine, was selected after irradiation of the avirulent strain TS. Both in the presence and absence of injected adenine, mutant T 3 shows the avirulent pattern of phagocytosis and reduction in numbers of viable organisms after intraperitoneal injection. Colonies of T 3 are readily distinguished by their small size on TMA from those of our other strains of *P. pestis*, which permits estimations of the relative numbers of this and any other strain in mixed suspensions to be made with ease. Determinations of the ratio of T 3:TS at intervals after injection showed that, in mixed infections consisting of equal numbers of T 3 and its parent TS, both types were eliminated at the same rate. Although over a 6 hr. period the numbers of each type had been reduced *c.* 10,000-fold, the ratio T 3:TS varied only between limits of 0·2–0·8 : 1. Since T 3 is nutritionally limited *in vivo* it would appear that TS is similarly incapable of multiplication during this period. No evidence of syntrophism between strains T 3 and TS has been observed *in vitro*.

Although apparently no multiplication of avirulent organisms occurs within 6 hr. after injection, they certainly increase in numbers after this period. For example, from injected doses of 114 million viable TS organisms two moribund animals yielded totals of 4850 million and 4121 million organisms respectively, most of which were present in the peritoneal cavity and the remainder in decreasing amounts in liver, spleen, kidney, pleural exudate, lungs, brain, muscle and heart blood. In an experiment in which each of ten mice received intraperitoneally 1000 million TS organisms, *c.* 1 million remained free in the peritoneal cavity 6 hr. after injection. All of the ten animals died between the 17th and 22nd hour after injection and yielded *c.* 10,000 million organisms from the peritoneal cavity alone, an increase in numbers which indicates a mean generation time for TS, under these conditions, of about 1 hr. Mice moribund from injections of 1000 million T3 organisms yielded from 20 to 60 millions, and those moribund from the same dose of M1 organisms yielded from 0·7 to 2·0 millions from the peritoneal cavity. Since in both these cases the injected doses had been reduced to *c.* 1 million free organisms 6 hr. after injection, the larger yield of T3 as compared with M1 organisms suggests that limited amounts of adenine, but not of guanine, xanthine, or hypoxanthine, become available in mice experiencing plague toxaemia. Mice moribund 3 days after the injection of ten virulent organisms yielded a total of 13,000 million organisms per mouse, representing a mean generation time, over the whole period, of just over 2 hr. Of this number 5000 million were recovered from the peritoneal cavity, 3600 million from the liver and 3600 million from the spleen.

Although observations from mixed infections of T3 + TS indicate that TS may be nutritionally handicapped *in vivo*, at least during the first 6 hr. after injection, we were unable to enhance the virulence of this strain by injection of factors known to be required by it for growth at 37° *in vitro*—namely, cystine, methionine, phenylalanine, glycine, valine, leucine, isoleucine, threonine, biotin, and pantothenate—either singly or in various combinations. This is in contrast to the great enhancement of virulence of certain *Salmonella typhi* mutants by specific growth factors (Bacon *et al.* 1951) and to the 1000-fold increase in virulence, in terms of the A.L.D., which resulted from injection of strain M1 together with a single dose of 4 mg. of hypoxanthine. Hog gastric mucin (Olitski, 1948) effected only a 5-fold enhancement of virulence of strain TS. Failure to enhance the virulence of this strain by growth-factor injection may have resulted from failure to supply the correct factor or factors, or it may indicate that apparent inability to multiply results not from nutritional limitation but from the action of an inhibitor. *In vitro*, however, neither TS nor MP6 showed any evidence of growth inhibition by undiluted fresh normal mouse serum or peritoneal washings.

In mixed infections of equal numbers of T3 and MP6 organisms, T3 was eliminated from the peritoneal cavity at a considerably lower rate than when injected alone or in mixed infection with TS. It was also eliminated at the high rate occurring in pure infections when injected with equal numbers of M1 organisms. The addition of hypoxanthine to such mixed infections, thus permitting metabolism of M1 to proceed, reduced the rate of elimination of T3 to the level occurring in mixed infections with strain MP6. In pure infections, neither hypoxanthine nor adenine injected with T3 affected its high rate of elimination. These observations support the deduction, drawn from *in vivo* phagocytosis experiments recorded above, that actively metabolizing virulent cells suppress the phagocytic activity of the mouse polymorphonuclear system.

The work recorded above brought to light a most obvious difference between our virulent and avirulent representatives. Virulent organisms after a short period of metabolism *in vivo* could alter in a manner not clearly understood to a condition in which they were phagocytosis-resistant, whereas avirulent organisms were apparently unable to effect such alteration. Attempts were made therefore to reproduce the development of resistance to phagocytosis by virulent organisms *in vitro* and to analyse the factors involved in the process.

DEVELOPMENT OF RESISTANCE TO PHAGOCYTOSIS BY VIRULENT CELLS *IN VITRO*

As harvested from 18 hr. growths at 37° on TMA the resistance of virulent organisms to phagocytosis was variable and was frequently higher than desirable in experiments designed to study factors controlling the development of resistance. From similar growths at 28° their resistance was uniformly low. For the majority of experiments we therefore used organisms harvested from growths at 28°. In view of the known temperature-dependence of the metabolic processes leading to the accumulation of envelope antigen in *P. pestis*, and of the importance associated with the possession of capsules for the manifestation of virulence in other pathogenic genera, careful microscopic observations were made on our organisms after all treatments leading to the resistant state. These observations will be referred to later, but it would be opportune to state here that no differences could be seen between the amount of capsulation of organisms showing full sensitivity to phagocytosis and those displaying the highest degree of resistance.

Virulent organisms harvested from agar and incubated at 37° in normal mouse serum were found to become phagocytosis-resistant. Incubation in horse or rabbit serum was equally effective. Serum factors were not essential for the process, because comparable resistance developed after incubation at this temperature in ordinary fresh tryptic meat broth (TMB). The optimum initial pH of TMB for the development of resistance after 2 hr. at 37° is within narrow limits of 7·0. With 3 hr. incubation equal resistance develops over the initial pH range of 6·2 to 7·4. No resistance is achieved within this time if the initial pH is 8·0 or higher. With a standard initial concentration of 250 million sensitive virulent organisms per ml., maximum resistance to phagocytosis is obtained after 3 hr. incubation at 37° in TMB of pH 7·0. Continued incubation beyond 3 hr. does not increase resistance. With organisms harvested from growths at 28° high resistance occurs under the above conditions at 37°, but there is no change in sensitivity if the temperature is maintained at 28° or reduced to 20°. With an inoculum of sensitive organisms harvested from growths at 37°, high resistance again develops on incubation at 37°, moderate resistance at 28°, and none at 20°. These observations suggest that organisms harvested from growths on TMA at 37° are enzymically equipped for the development of resistance on transfer to a physically and nutritionally adequate medium incubated at 28° or 37°, and that the necessary enzyme system, although functional at 28°, is not developed at this lower temperature. Apparently it is neither formed nor functional at 20°. Avirulent cells subjected to conditions which permit our virulent strain MP6 to develop maximum resistance to phagocytosis retain their initial high sensitivity.

To determine whether or not this easily observed, contrasting behaviour of our virulent and avirulent representative strains could be used for the differentiation of virulent and avirulent strains of *P. pestis* in general, we subjected a random collection of laboratory strains to conditions known to lead to high resistance to phagocytosis of strain MP6 and to high sensitivity to phagocytosis of strain TS. Their assessment as virulent or avirulent on the basis of their resistance or sensitivity to phagocytosis in an *in vitro* test system was checked by animal inoculation. The results are given in Table 1.

In this limited comparison all assessments, with one exception, were substantiated. The exception was the avirulent strain M1 previously referred to. From earlier studies we were aware that in media containing its specific growth requirement, e.g. in TMB, this mutant behaved as did its virulent parent MP6. Strain A2256/Ppl sent to us labelled virulent proved to be avirulent in both the phagocytic and animal tests.

It is not possible to differentiate virulent from avirulent strains by a phagocytic test employing organisms as customarily harvested from 18 hr. growths at 28° or 37° on TMA. Both types from growths at 28° are uniformly highly sensitive to phagocytosis, and from growths at 37° the correlation between resistance or sensitivity and virulence or avirulence is frequently poor. The observation that virulent organisms could be recovered in a relatively phagocytosis-sensitive state from TMA slopes incubated for 18 hr. at 37°, and that a few hours' incubation in

Table 1. *Differentiation of virulent and avirulent strains of* Pasteurella pestis *by* in vitro *phagocytosis*

Exp. no.	Strain	Phagocytosis*	Assessment by *in vitro* phagocytosis	Virulence† to mice
1	MP6	30:20	V	10
	TS	1522:99	AV	0
	A1122	1567:97	AV	0
	5341	1159:98	AV	0
	14	1842:98	AV	0
	I-72	119:52	V	8
	F9581	55:25	V	10
	L27	40:23	V	10
	L36	47:20	V	10
2	MP6	41:20	V	10
	TS	1541:94	AV	0
	Java	1883:100	AV	0
	Soemedang	1422:100	AV	0
	A2256Ppl	1203:98	AV	0
	H327	49:21	V	10
	139L	43:19	V	10
	Yokohama	22:13	V	10
	M1	51:22	V	10

Organisms harvested from 18 hr. growths on tryptic meat agar at 28°, incubated with rotation for 3 hrs. at 37° in tryptic meat broth (2·5 × 10⁸ organisms/ml.), centrifuged, and tested for sensitivity to phagocytosis.
* Phagocytosis recorded by numbers of organisms ingested per 100 polymorphs, followed by percentage of polymorphs containing ingested cells.
† Deaths out of 10 mice injected intraperitoneally with 10⁴ organisms in 0·2 ml. buffer.
V = virulent.　　AV = avirulent.

fresh TMB at this temperature would allow them to become phago-cytosis-resistant required explanation. Possible reasons were that agar inhibited the development of resistance to phagocytosis, that unfavourable pH resulted, or that factors essential for resistance became exhausted during the 18 hr. incubation period. To determine the factors essential for the development of resistance, observations were made on the behaviour of virulent organisms in chemically defined media.

The results of this aspect of our work are not satisfactory in that during recent months we have been unable consistently to demonstrate effects which in the past were readily obtained and reproduced. Using sensitive organisms harvested from growths on TMA at 28° or 37° it was possible to show that a level of resistance to phagocytosis similar to that developing in TMB resulted from their incubation at 37° in a medium containing glucose, ammonium salts, phosphate, cystine, methionine, phenylalanine, glycine, valine, and isoleucine—that is, in a medium permitting growth of *P. pestis* at 28°. From this medium all amino-acids except cystine could be omitted without loss of efficiency, but omission of cystine, glucose, or ammonium salts severely impaired its properties. These results were sufficiently reproducible to permit titration of optimal levels of cystine. For resistance to phagocytosis equal to the maximum obtainable in TMB, cystine concentrations of 25–100 μM were ncessary; and concentrations above 400 μM were inhibitory. Highest levels of resistance to phagocytosis in glucose-ammonium-phosphate-cystine medium (GAPC) occurred after 3 hr. at 37° with an initial pH range of 6·4–7·6. These experiments were conducted with unwashed cells. Thorough washing of cells harvested from TMA slopes resulted in loss of viability of a large proportion (50 % or greater reduction in viable count after four washings in buffer) which was reflected in the low level of resistance to phagocytosis developed by washed organisms after 3 hr. in TMB. This low level did not improve on continued incubation. Non-viable elements in a suspension would fail to develop resistance to phagocytosis, and their ingestion in a phagocytic system would obscure the behaviour of resistant viable organisms.

The fact that low levels of added cystine were necessary to permit resistance to develop in synthetic media suggested that the relatively high sensitivity to phagocytosis of organisms harvested from 37°, 18 hr. TMA slopes, resulted from exhaustion of cystine during growth. However, cystine is an essential factor for growth of our organism—certainly replaceable by thiosulphate, and no doubt also by the precursors of cystine postulated by Engelsberg (1952)—and 18 hr. growth under our conditions yields about one-third of the maximum numbers obtainable with 50 hr. incubation. Cystine or its equivalent is therefore unlikely to have been exhausted within 18 hr. Addition of cystine to 18 hr. slopes, followed by 2 hr. additional incubation did not yield cells showing increased resistance to phagocytosis, but addition of glucose or glucose + cystine yielded cells showing appreciable increase of resistance to phago-cytosis, indicating that exhaustion of glucose, or its equivalent, was responsible for the frequently low resistance to phagocytosis shown by virulent cells harvested from 18 hr., 37°, TMA slopes. The fact that cystine has to be added in low concentration to unwashed cells harvested from TMA in which cystine is available to permit them to develop resistance in glucose-ammonium-phosphate indicates that *P. pestis* does not accumulate cystine in its amino-acid pool. Provision of cystine presumably permits metabolism to proceed. In the absence of active metabolism, as has been shown earlier, resistance to phagocytosis cannot be developed.

Attempts have been made without conspicuous success to improve the reliability of GAPC medium for the development of phagocytosis-resistance by phagocytosis-sensitive, virulent, organisms harvested from 28° growths on TMA. The attempts have included varying the glucose concentration, time of incubation and initial pH, and the addition of haemin, bisulphite, various metals, amino-acids, and vitamins in many combinations. The conditions for consistent development of resistance in synthetic medium are apparently quite subtle and at present are incompletely defined. This inconstancy of behaviour of *P. pestis* in synthetic media at 37° appears to be a general experience of workers studying this organism.

THE MECHANISM OF RESISTANCE TO PHAGOCYTOSIS

It is conceivable that phagocytosis-resistant differ from phagocytosis-sensitive organisms in having surface properties which, by an obscure mechanism, prevent their ingestion by polymorphs, or in having surface charges which result in their repulsion from similarly charged polymorphs, or in their ability to produce and excrete a metabolic product which is inhibitory or repellent to polymorphs. In slide-cell preparations of phagocytosis-resistant, virulent organisms and normal mouse polymorphs examined by phase-contrast microscopy, we observed no apparent repellent effects. Polymorphs were frequently seen to make contact with organisms without attempting to engulf them.

In the search for antiphagocytic factors it was of interest to compare the changes in amino-acid composition of TMB after incubation with virulent and avirulent organisms for 3 hr. at 37°—that is, under conditions leading to high phagocytosis-resistance of virulent and low phagocytosis-resistance of avirulent organisms. The object was to detect any amino-acids specifically excreted by one or other. Incubation with virulent MP6 resulted in complete removal of cystine, asparagine, aspartic, and glutamic acids from the medium as judged by chromatography. Incubation with avirulent TS yielded an identical result. Resistant virulent organisms sedimented from TMB, washed once, and resuspended in distilled water + glucose and cystine to a final concentration of 2×10^{10} organisms/ml. released into the medium on incubation for 1 hr. at 37° small amounts of leucines, valine, histidine, methionine, lysine and alanine and relatively large amounts of glutamic acid. Similarly treated avirulent organisms did precisely the same. We have consistently been unable to demonstrate the presence of any polymorph-inhibiting agent in TMB in which virulent organisms at a concentration of 250 millions/ml. have been rendered resistant by incubation for 3 hr. at 37°. TMB itself was toxic to mouse polymorphs when added to our phagocytic system in final concentrations higher than 10 % (v/v), but non-toxic at high concentrations when supplemented with gelatin to 3 % (w/v). Demonstrations of this kind therefore have to be conducted in the presence of 3 % (w/v) gelatin, which, however, does not interfere with the development of phagocytosis-resistance of virulent organisms, the manifestation of their phagocytosis-resistance in a test system, or the ability of normal polymorphs to ingest phagocytosis-sensitive organisms.

The development of phagocytosis-resistance requires active metabolism of the virulent organism. It was argued that if resistance to phagocytosis resulted from the excretion of a metabolic product inhibitory to phagocytosis, suppression of the metabolism of resistant organisms would result in loss of their resistance, whereas if resistance resulted from alteration in structure this would be retained on cessation of metabolism. Resistant virulent organisms were found to remain phagocytosis-resistant in the presence of $1000\,\mu$g. of streptomycin/ml. or when exposed to this concentration of streptomycin for 1 hr. at 37° before being added to the test system. However, whereas this high level of streptomycin does not affect the phagocytosis-resistance of virulent organisms once they have become resistant, a low level of $10\,\mu$g/ml. in TMB prevents the change from sensitivity to resistance. Mutant M 1 harvested from growth *in vivo* in the presence of hypoxanthine retains its resistance to phagocytosis on transfer to normal mice, at least during a period of 2 hr. From these observations it could be concluded that resistance to phagocytosis does not result from the excretion of a metabolic product. However, it may be that although streptomycin inhibits the elaboration of enzyme systems necessary for synthesis of a hypothetical metabolite, it need not necessarily inhibit their activity once they are established. Similarly, M 1 organisms harvested from hypoxanthine-treated mice may or may not contain an intracellular reserve of purines permitting limited metabolism in normal mice. Streptomycin in concentrations up to $4000\,\mu$g/ml. was not inhibitory to mouse polymorphs in our tests.

Virulent organisms rendered resistant to phagocytosis by 3 hr. incubation in TMB at 37° retain high resistance over a 10 hr. period

of continued incubation at this temperature. However, if stored at
4° in this medium they retain high resistance to phagocytosis only
during a 4–5 hr. period of storage and then rapidly return to full
sensitivity—a situation which could result either from the loss by
diffusion of intracellular products, or by the slow solution of a surface
component which inhibits phagocytosis.

It will be remembered that the conditions necessary for the development of resistance to phagocytosis by virulent organisms are very
similar to those necessary for the elaboration of capsular or envelope
antigen by *P. pestis*. Although there is some controversy whether
'capsule' or 'envelope' better describes the poorly staining, indefinitely
delineated, viscous material enveloping plague organisms under certain
cultural conditions, or whether in fact the two terms are synonymous
when applied to this organism, we will purely for convenience use the
terms capsule and capsulation when making reference to this material
here. Neither virulent nor avirulent cells harvested from TMA slopes
grown at 28° have any capsule observable in wet or dry India-ink preparations (Rowland, 1914), and both types are highly sensitive to phagocytosis. After incubation in TMB at pH 7·0 for 3 hr. at 37° no development of capsule was observed with either strain, although as stated
earlier such treatment confers maximum resistance to phagocytosis on
virulent organisms but leaves avirulent cells highly sensitive. When
capsulation and phagocytosis of the two types were observed hourly
during the period 0 to 10 hr. incubation under the above conditions, just-
visible capsules arose by the 5th hr. in both. These increased in size with
further incubation so that both types were well capsulated by the 10th hr.
However, the heavily capsulated, avirulent organisms obtained after
10 hr. incubation, although less sensitive to phagocytosis than the
original non-capsulated organisms, showed a very much greater sensitivity to ingestion than the apparently non-capsulated virulent organisms
obtained after only 3 hr. incubation (Fig. 1).

Preparations of capsular material derived from virulent MP6 and
avirulent TS organisms by the method of Amies (1951), which involved
extraction of large numbers of capsulated organisms with KCNS
followed by repeated precipitations at pH 4·4, were not found to inhibit
mouse polymorphs in our tests. That is, mouse polymorphs incubated
at 37° for 1–3 hr. in the presence of 1 mg/ml. final concentration of
purified capsular material, derived from either strain, showed unimpaired phagocytic activity towards either virulent or avirulent organisms.
Assuming complete extraction and no loss of material in purification,
the above final concentration (1 mg./ml.) represented the amount of

capsular antigen derived from 2×10^{10} capsulated organisms, per ml. The yields of both crude extracts and purified materials obtained from similar numbers of the two types of organisms were approximately the same (crude extracts, MP6, 2·400 g.; TS, 2·563 g.; thrice precipitated, pH 4·4; MP6, 0·45 g.; TS, 0·444 g.). Crude extracts similarly showed no anti-phagocytic activity.

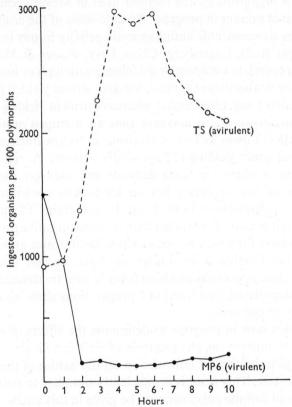

Fig. 1. Phagocytosis of virulent MP6 and avirulent TS strains of *P. pestis* with time of incubation in tryptic meat broth, pH 7·0 at 37°. Neither type was visibly capsulated between 0–4 hr., both were slightly capsulated at 5 hr., and well capsulated at 10 hr.

These observations contrast with those of Chen & Meyer (1954) who were able to demonstrate inhibition of phagocytosis by the addition of 0·25 mg./ml. of their fraction 1 to normal defibrinated guinea-pig blood. In view of the importance of capsular antigens for the development of a high degree of immunity in mice and their relative inefficiency in the guinea-pig, these divergent results are difficult to explain. From their study Chen & Meyer concluded that 'the presence or absence around the plague organism of an unaltered "envelope" containing greater than

10 % fraction 1 appears to be the decisive factor in phagocytosis'. It is possible that KCNS has a 'toxoiding' action on capsular material resulting in destruction of antiphagocytic activity but leaving it serologically active (cf. the 'toxoiding' effect of KCNS on diphtheria toxin reported by Hosoya & Yokoyama, 1953). Fractionation of saline extracts of acetone-killed and dried capsulated virulent MP6 and avirulent TS organisms by the method used in Meyer's school (Baker *et al.* 1952) is at present in progress. To date none of the crude fractions obtained has demonstrable antiphagocytic activity in our tests.

In a recent study Engelsberg, Chen, Levy, Foster & Meyer (1954) were able to correlate virulence or avirulence with high or low fraction 1 content in the strains they examined. Virulent strains yielded from 127 to 150 μg. fraction 1/mg. (dry weight), whereas avirulent yielded 10–121 μg. It is difficult, however, to conceive that an avirulent strain yielding 121 μg. fraction 1 owes its loss of virulence to its low fraction 1 content when another strain yielding 127 μg. is fully virulent. As rightly pointed out by these workers virulence depends not only on the antigenic complement of the organism but on all factors contributing to its survival and multiplication in the host. In our strains TS and MP6 we consider that it is a difference other than their quantitative production of fraction 1 *in vitro* for which we are seeking. Both strains appear capable of elaborating fraction 1 in similar amounts; certain phagocytosis-resistant virulent organisms resulting from *in vitro* treatments appear to be quite uncapsulated, and fraction 1 preparations show no antiphagocytic activity in our tests.

Experiments now in progress to determine the effects of highly protective rabbit antisera on phagocytosis of resistant virulent organisms promise to yield important information on the nature of the change to the resistant state. This work is insufficiently complete to permit factual statements and definite conclusions to be given in this article. However, subject to complete confirmation, the results to date may be summarized as follows. Antisera produced in rabbits or in mice using living phagocytosis-resistant virulent organisms are of higher passive protective power than sera similarly produced using living phagocytosis-sensitive cells. To obtain these sera, animals were first immunized with two doses of living strain M1 in the corresponding condition. Their protective values are directly related to their precipitin titres against our capsular extract prepared by Amies's method, and absorption with this material removes their protective action. (Purified capsular antigen of Amies is reported to be identical with fraction 1A by Landy & Webster, quoted by Engelsberg & Levy, 1954.) Incubation of phagocytosis-resistant organisms with highly protective rabbit antiserum (0·05 ml. protecting 10 of 10 mice for 25 days against challenge with 3000 resistant virulent cells) renders the resistant organisms sensitive to ingestion by polymorphs, but not to the high degree shown by the original organisms before conversion to the resistant state. Serum absorbed with capsular antigen in amounts sufficient to remove its protective properties does not appear to impair its ability to sensitize resistant organisms to phagocytosis. Phagocytosis of resistant organisms results to the same degree when either they or normal mouse polymorphs are pretreated with highly protective rabbit antiserum. Actively immunized mice capable of tolerating injected doses of 1 million resistant virulent organisms yield sera which, in 0·05 ml. amounts, passively protect only 1 of 10 mice, each challenged with 2000 resistant organisms.

DISCUSSION

It is apparent that a considerable amount of work remains to be done to disclose the fundamental difference or differences between our representative virulent and avirulent strains of *Pasteurella pestis*. The mechanism permitting virulent cells to resist phagocytosis remains obscure. We have obtained much information about the conditions requisite for resistance to develop and be expressed, and we have eliminated or, more correctly, failed to demonstrate, certain mechanisms which might lead to resistance to phagocytosis. With the reservation that excreted antiphagocytic factors may be highly unstable and easily 'toxoided', it is our opinion that change from sensitivity to resistance to phagocytosis results from a change in the surface properties of the organism. Resistant virulent organisms may have no observable capsule, but heavily capsulated virulent organisms are also phagocytosis-resistant, and very much more so than are avirulent cells capsulated to the same degree. It is probable that capsulated virulent organisms are resistant for the same reasons that non-capsulated virulent organisms are resistant—a situation which is understandable by assuming the presence of an invisible, but nevertheless effective, degree of capsulation in the latter. If this is so it must be presumed that the capsular material of virulent organisms has, *in its native state*, some different properties from that of avirulent organisms, despite the fact that extracted products from virulent and avirulent organisms apparently have identical properties. It is not unprecedented in immunology for biological materials to differ in physiological activity although serologically indistinguishable.

We could thus tentatively conclude that virulent organisms have the ability, under defined conditions *in vitro* and under the conditions occurring *in vivo*, to elaborate a soluble surface layer from few to many molecules thick which, on making contact with the polymorph surface, fails to evoke the stimulus necessary to initiate processes leading to their ingestion. Avirulent organisms, under the same conditions, produce a surface component in many respects identical with that of the virulent organism but sufficiently different to provide the necessary stimulus. This conclusion is not proven but is open to experimental investigation and receives considerable support from the observation that normal mouse polymorphs treated with plague antiserum, which in all probability modifies their surface properties, have enhanced ability to ingest resistant virulent organisms.

This article has been concerned mainly with observations on the development of resistance to phagocytosis by virulent organisms *in vitro*. With the reservations stated above, we have no evidence for the production of an extracellular antiphagocytic factor under the simple conditions which lead to resistance to phagocytosis. However, under the complex conditions found *in vivo* there is clear evidence that such a factor is produced. This aspect of virulence in *P. pestis* awaits investigation. To date the only circumstance under which we have been able to demonstrate the production of such a factor *in vitro* is after incubation of heparinized fresh whole mouse blood with virulent organisms at 37° under conditions of high aeration.

If a virulent organism can develop into a state in which it can resist ingestion by polymorphs, the production of an extracellular antiphagocytic factor would appear to be superfluous—at least as far as overcoming the polymorphonuclear defence mechanism is concerned. However, this mechanism is not the only one to be overcome by a pathogen capable of producing generalized infection resulting in the development of enormous numbers of progeny from a small inoculum. The efficient filtering and phagocytic activity of the whole reticulo-endothelial system constitutes a second formidable barrier to general infection, and it may well be that the condition of resistance to ingestion by polymorphs does not similarly confer resistance to ingestion by macrophages of the reticulo-endothelial system. Perhaps an extracellular antiphagocytic factor is instrumental in permitting virulent organisms to evade arrest by this barrier. The persistence of avirulent organisms in the liver and spleen during periods of 8 days or longer (Walker *et al.* 1953) suggests that they may not be dissimilar to virulent cells in this respect. Presumably avirulent organisms cannot give rise to generalized infection from small foci in these organs owing to their sensitivity to ingestion by circulating polymorphs.

That factors other than the ability to develop resistance to phago-cytosis are involved in determining virulence in *P. pestis* is indicated by the finding that phagocytosis-resistant organisms are occasionally no more virulent for mice than are the sensitive organisms from which they were derived. (They have never been observed to be less virulent.) If resistance to phagocytosis by polymorphs was the only factor of import-ance there would be no reason to expect the minimal lethal dose of resistant organisms to be greater than one. Frequently, however, the average lethal dose for mice has been observed to fall within the range of 5–15 organisms. It is not improbable that modification of the metabolism of the virulent organism to accentuate its properties with respect to resistance to phagocytosis adversely affects its metabolism with respect to other properties equally essential for virulence; with the net result that little reduction in average lethal dose is achieved by *in vitro* treatments yielding highly phagocytosis-resistant organisms.

By a two-step selection we have isolated from the virulent strain MP 6, a particular mutant which is characterized by methionine-independence and reduced ability to produce densely pigmented colonies on synthetic agar containing haemin. This mutant—M 7—is of especial interest in that, like its parent, it has the ability to develop resistance to phagocytosis and to inhibit polymorphs *in vivo*; but it is of low virulence for mice. As far as we have been able to determine, apart from its methio-nine-independence which in itself does not affect virulence, the mutant M 7 does not differ nutritionally from strains MP 6 and TS and pre-sumably therefore is not nutritionally handicapped *in vivo*. It is antici-pated that this mutant strain will be a useful tool in following the behaviour *in vivo* of virulent organisms after they have overcome the polymorphonuclear defence mechanism, and will help towards a better understanding of the basis of virulence in *Pasteurella pestis*.

I wish to thank Dr D. W. Henderson for his interest and advice throughout this work and for helpful suggestions concerning this manuscript. My thanks are also due to Mr G. A. Bacon, Miss Barbara Alkins and Miss Corinne Denham for excellent assistance in the laboratory, and to Mr R. E. Strange for chromatographic analyses.

Publication is by permission of the Chief Scientist, Ministry of Supply.

REFERENCES

Amies, C. R. (1951). The envelope substance of *Pasteurella pestis*. *Brit. J. exp. Path.* **32**, 259.

Avi-Dor, Y. & Yaniv, H. (1953). Relation between changes in the stability of *Pasteurella tularensis* suspensions and in its bacterial population. 1. The stability of suspensions of *Pasteurella tularensis* in the presence of electrolytes. *J. Bact.* **6**, 1.

174   T. W. BURROWS

BACON, G. A., BURROWS, T. W. & YATES, M. (1951). The effects of biochemical mutation on the virulence of *Bacterium typhosum*: the loss of virulence of certain mutants. *Brit. J. exp. Path.* **32**, 85.

BAKER, E. E., SOMMER, H., FOSTER, L. E., MEYER, E. & MEYER, K. F. (1947). Antigenic structure of *Pasteurella pestis* and the isolation of a crystalline antigen. *Proc. Soc. exp. Biol., N.Y.*, **64**, 193.

BAKER, E. E., SOMMER, H., FOSTER, L. E., MEYER, E. & MEYER, K. F. (1952). Studies on immunization against plague. 1. The isolation and characterisation of the soluble antigen of *Pasteurella pestis*. *J. Immunol.* **68**, 131.

BHATNAGAR, S. S. & SHRIVASTAVA, D. L. (1946). An experimental study on cellular immunity in *Pasteurella pestis* infection. *J. Hyg., Camb.*, **44**, 307.

BURROWS, T. W. & BACON, G. A. (1954). The basis of virulence in *Pasturella pestis*: attempts to induce mutation from avirulence to virulence. *Brit. J. exp. Path.* **35**, 129.

CHEN, T. H. & MEYER, K. F. (1954). Studies on immunization against plague. VII. A hemagglutination test with the protein fraction of *Pasteurella pestis*: a serologic comparison of virulent and avirulent strains with observations on the structure of the bacterial cells and its relationship to infection and immunity. *J. Immunol.* **72**, 282.

DOUDOROFF, M. (1943). Studies on the nutrition and metabolism of *Pasteurella pestis*. *Proc. Soc. exp. Biol., N.Y.*, **53**, 73.

ENGELSBERG, E. (1952). Irreversibility of methionine synthesis from cysteine in *Pasteurella pestis*. *J. Bact.* **63**, 675.

ENGELSBERG, E., CHEN, T. H., LEVY, J. B., FOSTER, L. E. & MEYER, K. F. (1954). Virulence in *Pasteurella pestis*. *Science*, **119**, 413.

ENGELSBERG, E. & LEVY, J. B. (1954). Studies on immunization against plague. VI. Growth of *Pasteurella pestis* and the production of the envelope and other soluble antigens in a casein hydrolysate mineral glucose medium. *J. Bact.* **67**, 438.

FADEEVA, T. (1939). Relations sérologiques entre différentes souches de la peste et de la pseudotuberculose. *Rev. Microbiol. Saratov*, **18**, 44. (French summary.)

GARBER, E. D., HACKETT, A. J. & FRANKLIN, R. (1952). The virulence of biochemical mutants of *Klebsiella pneumoniae*. *Proc. Nat. Acad. Sci.* **38**, 693.

HERBERT, D. (1949). Studies on the nutrition of *Pasteurella pestis* and factors affecting the growth of isolated cells on an agar surface. *Brit. J. exp. Path.* **30**, 509.

HILLS, G. M. & SPURR, E. D. (1952). The effect of temperature on the nutritional requirements of *Pasteurella pestis*. *J. gen. Microbiol.* **6**, 64.

HOSOYA, S. & YOKOYAMA, M. (1953). Conversion of diphtheria toxin to toxoid with KCNS. *Yoko. med. Bull.* **4**, 69.

JAWETZ, E. & MEYER, K. F. (1943). Avirulent strains of *Pasteurella pestis*. *J. infect. Dis.* **73**, 124.

JAWETZ, E. & MEYER, K. F. (1944). The behaviour of virulent and avirulent *P. pestis* in normal and immune experimental animals. *J. infect. Dis.* **74**, 1.

JENNINGS, R. K. (1954). Diffusion precipitin studies of the complexity of antigen mixtures. II. The number of zones formed by one antigen. *J. Bact.* **67**, 565.

OAKLEY, C. L. & FULTHORPE, A. J. (1953). Antigenic analysis by diffusion. *J. Path. Bact.* **65**, 49.

OLITSKI, L. (1948). Mucin as a resistance-lowering substance. *Bact. Rev.* **12**, 149.

OTTEN, L. (1936). Immunization against plague with live vaccines. *Ind. J. med. Res.* **24**, 73.

OUDIN, J. (1948). L'analyse immunochémique qualitative; méthode par diffusion des antigènes au sein de l'immunsérum précipitant gélosé. *Ann. Inst. Pasteur*, **75**, 30.

RAO, M. S. (1939). The nutritional requirements of the plague bacillus. *Ind. J. Med. Res.* **27**, 75.

ROWLAND, S. (1914). The morphology of the plague bacillus. *J. Hyg.*, Plague suppl., **3**, 418.

SCHÜTZE, H. (1932a). Studies in *B. pestis* antigens. 1. The antigens and immunity reactions in *B. pestis*. *Brit. J. exp. Path.* **13**, 284.

SCHÜTZE, H. (1932b). Studies in *B. pestis* antigens. II. The antigenic relationship of *B. pestis* and *B. pseudotuberculosis rodentium*. *Brit. J. exp. Path.* **13**, 289.

SCHÜTZE, H. (1934). The envelope antigen of *B. pestis* and its antibody. *Brit. J. exp. Path.* **15**, 200.

SCHÜTZE, H. (1939). Studies on *B. pestis* antigens as prophylactic agents. *Brit. J. exp. Path.* **20**, 235.

SEAL, S. C. (1951). Studies on the specific soluble protein of *Pasteurella pestis* and allied organisms. I. Isolation, fractionation and certain physical, chemical and serological properties. *J. Immunol.* **67**, 93.

SOKHEY, S. S. & HABBU, M. K. (1943a). Optimum and limiting temperatures for the growth of the plague bacillus in broth. *J. Bact.* **46**, 25.

SOKHEY, S. S. & HABBU, M. K. (1943b). Optimum and limiting hydrogen ion concentrations for growth of the plague bacillus in broth. *J. Bact.* **46**, 33.

WALKER, D. L., FOSTER, L. E., CHEN, T. H., LARSON, A. & MEYER, K. F. (1953). Studies on immunisation against plague. V. Multiplication and persistence of virulent and avirulent *Pasteurella pestis* in mice and guinea pigs. *J. Immunol.* **60**, 245.

WATS, R. C., WAGLE, P. M. & PUDUVAL, T. K. (1939). A serological study of some strains of *Pasteurella pestis*. *Ind. J. med. Res.* **27**, 375.

YANIV, H. & AVI-DOR, Y. (1953). Relation between changes in the stability of *Pasteurella tularensis* suspensions and in its bacterial population. II. Mutual influence between salt-agglutinable and salt non-agglutinable types. *J. Bact.* **66**, 6.

THE PATHOGENICITY OF PROTOZOAL AND OTHER PARASITES: GENERAL CONSIDERATIONS

F. HAWKING

National Institute for Medical Research, Mill Hill, London

INTRODUCTION

Man's study of parasites has been activated mostly by the desire to prevent or to cure disease, and this motive has coloured his conceptions of the host-parasite relationship. Most people tend to think in terms of attack and defence—attack by the parasite and defence by the host. Actually, as all parasitologists have long recognized theoretically if not subconsciously, the true position is quite different. The motto of parasites —if they had one—would be: 'Live and let live.' Not only is the parasite free from hostility to its host, apart from the necessary satisfaction of its own modest needs, but it has in fact a vested interest in the host's well-being, and most of all in the host's continued survival; for death of the host inevitably entails death of almost all the endoparasites which it contains. The perfect parasite is one which has adapted itself so well that it causes no harm to the host, and the host takes no notice of it. Such parasites are exemplified by *Entamoeba coli* and many other protozoa living in the intestine, and to some extent by *Trypanosoma lewisi* living in the blood of rats. Presumably such harmonious host-parasite relationships have been reached only by gradual evolution, so non-pathogenic parasites are probably old and long-established ones.

The attitude of the host towards the parasite, however, is quite different. The host can survive very well without the parasite and seldom derives any benefit from association with protozoal or helminthic parasites. With bacteria, indeed, there are many examples of the host deriving advantage from organisms, perhaps owing to their synthesis of important growth factors, and such associations are named symbiosis rather than parasitism. With protozoa, however, symbiosis is rare, the best investigated case being that of the flagellates in the intestine of termites and other invertebrates which eat wood. Thus the roach, *Cryptocercus punctulatus*, contains great numbers of flagellates which can dissolve the pieces of wood which it has swallowed. These flagellates occur only in the intestines of the individuals which eat wood. If the intestine is freed from flagellates (by warming the host to 36° for 25 hr.)

the roach loses its power of digesting wood; the power can be restored by feeding it with faeces containing flagellates (Cleveland, 1934; Goetsch, 1946). In most cases the parasite is a nuisance which may be overlooked, or which remains unnoticed; in a few cases it is an obnoxious invader to be combated by all possible means. Accordingly, the host may ignore the parasite (non-pathogenic parasite) or it may try to destroy it either with success (in which case, the protozoon is non-parasitic) or with partial or complete failure (in which case the parasite is pathogenic).

Pathological effects are produced when (i) a parasite has succeeded in establishing itself in a host and (ii) when the harmonious balance of this parasite to its host is in some way incomplete. Accordingly we may consider first the factors which determine whether a parasite can establish itself and secondly the ways in which the harmony between parasite and host may be incomplete.

ESTABLISHMENT OF THE PARASITE IN ITS HOST

As already mentioned, a parasite cannot become pathogenic unless it succeeds in establishing and maintaining itself in or on the host. Absence of pathogenicity may be due simply to lack of success of the micro-organism at this stage, as with the free-living non-pathogenic protozoa of many kinds. Moreover, many so-called pathogenic protozoa are not pathogenic to animals other than their own specific hosts, simply because they cannot live and multiply in them, e.g. human malaria parasites are not pathogenic for other mammals, not even for monkeys, because they are so narrowly adapted to their own hosts that they cannot multiply in other ones. Trypanosomes and leishmanias are much less specialized and are pathogenic for many mammals; entamoebas occupy an intermediate position.

However, many protozoa succeed in establishing themselves in the bodies of higher animals or plants and these constitute the well-known parasites. As indicated above, the best strategy for the parasite to employ is to adapt itself so closely to the host, especially as regards its immunological pattern, that the host does not notice its presence; such close adaptation, on the other hand, has the disadvantage of severely limiting the kind of host which the parasite can utilize.

The factors in the host and in the parasite which determine whether or not the parasite can establish itself are of two kinds. On the one hand, the parasite must be able to secure all its physico-chemical requirements—food, temperature, and so forth—in the body of the host. On the other hand, it must be able to evade attempts made by the host to rid itself of the parasite—either the parasite must be so innocuous as not to excite the host's reactions—for example, non-pathogenic parasites such as *Entamoeba coli* or *Dipetalonema perstans*—or it must be able to circumvent the immune responses of the host—for example, trypanosomes which change their antigenic structure at each relapse.

FOOD REQUIREMENTS OF THE PARASITE

The food requirements of a parasite may be grouped like those of larger animals into carbohydrate, fats, proteins and accessory growth factors. The carbohydrate requirements, which are mainly glucose, are usually secured with little difficulty. About the fats required by protozoa, little is known. The protein requirements are extremely exacting, as is well known. Probably most of the narrow specificity of certain parasites for certain hosts, e.g. *Plasmodium vivax* specific for *Homo sapiens*, is due to the close adaptation of the parasite to the proteins of its host; as already noted, unless the animal's proteins are of the correct pattern required by the parasite, the parasite is perforce non-pathogenic for that species of animal. The accessory growth factors required by parasites have received considerable attention during recent years. In many cases these growth factors consist of important metabolites or enzymatic substances which the host can synthesize but which the parasite has ceased to produce, thus depending on what it can extract from the host. In other cases the growth factors can be synthesized neither by the parasite nor by its host but must be obtained from the chemical activities of plants or bacteria. When this is the position, the diet of the host may be of great importance to the successful development of the parasite. Thus the growth of malaria parasites may be depressed by feeding the host on diets deficient in methionine, ascorbic acid, vitamin A, riboflavin, or pantothenic acid, but may be increased by feeding diets deficient in biotin, nicotinic acid, choline, or protein (review by McKee, 1951). Similarly, the multiplication of *Trypanosoma congolense* in mice tends to be depressed if the mice are fed on a special diet, which is adequate for the mice but apparently inadequate for the parasites (Keppie, 1953). Unpublished work by Godfrey has confirmed this phenomenon, although it is not clear what is the factor missing from the diet. In most of these cases, the parasite requires growth factors which are also required by the host. Recent work, however, has revealed one instance in which the host's diet may be defective for the parasite although quite adequate for the host.

This work began with the finding by Maegraith, Deegan & Jones (1952) that if rats are given a milk diet, they are not susceptible to infection by the malaria parasite, *Plasmodium berghei*. Further work in our own laboratory (Hawking, 1954) has shown that if *p*-aminobenzoic acid is added to the milk diet, the susceptibility of rats (to *P. berghei*) or of monkeys (to *P. knowlesi* and *P. cynomolgi*) is fully restored. Accordingly, it seems probable that these malaria parasites require *p*-aminobenzoic acid as one of their many growth factors and this view is supported by much other evidence (especially the work of Geiman & McKee (1948) and Anfinsen, Geiman, McKee, Ormsbee & Ball (1946) on the growth of *P. knowlesi in vitro*). Apart from its biochemical interest, the suppression of malaria by a milk diet and by *p*-aminobenzoic acid deficiency may be of practical importance as offering an explanation of the relatively low pathogenicity of malaria parasites for infants. It has long been noticed that infants in West Africa and other malarious areas do not experience as much or as severe malaria as might have been anticipated from their exposure to infected mosquitoes. Thus African babies suffer much less from malaria than non-immune Europeans used to suffer before modern methods of protection by mosquito nets and prophylactic drugs were perfected. In the past, this partial immunity of African infants has usually been attributed to immune bodies trans-mitted from their mothers. In view of the above work, however, and because during their early months the babies subsist wholly on a milk diet, it is quite possible that the low pathogenicity of the malaria parasite for these babies may be due to a deficiency of *p*-aminobenzoic acid (and other factors) induced by the milk diet. The question, however, is complex and difficult to investigate, and it is further complicated by the fact that bacteria present in some individual rats and human beings probably synthesize *p*-aminobenzoic acid irrespective of the composition of the diet.

IMMUNOLOGICAL RELATIONS BETWEEN HOST AND PARASITE

In protozoal infections the immunological relations between host and parasite are complex and difficult to interpret.

Trypanosomes

In trypanosome infections in the laboratory it is easy to demonstrate that the serum of an infected animal contains antibodies which agglu-tinate and lyse the trypanosomes, often in great dilution. But these antibodies remain effective only so long as the infection is prevented from relapsing. If most of the trypanosomes are destroyed (by an immunological crisis or by a drug) and a fresh relapse strain of trypanosomes is formed, the new trypanosomes are found to be unaffected by the antibodies which were so deadly for the original strain (Browning, Adamson & Keppie, 1953). Apparently at each relapse the trypanosome can modify the pattern of antigens on its surface, so that it becomes insusceptible to the previously effective antibodies. The number of these possible modifications seems to be great; certainly it has not been exhausted in any experimental trial. It is this capacity for repeated modification of its antigen pattern which gives the trypanosome its power to maintain itself in its animal host; although continually being decimated by immunological crises, the trypanosome can form a relapse strain and multiply once again.

Actually the immunological relations between trypanosomes and their host are even more complex than has been realized hitherto. This is indicated by recent work of Desowitz & Watson (1951, 1952, 1953a) which is worth considering in detail. They worked with *Trypanosoma vivax*, well known as an important parasite of cattle, sheep and antelopes in Africa. Usually this parasite cannot be transmitted to rats and similar laboratory animals. But, as Desowitz & Watson discovered, if a quantity of clean sheep serum is injected into the rat at the same time as the trypanosomes are injected, the latter can multiply and set up an infection of moderate intensity. This infection can be passed on to other rats, provided that each time trypanosomes are passed a further dose of sheep serum is provided to help them to establish themselves. To explain these phenomena it is postulated that the serum of sheep and of other animals which are the natural hosts of *T. vivax*, contains a 'supplementary factor' which facilitates growth of the trypanosome in the rat. This factor is associated with the serum proteins, but its chemical identification has not yet been completed.

Further work has shown that when a sheep is infected with *T. vivax* it gradually forms antibodies which can agglutinate and kill the trypanosomes in certain circumstances. Thus, if the trypanosomes of the homologous strain are taken from a rat, or if they are washed free from sheep serum, they are found to be susceptible to the sheep's antibodies and are rapidly destroyed by them *in vitro*. But while the trypanosomes are present in the sheep's own blood, they are somehow protected from the antibodies which are also present there. Accordingly, Desowitz & Watson postulate that *T. vivax* has the power to draw a specific substance from the blood of its host the sheep and to use it to protect itself against the host's antibodies. Possibly this antibody-protection factor is identical with the supplementary factor already mentioned, which enables *T. vivax* to develop in rats; perhaps the substance protects the trypanosomes against antibodies of the rat which would otherwise destroy it. We may imagine that the receptor groups on the surface of the trypanosome are able to combine with some harmless substance in the sheep's serum, and they are then protected against fatal combination with the sheep's antibodies. This conception has wide implications and more work will be needed before it is generally accepted. But if confirmed it will form an important contribution to our understanding of the parasite-host relationship.

Plasmodia

In plasmodial infections, such as malaria, the immunological relations between the parasite and its host are again complex and obscure but important. An enormous amount of work has been done on the subject and the position will be briefly presented in what follows.

When the malarial parasites first multiply in a man or animal they produce an immunological response which ultimately cuts the attack short and destroys most but not all of the parasites. This immunological counter-attack depends partly on humoral antibodies, largely on phagocytosis increased by opsonins and the like. Later the level of the immunological response diminishes, and another multiplication of the parasites becomes possible, leading to a heightened immunological response. In this way a series of relapses occurs, until eventually the parasites are all destroyed or persist at only a very low level, presumably held down by the host's immune response. With some plasmodia this state of equilibrium between host and parasite may persist for a surprising number of years, and there are many records of latent infections of *Plasmodium malariae* (quartan malaria) persisting for over 26 years. Unfortunately, the immunity produced by plasmodia is strain-specific, and does not protect the host against infection by other strains. By repeated infection with all the strains of one locality, however, the inhabitants of that locality gradually build up a strong but not complete immunity to all the strains to which they are exposed. Consequently the strains of *P. falciparum* in West Africa are not appreciably pathogenic to adult West Africans, although they are highly pathogenic to immigrant Europeans and moderately pathogenic for African children who have not yet acquired immunity. This immunity to malaria, acquired only by repeated and prolonged exposure to infection, has been of great historical importance for the development of Africa as compared with that of America; for the prevalence of malaria in Africa and the immunity of the local population have preserved tropical Africa from the European colonization which occurred in America.

The immunological responses excited by plasmodia, although of great epidemiological importance, are of little or no value for diagnosis owing to their limitation to the particular strain involved. Similarly, attempts to produce immunization by the injection of malarial antigens have also proved useless in practice, although during the 1939–45 war the possibility was intensively studied in America and elsewhere.

PRODUCTION OF PATHOLOGICAL EFFECTS

The parasite having succeeded in establishing itself, we may next consider why some parasites should produce pathological effects. As we have already said, the successful parasite is one which is so well adapted that its presence is unnoticed and excites no reaction. Pathological effects follow when the parasite establishes itself but is not so successful as to remain harmless and unobserved. From this point of view, the non-pathogenic parasite is the skilful one; the pathogen is the blunderer. From an evolutionary point of view, the non-pathogenic parasite is the long-established resident and the pathogen is the awkward newcomer who cannot avoid wounding local susceptibilities. Pathogenic effects occur because the balance between parasite and host has broken down, or has never existed. Such lack of balance may occur in many ways, of which seven will be discussed here.

(1) *Number of parasites.* There may be excessive numbers of parasites, due to unrestrained multiplication or too great invasion. The simplest example of this is given by the laboratory infection of mice by old strains of trypanosomes, e.g. *Trypanosoma equiperdum*. The trypanosomes rapidly multiply in the blood until there are as many trypanosomes as red blood corpuscles. Although the parasites seem to have little direct harmful effect, there is obviously a limit to the number of extraneous organisms which the mouse can carry in its blood and remain alive. Such excessive multiplication probably does not occur in nature, except in the terminal stage of trypanosome and similar infections.

(2) *Destruction of host tissue.* Another simple cause of pathogenic action is the consumption or destruction by the parasite of the host's substance. Thus a red blood corpuscle is destroyed each time a malaria parasite passes through its cycle of asexual development, and *Entamoeba histolytica* destroys cells of the intestinal mucous membrane and erythrocytes. Usually the amount of tissue consumed in this way is negligible compared with the bulk of the host; but in severe infections with malaria it may contribute appreciably to the anaemia which develops. The death of mice infected by large numbers of trypanosomes is often attributed to excessive consumption of glucose by the parasites.

Certainly the life of the mice can be prolonged for a few hours by the administration of this sugar. But for reasons given below, it is more probable that death is due to intoxication by the disintegrating products of the trypanosomes, and that the hypoglycaemia, which certainly occurs in the final stage of these infections, is due to this intoxication rather than to failure of the host to make good the glucose consumed by the parasites.

(3) *Mechanical effects.* The development of the parasite may produce mechanical effects such as pressure on important tissues or interference with tubes. Protozoa are usually too small, even in conglomerations, to cause such effects directly, although the exoerythrocytic forms of *Plasmodium gallinaceum*, which develop in the endothelium of small blood vessels, are big enough to block the capillaries of the brain, thus causing death of young chicks. Helminthic parasites often cause such obstruction; for example, hydatid cysts may compress the liver or spinal cord, and bunches of *Ascaris* may block the intestine. Indirectly, such mechanical effects may be produced in various ways. (i) The presence of the parasite may excite local inflammation which may form granulomatous masses—for example, the gummata of syphilis, which themselves cause pressure effects; or the parasite may cause abscesses, like the liver abscess due to *Entamoeba histolytica*; alternatively, the subsequent scar tissue may cause obstruction to lymphatics, leading to lymphstasis and elephantiasis as in filariasis due to *Wuchereria bancrofti*. (ii) The destructive action of parasites may open up blood vessels, leading to haemorrhage, as happens with *Entamoeba histolytica* in the intestine; similarly, the ulcerative action of this protozoon may occasionally cause perforation of the intestine. The ulcers caused by protozoa may also form a portal of entry for secondary infections by bacteria which often cause far more damage than the original protozoal parasites would have done. (iii) Some intestinal protozoa, e.g. *Lamblia*, may congregate in such enormous numbers on the mucous membrane lining the intestine, that they eventually obstruct the normal processes of absorption.

(4) *Physico-chemical effects.* The presence of the parasite may alter the physico-chemical properties of the cells in which it lives, so that mechanical disturbances arise. The classical example of this kind of reaction is the way in which the malaria parasite alters the surface properties of red blood corpuscles so that they no longer pass smoothly through the capillaries, but adhere to each other in large clumps and cause capillary obstruction with disastrous effects. This phenomenon is very important, since it probably underlies many of the pathological lesions of malaria.

(5) *Inflammatory reactions*. The presence of the parasite and the resultant inflammation may irritate the local muscular and glandular mechanisms, so that they are too active for optimum physiological functioning. Thus the presence of many *histolytica* amoebae in the wall of the intestine leads to increased peristalsis and to increased discharge of mucus and other excretions, which form important parts of the syndrome of dysentery; and the body fails to absorb food, and loses excessive quantities of water and salts.

(6) *Toxic products*. Another way in which pathogenic effects may theoretically follow from the presence of parasites is the liberation of toxic products. These are extremely important in many bacteria, in which they have been studied in great detail; but in protozoal infections the identification of specific toxic substances is rare. True exotoxins, such as those of tetanus and diphtheria, are unknown among protozoa, unless a substance produced by Sarcosporidia is included under this heading. This substance, which has been named 'Sarcocystin' or 'Sarcosporidiotoxin', is lethal for rabbits if injected intravenously in small doses, but it is much less toxic for other animals such as rats and guinea-pigs. Rabbits can be immunized against it. Paradoxically Sarcosporidia, from which this toxin can be obtained, cause little pathological effect in their natural hosts (cattle and pigs) unless they are present in very large numbers (Sato, 1926; Teichmann, 1910). Protozoa which invade the wall of the intestine such as *Entamoeba histolytica* and *Balantidium coli* cause necrosis and lysis of the tissues round about them; presumably this is effected by means of toxins, but these have not been isolated.

The metabolic waste products which are liberated by protozoa during their normal development seem to be relatively innocuous. But if large numbers of parasites are simultaneously destroyed in the body acute febrile disturbances may be caused. Such large-scale destruction may be due to the administration of a drug, which rapidly destroys the parasites, liberating their proteins and other constituents. This may happen, for example, after injection of tryparsamide into a patient with many trypanosomes, or it may result from the host's own immunological processes, as in the well-known crises of many infections produced by trypanosomes and plasmodia. In these instances the host's production of lytic antibodies seems suddenly to reach an effective level, and great numbers of parasites circulating freely in the blood stream are destroyed in a short space of time, setting free disintegration products in relatively high concentration. A dramatic illustration of this type of reaction has recently been observed by Desowitz & Watson (1953*b*) in pigs infected with *Trypanosoma simiae*. This trypanosome multiplies rapidly in the blood of domestic pigs, normally causing death in 8–9 days apparently from simple excess of numbers, as discussed above. Certain pigs, however, were able to build up an effective immunological response, and a crisis ensued during which most of the trypanosomes in the blood were destroyed. This successful counter-attack by the host did not, however, improve the immediate clinical picture; rather the reverse. While the trypanosomes had been swarming in its blood to an apparently dangerous extent, the pig did not appear acutely ill and was able to take food and to stand up. But when the immunological crisis occurred, and the trypanosomes were suddenly destroyed, the pig showed severe symptoms. It was extremely distressed, its breathing was shallow, it lay on its side and took no food. Recovery after this period was rapid and the pig remained in apparently good health until the next parasitic crisis. Presumably these severe, but non-fatal, symptoms were caused by the disintegration products of the trypanosomes which had undergone lysis.

Many workers have endeavoured more precisely to demonstrate the production of toxins by trypanosomes, but usually they have not succeeded. However, if a suspension of trypanosomes killed by a temperature of 45° is injected into mice, rats or guinea-pigs, toxic effects and death can be produced. The suspension becomes toxic after incubation for about 1 hr. after the death of the trypanosomes; and the toxic factors are presumably bound to the cell remnants. If the suspension is incubated at 37° for 8–18 hr. the toxicity diminishes and disappears. Apparently the formation of toxin depends upon the disintegration of the trypanosome protoplasm; if the disintegration proceeds beyond a certain stage, the products become non-toxic. It may be that the death of mice during heavy infections with trypanosomes in the laboratory is due to these toxic disintegration products rather than to the excessive consumption of glucose described above. This explanation (by toxic factors) is supported by the observation that rats die from a heavy infection with the pathogenic *T. brucei*, whereas they show practically no symptoms during an equally heavy infection with the non-pathogenic *T. lewisi*.

In malaria, as is well known, schizogony of the parasites inside the red blood corpuscle leaves a portion of parasitic substance behind as a reminder, and when this is done simultaneously by large numbers of parasites, an acute febrile reaction (the 'attack of malaria') is produced in the host.

(7) *Allergic and immunological reactions.* Yet another way in which the host may suffer from the presence of the parasite is by the develop-

ment of allergy to the parasite or its products. The precise nature and causation of allergy are not fully understood, so it is not surprising if we often cannot explain why such allergic manifestations occur when they do and why they do not occur more frequently. The problems concerning allergy are well illustrated by the infections with filarial worms such as *Wuchereria bancrofti* or *Loa loa*. In these infections many adult worms and millions of microfilariae may live and circulate in the body for months without causing any symptoms whatsoever. Presumably the parasites are so well adapted to their host that they are not noticed by it. The immunological reactions during these latent periods of filarial infections are very interesting as they illustrate many aspects of the host-parasite relationship; so we may make a digression at this point to consider them in more detail.

Relation of immunological response to extent of pathological effects

As explained above, the host commonly shows no symptoms of the parasite's presence, but appropriate investigations show that the host is sensitized to some extent to the products of the parasite. Thus intradermal injection of dried parasite or its products, as in the ordinary skin test, produces a wheal in an infected person which is greater than that in a non-infected one. Similarly, complement-fixation with antigens prepared from filarial worms can often be demonstrated in sera from infected patients. But in both these reactions the results are much less clear-cut than those obtained with some bacterial infections. Some normal persons give positive skin tests or positive complement-fixation; whereas many patients or animals whose blood contains thousands of microfilariae may consistently give negative responses to both these tests. Thus in Surinam, Dutch Guiana, among the negro adults carrying *Microfilaria bancrofti*, 27 % showed a positive skin reaction to the intradermal injection of Dirofilarial antigen, but 73 % gave only a wheal which was no greater than that given by European controls (Lampe, 1950). Similarly, in a series of West Africans with *Mf. bancrofti*, only 57 % gave a positive complement-fixation reaction (Minning & McFadzean, 1955). The positive responses obtained from uninfected persons might easily be interpreted as due to the use of antigens containing groups which react with antibodies to non-filarial infections or to the presence of antibodies of other types; because the substances used in these immunological tests commonly contain many different compounds and always many different chemical groupings. But the negative responses yielded by persons with many microfilariae in their blood raise much more fundamental questions. Since the weakness of antigen preparations lies in the broadness of their spectra, not in their narrowness, it is improbable that antigens satisfactory for 60 % of patients should completely fail to contain the appropriate grouping for the other 40 %, if these actually carried antibodies to filariae. A more plausible explanation would be that the antibodies might be absorbed as soon as they appeared by the microfilariae present in the blood, leaving no surplus for detection by complement-fixation tests. But this explanation also is not completely satisfactory, because some persons with many microfilariae show no complement-fixation, whereas others show fixation readily. The most probable explanation is also the simplest, viz. that antibodies have not been produced by the host in these cases; and if the whole field of immunological responses is surveyed in a broad way, the reason for this non-production becomes clear. Antibody reactions are most clearly marked in the infections which produce acute and serious disturbance of the host, e.g. the bacterial infections such as typhoid. The foreign organism causes serious disturbance of the host, the host delivers a strong immunological counter-attack, and the foreign organism is eliminated. Among helminthic infections, the schistosomes cause considerable tissue damage to the host (for the eggs must produce lysis of the adjacent tissues, so that they may make their way to the surface of some excretory duct) and the immunological responses of the host as measured by complement-fixation and skin tests are well marked. But in the case of filarial worms, the parasite is extremely well adapted to its host, so that disturbance of the host is minimal or even completely absent. Consequently it is not surprising if the usual immunological response of the host is also slight, and if in some cases it is absent altogether. The broad rule might be enunciated that the extent of the immunological response to an infection is generally proportional to the extent and acuteness of the pathogenic effects which the infection causes. Although there are exceptions, this rule would be true in many instances.

Pathogenicity in filarial infections

We now resume consideration of filarial infections such as loiasis. In most persons and at most times this infection causes no symptoms; but from time to time a local manifestation called a Calabar swelling tends to occur. This is a localized swelling, 6–12 in. across, usually situated on a forearm, hand, knee or leg. It involves mostly the skin and subcutaneous tissue, and consists of localized oedema or transudation of fluid with a few inflammatory cells. The patient feels a mild dull ache at the site. The swelling comes up in a few hours, persists a few days, and then goes down again leaving no permanent ill effects. Sometimes there is a history of a knock at the site, but often there has been no obvious cause for the precipitation of the swelling. There has been much speculation about these Calabar swellings, but their investigation is difficult because of their irregular occurrence and transitory nature. Apparently they are a localized allergic reaction to some product of the adult worms. They cannot be due to the ordinary microfilariae circulating in the blood, since these are distributed generally all over the body. On the other hand, their location in subcutaneous tissue would agree with the location of adult worms which tend to occur in this stratum. Yet the region of the spermatic cord is one of the commonest sites for the adult worms of *Loa*, but Calabar swellings in this region are rare—perhaps because the area is shielded from trauma. Provisionally we may interpret them as a local response to products liberated in an abnormal way or to an abnormal extent from the adult worms; possibly these products are released by trauma which may or may not have been noticed by the patient. Normally the liberation of microfilariae by the adult worm proceeds unnoticed by the host. It would be an attractive hypothesis, however, that in response to trauma or some other stimulus an adult worm suddenly extrudes an unusually large number of microfilariae and that these precipitate the allergic response. Alternatively, it might be postulated that the extruded larvae sometimes encounter abnormally unfavourable local circumstances (e.g. local mechanical blocking in the tissues or an infrequent high concentration of antibodies), so that many of the larvae are destroyed in the tissues before they can reach the blood stream, and their disintegration products excite the allergic response.

Somewhat similar allergic phenomena occur in bancroftian filariasis. Here again there may be many adult worms living in the lymphatics and millions of microfilariae circulating in the blood without causing any appreciable pathogenic effects. But from time to time (every 6 weeks or 3 months) there may be a violent attack of acute lymphangitis usually in a leg or in the scrotum; the affected part is greatly swollen, hot, red, extremely tender, and painful; there is acute fever and the unfortunate patient is prostrated; in a few days the whole attack subsides, only to return at a later date; these attacks may recur for several years. In these cases the inflammation appears definitely to be localized round the adult worms lying in the lymphatics, but it is not clear why worms can normally persist in this situation for long periods without causing reaction, and why on some occasions they should suddenly excite these violent attacks. At one time it was supposed that the attacks were due to superadded infections by streptococci; but this has been disproved, and it is now believed that most of these attacks are allergic reactions to the worms themselves, although the reason for their abrupt precipitation is still unknown.

Blackwater fever

Immunological processes usually limit the pathogenicity of malaria parasites, but in blackwater fever they seem greatly to increase it. This phenomenon is very complex and it is also referred to by Maegraith (see p. 215 of this volume), so only a brief indication will be given here. In a typical case, a patient who has been repeatedly infected with *Plasmodium falciparum* takes a dose of quinine to treat a fresh infection; in a very short time there is acute haemolysis of many of his erythrocytes and he becomes dangerously ill from this and related causes. It is generally believed that the previous attacks of malarial infection have sensitized the person to antigens from the plasmodia and possibly from his own erythrocytes, and when more malaria parasites and erythrocytes are suddenly destroyed by the quinine, their disintegration products precipitate the acute haemolysis just described, apparently by some kind of allergic reaction.

CONCLUSION

We may summarize this survey by saying that the pathogenicity of a protozoal or other parasite depends in the first place on whether the parasite is able to establish itself in a host. Any resultant pathological effects are in essence only unfortunate accidents, most of which are due to imperfect adaptation of the parasite to the host. These accidents may arise in various ways—for example, mechanical obstruction or disturbance of the host's mechanisms by excessive numbers of parasites. But the most serious disturbances usually arise from the host's own immunological reactions. Either the host becomes allergic to products of the parasite, or its parasiticidal antibodies kill off many parasites at one time and thus liberate innumerable disintegration products which excite the usual reactions to foreign proteins and similar substances. A potential host with ambition to survive should learn how not to admit parasites and how, if they gain entry, to get rid of them without disturbance.

REFERENCES

ANFINSEN, C. G., GEIMAN, Q. M., MCKEE, R. W., ORMSBEE, R. A. & BALL, E. G. (1946). Studies on malarial parasites; factors affecting growth of *Plasmodia knowlesi in vitro. J. exp. Med.* **84**, 607.

BROWNING, C. H., ADAMSON, H. & KEPPIE, A. A. N. (1953). Acquired immunity to *Trypanosoma congolense*: further observations. *J. Path. Bact.* **65**, 137.

CLEVELAND, L. R. (1934). The wood-feeding roach *Cryptocercus*, its protozoa and the symbiosis between protozoa and roach. *Mem. Amer. Acad. Arts Sci.* **17**, 185.

DESOWITZ, R. S. & WATSON, H. J. C. (1951). Studies on *Trypanosoma vivax*. I. Susceptibility of white rats to infection. *Ann. trop. Med. Parasit.* **45**, 207.

DESOWITZ, R. S. & WATSON, H. J. C. (1952). Studies on *Trypanosoma vivax*. III. Observations on the maintenance of a strain in white rats. *Ann. trop. Med. Parasit.* **46**, 92.

DESOWITZ, R. S. & WATSON, H. J. C. (1953a). Studies on *Trypanosoma vivax*. VI. The occurrence of antibodies in the sera of infected sheep and white rats, and their influence on the course of infection in white rats. *Ann. trop. Med. Parasit.* **47**, 247.

DESOWITZ, R. S. & WATSON, H. J. C. (1953b). The maintenance of a strain of *Trypanosoma simiae* in rabbits; the effect of splenectomy on the course of infection. *Ann. trop. Med. Parasit.* **47**, 324.

GEIMAN, Q. M. & McKEE, R. W. (1948). Malarial parasites and their mode of life. *Sci. Mon. N.Y.* **67**, 217.

GOETSCH, W. (1946). Darmsymbionten als Eiweissquelle und als Vitaminspender. *Öst. zool. Z.* **1**, 58.

HAWKING, F. (1954). Milk, *p*-aminobenzoate and malaria of rats and monkeys. *Brit. med. J.* i, 425.

KEPPIE, A. A. N. (1953). Modified course of *T. congolense* infection in mice given diets of milk casein. *Brit. med. J.* **2**, 853.

LAMPE, P. H. J. (1950). Study on filariasis in Surinam. *Docum. neerl. indones. Morb. trop.* **2**, 193.

MAEGRAITH, B. G., DEEGAN, T. & JONES, E. S. (1952). Suppression of malaria (*P. berghei*) by milk. *Brit. med. J.* ii, 1382.

McKEE, R. W. (1951). *Biochemistry and Physiology of Protozoa*, edited by A. Lwoff, p. 251. New York.

MINNING, W. & McFADZEAN, J. A. (1955). In preparation for publication.

SATO, S. (1926). On the toxic action of sarcosporidiotoxin and its serological study. *Jap. med. World*, **6**, 62.

TEICHMANN, E. (1910). Ueber das Gift der Sarkosporidien. *Arch. Protistenk.* **20**, 97.

THE COMPARATIVE PATHOGENICITY OF PROTOZOA IN THEIR VERTEBRATE AND INVERTEBRATE HOSTS

P. C. C. GARNHAM

Department of Parasitology, London School of Hygiene and Tropical Medicine

Many groups of parasitic protozoa possess both an arthropod and a vertebrate host. The life cycles of these parasites have been extensively studied, and when the vertebrate has happened to be man or domestic animal, the pathogenic effect also has received considerable attention. In recent years research has been carried out on the disturbances of physiology brought about by some of these organisms in the vertebrate host, and the mechanism of pathogenesis was thus determined. These mechanisms will be described by other contributors to the Symposium, and will only be mentioned here when they have a direct bearing on the other side of the picture—pathogenicity in the invertebrate host. But here one meets an almost complete blank. What effect has the parasite on the arthropod? Practically nothing is known about this problem; it has been assumed in many instances that the protozoon causes little harm to the invertebrate, but without much factual basis. Still less is known about the exact cause of any ill effects produced by the parasite. The purpose of this paper is to speculate on the possible mechanisms of pathogenicity in the arthropod or the reasons for its absence; but first it will be necessary to consider very briefly the action of the same organisms on the vertebrate in order to see if a clue may exist there. Some protozoa are parasitic in invertebrates only, and in a few cases they are highly pathogenic. It is often possible in the latter cases to attribute the harmful effect to some definite mechanism. Although these one-host protozoa do not come exactly into the scope of this paper it will be useful to consider them briefly, because their action on the arthropod may throw light on the phenomenon in the group which lives in two hosts.

The subject will therefore be discussed under the following headings:

(1) Main features of pathogenic action of certain protozoa in vertebrates. This aspect is described in detail by other contributors to this Symposium.

(2) Pathogenic action of certain protozoa parasitic in invertebrates.

(3) Reaction of invertebrates to protozoa when part of the life cycle occurs also in a vertebrate host.

(4) Discussion: comparative pathogenicity of protozoa in the vertebrate and invertebrate host.

PATHOGENIC ACTION OF PROTOZOA IN VERTEBRATES

Parasitic protozoa affect vertebrates in many ways, some highly complicated, others relatively simple; the reaction of man to the malaria parasite provides a good example of the former. The parasite acts directly and indirectly as follows:

Direct action. (1) By the production of toxins. While the parasite grows, whether in a red blood cell or a liver cell, little or no toxin appears to be liberated; when the mature schizont ruptures, various toxic products are thrown into the blood stream. These include malaria pigment, residual body, and the remains of the host cell. The fever and rigours characteristic of a malaria paroxysm are probably caused by these substances, and according to Maegraith (1948), their presence is also responsible for venous constriction in certain organs which leads to a gradually worsening anoxaemia.

(2) By interference with the blood supply of organs. This may be started by peripheral vaso-constriction, but mechanical obstruction of capillaries is an important and constant feature of infections.

(3) By destroying the host cells—erythrocytes or liver parenchyma.

Indirect action. (4) Secondary changes in organs after the blood supply has been cut off.

(5) Reticulo-endothelial response—splenomegaly, etc.

(6) Sensitization and occurrence of blackwater fever.

The different species of a single genus may cause disease in entirely different ways and this is well illustrated by the trypanosomes. Some may kill by sheer weight of numbers, probably by absorbing all the available food supply or by gross interference with the vital processes; others, like *Trypanosoma cruzi*, develop in heart muscle and cause acute or chronic heart failure, while the trypanosomes responsible for sleeping sickness have an obscure action on the vessels of the brain which produces inflammatory and degenerative changes in the surrounding tissues, meninges, or brain itself.

Leishmania donovani prevents the normal development of granulocytes, an excessive leucopenia arises, and the patient dies of cancrum oris.

Entamoeba histolytica multiplies in a nidus in the sub-mucosa of the large bowel and so causes an abscess which breaks through the epithelium and leads to ulceration; at the same time blood vessels are eroded, giving rise to haemorrhage and to transport of the amoeba via the portal vein to distant parts of the body where metastatic abscesses arise.

Eimeria stiedae grows in the epithelium of the bile ducts in the liver of rabbits. Gross hypertrophy of this tissue ensues, leading eventually to tumour-like masses occupying practically the whole of the organ, and the animal dies of hepatic insufficiency; other species of *Eimeria* in birds and rabbits have an even simpler action, merely destroying the intestinal mucosa and causing a fatal form of dysentery.

Myxosporidia (and less often microsporidia) infections of fish may be severe, affecting the muscle and connective tissue of all parts of the body, especially the skin, gills and gall bladder. The process is largely one of infiltration, with little or no tissue reaction; finally, tumour-like masses form which interfere—largely mechanically—with the vital processes of the fish. Occasionally the eye is affected and the fish becomes blind; with others—e.g. Black Forest trout—the brain is attacked (by *Myxobolus neurobius*) and the fish dies. Fish are sometimes badly affected by myxosporidian cysts in the muscles, much in the same way that *Sarcocystis muris* harms mice.

These examples serve to illustrate some of the important ways in which protozoa affect vertebrates; the types of pathogenicity may now be compared with the lesions found in arthropods.

PATHOGENICITY OF PROTOZOA IN ARTHROPODS

Steinhaus (1949) devotes several chapters in his book on insect pathology to protozoal infections and shows that all classes of these organisms may be involved. It is hardly surprising that much less is known about this subject than the foregoing, and it is equally obvious that in this simpler form of animal life the pathological reactions will be less complex; in fact, in most of them, when pathogenicity exists at all, it corresponds to the simpler forms seen in vertebrates where the animal dies because of total loss of an organ. There is a major difference, however, in the way that vertebrates and invertebrates respond to an invader. At some time or other cellular reaction practically always occurs when a vertebrate is attacked by a protozoon, and this in itself is a major cause of disease; on the other hand, cellular reaction is hardly ever seen in arthropods, in which resistance is usually humoral in character and unaccompanied by any visible changes.

Steinhaus (1949) considers that protozoa, particularly microsporidia, are probably of great importance in the destruction of insects in nature.

It is interesting to observe how these parasites kill larval and adult stages. The infection usually spreads and is most severe when conditions in the external environment are adverse, e.g. *Simulium* larvae and pupae are frequently parasitized with *Thelohania* at the end of the dry weather. *Nosema* infection in bees and locusts is most prevalent at special seasons. *Thelohania* first invades the cells of the fat body; growth is so extensive that most of the body cavity becomes occupied by spores and sporonts, and the insects die, usually in the pupal stage, though parasitization may continue in the imago. *Nosema locustae* is a parasite of locusts, recently discovered by Canning (1953), which is capable of causing heavy mortality amongst these insects. Again the fat body is the site of invasion, and the locust dies, not from destruction of any organ, nor from pathological changes, but merely by sheer weight of numbers of the parasite. Recent work at Rothamsted (Bailey, 1954) has shown that pathogenicity of microsporidia in insects is not necessarily as simple as in the above examples. For example, the epithelial cells of the gut of bees normally contain granules of calcium phosphate, required for maintaining the pH of the intestinal contents at a sufficiently high level to allow the gut protease to act on the food. When the parasite *N. apis* invades these cells, the phosphate disappears, digestion is interfered with, and the bee becomes ill. Also, the protease itself is produced by the epithelium, and the partial destruction of these cells by the parasite results in a diminished supply of the enzyme. Beutler & Opfinger (1950) demonstrated that bees infected with *Nosema* had their life-span reduced by as much as 40 %.

Gregarines are often found in arthropods, and as a rule do little damage; they are large protozoa, however, and by their size alone (up to several millimetres) may incapacitate their hosts. An interesting histopathological change has been observed after the sporozoite of the gregarine has penetrated the host cell: the nucleus divides repeatedly and gross hypertrophy of the tissue cell takes place. Such changes have been seen also in haemosporidian infections of vertebrates (*Hepatocystis kochi* and *Leucocytozoon*), where the volume of the parasitized cell may be increased many thousand times. The stimulus to growth is thought to be due to some chemical substance secreted by the parasite, though there is no experimental verification of this assumption. Cuénot (1896) has shown that in gregarine infection of *Gryllus domesticus*, once the gametocyst stage is reached, the host begins to react by forming a mantle —two cells thick—of phagocytes around the cyst; these secrete a toxic substance which often leads to the death of the parasite. Cameron (1934) has also pointed out that these changes continue in concentric layers of leucocytes and lymphocytes around the parasite, leading finally to the production of a nodule. Gregarine infections in mosquitoes have been known for a long time. *Culex* and *Aedes* are attacked more often than *Anopheles*, and the infections are usually seen in wild adults. The parasite, *Lankesteria culicis*, produces enormous numbers of boat-shaped oocysts which fill the body cavity of the insect but do not apparently interfere seriously with its activity.

An important cause of insect mortality is amoebic disease—for example, bees become infected with *Walkampfia*, which grows inside the Malpighian tubes and finally destroys them entirely. The insect is then unable to excrete the toxic products of metabolism, and dies.

Coccidian infections of arthropods are interesting, because of the importance of this order in vertebrates. They affect primarily the intestine, but in many types pass through the gut wall and invade every part of the body. Schizogony and sporogony take place in these tissues, but give rise to little or no visible reaction on the part of the host. Nevertheless, when the infection is heavy, the functions of the insect are upset. Steinhaus (1949) states that larvae of the wood-eating roach, heavily infected with *Adelina*, are sluggish and slow to respond to stimuli, while the adults lose their reproductive capacity and a colony may die out.

This short survey suggests that the two principal features of ento-pathology are the following:

(1) The arthropod resists the protozoal invader by means of humoral immunity rather than by phagocytosis—thus true inflammatory changes are rare or absent.

(2) The protozoon produces its effect either by complete obliteration of an organ or by compression of most tissues in the body through sheer size or numbers of the parasite. In both cases, the mechanism of pathogenicity is usually easy to understand.

In very many instances, the parasite is completely harmless, and in one large category—the flagellates of termites—the parasites are symbionts essential to the life of the insect.

PATHOGENICITY IN ARTHROPODS OF PROTOZOA WHICH HAVE ALSO A VERTEBRATE HOST

Metalnikow & Chorine (1929) stated that organisms pathogenic to man are not necessarily pathogenic to insects, while saprophytes in man may be highly pathogenic to insects. This principle is chiefly applicable to bacteria, but the first part of it is true—both for man and other vertebrates—in the case of protozoa. In fact, it is difficult to detect even mild

13-2

pathogenicity in arthropods due to organisms which yet have had profound effects upon their vertebrate hosts.

In nearly all the examples which will be considered here, the protozoon
undergoes metacyclic change in the arthropod; often several tissues or
organs are invaded by the parasite, which is usually present in enormous
numbers. In *Babesia canis*, after partial development of the parasite in
the gut and body cavity of the adult tick, the motile sporokinete attacks
the ovary, and the final development takes place in the larva and nymph
of the next generation, where the salivary glands become filled with the
so-called sporozoites. Although host cells are destroyed or injured
during this process, no major damage is done, because the egg hatches
without difficulty, and the tick develops normally. The classical work of
Reichenow (1921) on *Karyolysus* shows how this haemogregarine likewise goes through part of its sporogonic cycle in the adult mite and part
in the immature stages of the next generation after invasion of the
ovaries by sporokinetes—all without apparent harm to the arthropod:
the egg may actually contain thousands of sporokinetes. I (Garnham,
1954) have been working recently with another haemo-gregarine which
develops in *Argas* ticks instead of mites; in the final infection, thousands
of large sporocysts collect not only in the interior of the gut, but throughout the haemocoelome, so that if a leg is pulled off the exuding fluid will
be found to contain numerous sporocysts. In spite of this heavy infection, the numphs continue to grow, moult and eventually reach maturity
with no apparent damage—heavily infected ticks move and behave just
like uninfected individuals from which they are indistinguishable.

These two examples—*Babesia* and *Karyolysus*—illustrate how even
congenital infection, involving most tissues of the embryo, fails to
harm the arthropod. Naturally, therefore, the less intimate association
of parasite and host occurring during mechanical transmission would
be expected to be found free from signs of pathogenicity. Houseflies and
cockroaches may ingest the cysts of *Entamoeba histolytica* and of other
intestinal protozoa; the cysts pass through the gut of the insects unchanged and are of course harmless, unlike another amoeba (*Walkampfia*)
which excystates, passes through the gut wall of the insect, and causes
extensive damage. The intestinal fluid of the fly is unable to dissolve the
cyst wall of *E. histolytica*, so the trophozoite never gets a chance to
invade; I think that no one has ever deliberately observed the effects
upon flies of ingestion of *trophozoites* of human intestinal protozoa—
possibly they will be found to have invasive properties.

Our study in the preceding section showed that protozoa affect
arthropods in two principal ways—by obliteration of organs and by

compression. In the present section, no obliteration of organs is known to occur; the effects are confined therefore to compression or inter-ference with vital functions by sheer numbers. The best example of the former is probably provided by the huge oocysts of the haemo-gregarine, *Hepatozoon*—e.g. the oocyst of *H. muris*, 0·25 mm. in size. Many hundreds may be present in the body cavity of the mite host. Miller (1908) noted that when the parasite was present in moderate numbers, it did not appear to be injurious to the mite; when present in great density, it killed it. Brumpt (1938) found that a haemogregarine of the tortoise was pathogenic to its tick host: infected ticks would not feed properly, and more than 50 % succumbed to the infection. But a remarkable feature about this genus of haemogregarines is that in spite of their size, not only are they usually harmless to the arthropod but they invade a wide range of hosts—mites, ticks, *Culex* mosquitoes, fleas, lice, sandflies and tsetse flies. This lack of host-specificity indicates an unusual degree of tolerance, and suggests that the pathogenicity of the parasite is extremely slight.

Flagellates are commonly found in insects, and usually form part of a cycle involving a vertebrate host. They are confined to the alimentary tract in which they may be present in enormous numbers. The effect of *Pasteurella pestis* in blocking the gut of fleas is well known, and causes a heavy mortality; obstruction by flagellates, although on as great a scale, is not known to have any effect. Shortt (1929) noted that a sandfly infected with *Leishmania donovani* first shows huge rosette agglomera-tions in the mid-gut, then a seething mass of motile forms is found anteriorly with the proventriculus entirely lined by sessile leptomonads many layers deep; later, forward migration of the infection causes dilation of the oesophagus and massive parasitic growth in the pharynx and buccal cavity. The alimentary tract thus becomes practically blocked by flagellates, and when the sandfly attempts to feed, a plug of parasites is expelled but little or no blood can be imbibed. Sandflies in this condition are alive and able to feed, and no particular mortality has been noted; nevertheless, it is difficult to believe that they would survive for long.

When flagellates develop in the posterior station, such intensity of infection does not occur, although organisms may be very numerous, as is the case with *Trypanosoma cruzi* in reduviid bugs. The life of these insects seems nevertheless to be totally unaffected by the infection. The parasite *T. lewisi* actually invades the epithelial cells of the stomach of the flea, and according to Wenyon (1926) the host cell is reduced to a mere membrane, enclosing the developing trypanosomes. No observations seem to have been made to see if damage to the stomach cells harms the flea. The following experiment was therefore carried out on *Xenopsylla cheopis* infected with *Trypanosoma lewisi*. In 1953, a strain of *T. lewisi* was isolated at Winches Farm Field Research Station (of the London School of Hygiene and Tropical Medicine) from a wild rat (*Rattus norvegicus*) and was subsequently maintained in white rats. *Xenopsylla cheopis* was kindly supplied by the Entomological Department of the London School of Hygiene and Tropical Medicine, and 200 adults which emerged from pupae within a few days of each other were used in the experiment. The fleas were divided into two groups (A and B) of 100 each, and were placed on two rats, one uninfected (A) and the other infected with *Trypanosoma lewisi* (B). The fleas were placed on the rats when the infected rat was on the ninth day of infection with the trypanosomes fully settled down. The fleas were kept on the rats for 2 days, and were then removed; sixty-two were recovered from rat A and sixty-two from rat B. They were then kept at 25° in 3 × 1 in. tubes at a humidity of 80 %, six in a tube, and daily deaths were recorded from each group (see Table 1).

Table 1. *Effect of* Trypanosoma lewisi *on* Xenopsylla cheopis: *first experiment*

	Group A (uninfected)	Group B (infected)
Original no. of fleas	100	100
No. collected after 2 days' feeding	62	62
Percentage deaths:* 1st day	5	32
2nd day	12	15
3rd day	4	15
4th day	...	...
5th day	45	54
6th day	33	28
7th day	38	50

* Deaths are expressed as percentages of those actually alive each day, because a few were lost accidentally and others were killed for examination.

One flea from the infected batch was dissected daily and flagellates in large numbers were found in the gut contents. Sections revealed the presence of leishmanial and other forms practically blocking the hind gut; numerous flagellates were also present in the rectum, and fewer in the mid gut.

The results of this experiment show clearly that there was a significantly higher mortality in the infected fleas during the first 3 days—twenty dying instead of three; in the following week death-rates in the uninfected and infected batches were approximately similar. It seems probable that the early deaths in the infected fleas were due to invasion of the gut cells by the trypanosomes, which is known to take place in this period. A second experiment (see Table 2) confirmed these observations; this time, fleas were left in contact with the rats for 24 instead of 48 hr. in order to define more precisely the date of the high mortality period, which is now seen to be during the day following infection, but only in newly emerged fleas. Under the marginal or unfavourable conditions surrounding the early adult life of an insect, these forms might be expected to be more susceptible to infections. Thus in both experiment I and II there is a heavy death rate among the infected as compared with

Table 2. *Effect of* Trypanosoma lewisi *on* Xenopsylla cheopis: *second experiment*

	Group A (uninfected)	Group B (infected)
No. of fleas collected after 1 day's feeding	186	288
Percentage deaths:* 1st day	9	19
2nd day	4	3
3rd day	2	7
4th day	13	12
No. of fleas collected after refeeding on 5th day	66	108
Percentage deaths:* 6th day	5	4
7th day	3	7
8th day	15	8
9th day	41	57
10th day	69	72

* The death rate is expressed as a percentage of those actually alive each day, because a few were lost in each batch and others were killed for dissection or sectioning.

the controls after the original feedings; in experiment II when the fleas, which are now older and presumably more stable, are re-fed, the infection has no apparent effect.

Polymorphic trypanosomes in *Glossina* were originally thought by Duke (1928) actually to have a beneficial action on the fly; he was unable to confirm this by experiment though he showed at least that the organism was not injurious to the insect in that its life was not shortened.

Probably the parasite most studied in its insect host is *Plasmodium*, and yet observations on the effect of the organism on the mosquito are remarkably scanty and the few records that exist are conflicting. Buxton

200 P. C. C. GARNHAM

(1935) analysed statistically the effect of *Proteosoma praecox* (= *Plasmodium relictum*) on the survival of *Culex fatigans* kept at constant temperatures (23° or 30°) and humidity. At the higher temperature, an infected batch of mosquitoes showed a higher death-rate on the first day than the uninfected controls; at the lower temperature the same difference was apparent on the second day. Mortality rates were approximately the same for the subsequent few days, but showed a sharp rise, in the infected group, on the seventh day. Buxton stated that the early deaths were doubtless due to invasion of the wall of the midgut by ookinetes, and the later deaths probably due to the growth of the oocyst, but he made no suggestion why these changes should kill the insect. It may be noted here that though the rate of infection in some of the above experiments was as high as 80 %, only one infective feed was given, and the number of oocysts was not particularly high. In the *Annual Report of the Rockefeller Foundation* (1950), an experiment is briefly described which showed that specially high oocyst infection (amounting to 'many thousands of oocysts') in *Anopheles* was associated with a high death-rate within a few days of the infecting blood meal (*Plasmodium gallinaceum*). In contrast to these observations, other workers have failed to note any pathogenicity of the parasite for the mosquito: Sergent (1919) kept under similar conditions three groups of *Culex*, one group with 100 or more oocysts per gut, one with few oocysts, and one with none, and all showed the same mortality rates. Sinton & Shute (1938) from their own records on *Anopheles maculipennis* and *Plasmodium vivax*, and from an analysis of earlier work, concluded that malaria did not affect the longevity of mosquitoes, except perhaps when they were in a debilitated condition, as when they had been kept on an inadequate diet. My own work in recent years involving transmission of monkey malaria by *Anopheles maculipennis* has never suggested that there was any undue mortality in the infected mosquitoes, which often survived for two months or longer.

None of the above experiments was designed to test the effect of a constantly maintained stream of ookinetes, oocysts, and sporozoites in the insects. A single sporogonic cycle in the mosquito is transitory, and would hardly be expected to have a profound effect; if, however, continuous invasion of the gut wall could be effected by repeated infective feeds, the pathogenic action of the parasite—if such exists—should become more apparent. It is known (Sergent & Sergent, 1906) that no immunity to repeated infection with malaria occurs in mosquitoes, and an experiment on these lines was therefore devised with *Plasmodium gallinaceum* (long maintained in this country by irregular blood and mosquito passages) and *Aedes aegypti* var. *queenslandensis* (from a newly established colony bred from eggs sent by Dr D. J. Lewis and originally derived from Jeddah on the Red Sea). A subsidiary purpose of the experiment was to determine how *Plasmodium gallinaceum* developed in this variety of *Aedes aegypti*. Details of the work are given below.

Several bowls of larvae were used in order that 600–700 pupae could be collected within a few days of each other. Male and female adults were allowed to emerge into a cube foot cage, and when sufficient were present, about 200 females were separated into two new cages in equal quantities. The mosquitoes in one cage were offered daily (except on Sundays) a feed on an uninfected chick, in the other on an infected chick. The chick had been infected some days previously either by sporozoites or by blood with *Plasmodium gallinaceum* and always showed numerous male and female gametocytes. A constant supply of infected chicks had to be kept available, for a single bird was suitable for feeding mosquitoes for only 2 or 3 days. The cages were kept at 28° and at a humidity of 70 %, and dead mosquitoes were counted daily. The death-rate was high in both cages, and after 10 days the survivors were transferred to Lumsden's tubes and were fed individually. In the later experiments they were kept in these tubes from the start.

The results may be discussed under three headings, infection in the mosquito, effect on longevity, and pathological changes.

Infection in the mosquito. Relatively few mosquitoes were dissected in each batch, but not a single one was found uninfected, and the oocyst rate was always very high. As the days progressed, the midgut showed an increasing number of oocysts of all sizes from tiny to mature, and sometimes at least 1000 must have been present almost completely covering the major portion of the midgut. The salivary glands became invaded by sporozoites on the eighth day, and remained heavily infected. Fourteen dissections were done in the first experiment, six in the second and five in the third. These results indicate that *Aedes aegypti* var. *queenslandensis* is at least as good a vector of the parasite as the type species. They also showed that the infected series were in a highly parasitized condition throughout the experiment.

Effect on longevity. Tables 3–5 give the death-rates in infected and uninfected mosquitoes respectively. There is little difference in the two groups; the absence of a feed on Sundays caused many deaths in the younger insects—as is shown by the high figures on 28 June (days 4 and 5 of Table 3) and 12 July (days 3 and 4 of Table 4). Otherwise the numbers of survivors declined steadily in the infected and uninfected batches. There was certainly nothing suggestive of a mortality due to 'ookinete penetration' or 'oocyst rupture' on the second and eighth days respectively. A small minority of both groups of mosquitoes lived for a month or longer.

There is nearly always a high and erratic mortality in newly emerged mosquitoes, and this may make it difficult to interpret mortality rates

Table 3. *Longevity of infected and uninfected mosquitoes.* * Exp.* 1.
Mosquitoes kept in cages for 10 *days, then in tubes*

	No. of deaths of	
Day	Infected mosquitoes (105)	Uninfected mosquitoes (105)
1	2	5
2	8	4
3	5	6
4 and 5	33	43
6	1	3
7	5	1
8	11	10
9	1	0
10–16	0	3
17	0	1
18	1	2
19	0	1
20–23	2	1
24	4	0
25	5	4
26	0	0
27	0	1
Total deaths	78	85

* Mosquito: *Aedes aegypti* var. *queenslandensis*; infection: *Plasmodium gallinaceum*.

Table 4. *Longevity of infected and uninfected mosquitoes.* *
Exp. 2. *Mosquitoes kept in tubes*

	No. of deaths of	
Day	Infected mosquitoes (45)	Uninfected mosquitoes (46)
1	0	4
2	3	1
3 and 4	25	14
5	4	6
6–8	0	2
9	0	1
10	1	2
11	0	2
12	2	0
13	1	1
14	0	1
15	3	1
16	1	0
Total deaths	40	35

* Mosquito: *Aedes aegypti* var. *queenslandensis*; infection: *Plasmodium gallinaceum*.

Table 5. *Longevity of infected and uninfected mosquitoes.* * *Exp.* 3. *Mosquitoes kept in tubes and fed on raisins for* 1 *week before experiment began*

No. of deaths of

Day	Infected mosquitoes (90)	Uninfected mosquitoes (90)
1	0	0
2	2	1
3	0	1
4	0	0
5	2	5
6 and 7	5	4
8	9	5
9	11	6
10	1	3
11	2	1
12	0	0
Total deaths	32	26

* Mosquito: *Aedes aegypti* var. *queenslandensis*; infection: *Plasmodium gallinaceum*.

if young insects are used; in the third experiment, therefore, the mosquitoes were kept in tubes for a week before starting the observations. During this time they were fed on raisins. The results are shown in Table 5. Few mosquitoes of either group died during the first week but in the first 3 days of the second week twenty-five infected mosquitoes died, in contrast to fifteen uninfected; this was the time when the first oocysts rupture, and possibly the higher mortality in the infected group was due to this occurrence, but the number of survivors at the end of a fortnight was scarcely different in the two groups—sixty-four in the uninfected and fifty-eight in the infected.

Pathological changes. No attempt was made in these experiments to look for any histological changes in the midgut or salivary glands attributable to the parasite, but in the past many sections of such infected organs have been examined without finding the slightest evidence of any reactions on the part of the host. It has been frequently noticed, however, that heavily infected salivary glands appear to the naked eye swollen and opaque compared with uninfected ones. Histological examination of such glands reveals the presence of large numbers of sporozoites both inside the cells and in the ducts, but there is no infiltration with adventitious cells and the nuclei and cytoplasm of the secretory cells appear normal. In the present series of experiments, marked pathological effects were observed in the midguts of practically all mosquitoes infected for 11 days or more—namely, the presence of Ross's black spores. These bodies can be regarded as the result of interaction between host and degenerating parasite, because they are nearly always associated with the presence of abnormal oocysts—that is, oocysts with vacuolation, or the contents shrunk away from the cyst wall. It is usually stated (e.g. Vargas, 1949) that the brownish black 'spores' are chitinized sporozoites derived from the tracheae of the midgut, but the evidence for such an origin is slender. Sections of an infected gut were examined in order to see if cellular reaction was present around the Ross's black spores—such as occurs, for instance, around gregarine cysts (see above)—but the sections showed no changes in adjacent tissue of the midgut. All stages in the formation of 'spores' could be traced from small yellowish brown rings to fully formed dark brown banana-shaped 'spores'. The smaller structures were seen to lie quite clearly *inside* the cyst, which had an apparently undamaged wall; it seems therefore that the change arises from within the cyst and does not originate from the tracheae. It is doubtful also if the structures originate from sporozoites; it is much more likely that they are degenerating partitions or septum walls of the immature oocysts. Histochemical tests failed to demonstrate chitin in the 'spores'.

Theoretically, it is difficult to see why passage of the ookinete between the cells of the midgut should be accompanied by pathogenicity—there is certainly no visible reaction in the beautiful sections prepared by Shute (1951); if any pathological change is to be expected, it is much more likely to develop when the mature oocysts rupture through the musculo-elastic membrane which covers the midgut. But no signs of damage are ever apparent, nor is there any evidence that toxins are liberated at this time. It might be thought also that the growth of innumerable oocysts would deprive the mosquito of essential nutriment, and thus shorten its life, but the results of the experiments described here show that this does not happen.

Finally, the recent work of Weathersbee (1952) illustrates how utterly harmless the malaria parasite must be to the mosquito: blood containing gametocytes was inoculated into the haemocoelome, zygotes formed, and oocysts grew to maturity in practically every part of the body of the mosquito, which suffered no ill-effects—a remarkable example of adaptability on the part of both host and parasite.

DISCUSSION

The mechanisms of pathogenicity of protozoa in vertebrates are principally two: (i) direct destruction of tissue, and (ii) secondary effects following the production of toxins. In arthropods only the first mechanism appears to operate, and even so is rarely seen in infections involving both hosts. On the few occasions when the organism is pathogenic in both hosts, the mechanism does not appear to be in any way related; there is no production of a toxin with a similar action on each host. Instead the parasite injures where it happens to be situated; *Hepatozoon* damages the liver of the vertebrate but harms the arthropod by general compression of the organs, *Trypanosoma lewisi* may kill the white rat by sheer intensity of infection, but injures the flea by interfering with its digestive processes.

Criteria for the determination of pathogenicity of protozoa in arthropods are naturally less fine than those used in vertebrates, and it is usually possible to assess effects only by seeing if there is an increased mortality; the mechanism causing this is some gross change produced by the parasite, leading to compression, blockage, or total replacement of tissue.

The reaction in the two types of host is different not only because the invertebrate possesses different defences, but more fundamentally because of the greater degree of tolerance shown by the original (i.e. phylogenetically older) host. Protozoa can be exceedingly virulent in the arthropod, when this is the sole host. A principle of parasitology is that the longer a parasite has lived in its host, the more adapted it becomes. Now it is thought that most protozoa which to-day live in two hosts originally were parasites of the invertebrate alone, and that the cycle in the vertebrate is a fairly recent development. It follows then that the arthropod being the older host will react less; in fact the protozoon will be a commensal in this host, and a true parasite only in the vertebrate. When the parasite has persisted in the vertebrate for a long time, it may lose most of its pathogenicity for this host also, and become commensal, as we see to-day in countless examples in the animal kingdom.

It would be undesirable to push this phylogenetic argument too far in the absence of real evidence, but it provides a reason for the variable pathogenicity of protozoa in arthropods and vertebrates. Apart from this it appears that the parasite produces toxins and tissue response only in the vertebrate; it is capable of destroying tissue or blocking vital passages in both hosts, but such overgrowth is less liable to occur in the older, invertebrate host, where tolerance has already been achieved.

Grateful acknowledgements are made for technical assistance from Mr W. Cooper and Mr R. R. Killick in the longevity experiments described in this paper.

REFERENCES

Annual Report of the Rockefeller Foundation, International Health Division, 1950, p. 30.

BAILEY, L. (1954). *Nosema* infections of the honey-bee. Unpublished thesis for the Ph.D. degree of the University of London.

BEUTLER, R. & OPFINGER, E. (1950). Pollenernährung und Nosemabefall der Honigbiene (*Apis mellifica*). *Z. vergl. Physiol.* **32**, 383–421.

BRUMPT, E. (1938). Formes évolutives d'*Haemogregarina mauritanica* chez la tique *Hyaloma syriacum*. *Ann. Parasit.* **16**, 350–61.

BUXTON, P. A. (1935). Effect of *Proteosoma* upon the survival of *Culex*. *Parasitology*, **27**, 547–50.

CAMERON, G. R. (1934). Inflammation in the caterpillars of *Lepidoptera*. *J. Path. Bact.* **38**, 441–66.

CANNING, E. U. (1953). A new microsporidian, *Nosema locustae* n.sp., from the fat body of the African migratory locust, *Locusta migratoria migratorioides* R. & F. *Parasitology*, **43**, 287–90.

CUÉNOT, L. (1896). Etudes physiologiques sur les orthoptères. *Arch. Biol.*, *Paris*, **14**, 293–341.

DUKE, H. L. (1928). On the effect on the longevity of *G. palpalis* of trypanosome infections. *Ann. trop. Med. Parasit.* **32**, 25–32.

GARNHAM, P. C. C. (1954). A haemogregarine in *Argas brumpti*. *Riv. Parassit.* (in the Press).

MAEGRAITH, B. G. (1948). *Pathological Processes in Malaria and Blackwater Fever.* Oxford: Basil Blackwell.

METALNIKOW, S. & CHORINE, V. (1929). Maladies microbiennes chez les chenilles de *Pyrausta nubilalis*. *Ann. Inst. Pasteur*, **43**, 136–51.

MILLER, W. W. (1908). *Hepatozoon perniciosum* (n.g., n.sp.). A haemogregarine pathogenic for white rats; with a description of the sexual cycle in the intermediate host, a mite (*Lelaps echininus*). *Bull. U.S. hyg. Lab.* no. 46.

REICHENOW, E. (1921). Die Hämococcidien der Eidechsen. *Arch. Protistenk.* **42**, 226.

SERGENT, ED. & SERGENT, ET. (1906). *Arch. Inst. Pasteur*, **21**, 251–80.

SERGENT, ET. (1919). Le *Plasmodium relictum*, agent pathogène du paludisme des oiseaux, ne donne pas une maladie mortelle au moustique transmetteur. *Bull. Soc. Path. exot.* **12**, 601–3.

SHORTT, H. E. (1929). The life-history of *Leishmania donovani* in its insect and mammalian hosts. *Trans. F.E.A.T.M. Seventh congr.*, **3**, 12–18.

SHUTE, P. G. (1951). Specimens demonstrating the passage of *Plasmodium vivax* ookinetes through the stomach wall of *Anopheles*. *Trans. R. Soc. trop. Med. Hyg.* **44**, 367–8.

SINTON, J. A. & SHUTE, P. G. (1938). A report on the longevity of mosquitoes in relation to the transmission of malaria in nature. *Rep. Publ. Hlth med. Subj.*, *Lond.*, no. 85.

STEINHAUS, E. A. (1949). *Principles of Insect Pathology.* New York: McGraw-Hill Book Co.

VARGAS, L. (1949). Culicine and Aedine mosquitoes and the malaria infections of lower animals. In *Malariology*, ed. Boyd, M. F., vol. 1. Philadelphia. W. B. Saunders Co.

WEATHERSBEE, A. B. (1952). The role of the stomach wall in the exogenous development of *Plasmodium gallinaceum* as studied by means of haemocoel injections of susceptible and refractory mosquitoes. *J. infect. Dis.* **91**, 198–205.

WENYON, C. M. (1926). *Protozoology.* London: Baillière, Tindall and Cox.

THE PATHOGENICITY OF PLASMODIA AND ENTAMOEBAE

B. G. MAEGRAITH

Department of Tropical Medicine, Liverpool School of Tropical Medicine

Pathogenicity is a difficult term to define. It is used in this text to refer to the potential possessed by the parasite of causing changes, physiological and pathological, in the host, directly or indirectly, as the result of invasion.

The potential for pathogenicity is presumed to be ultimately inherent in the parasite. Nevertheless, in a large measure the pathological consequences of invasion appear to depend on local and general factors which determine the circumstances under which the parasite and host interact. To this extent the host plays a significant part in the fulfilment or otherwise of the pathogenic potentialities of the parasite. Pathological changes in the host follow the successful invasion of the host by the parasite, but they represent also the failure of perfect parasite-host adaptation which would be the successful survival and existence of both in the same circumstances.

The study of pathogenicity thus includes the direct reactions of host at the site of invasion and at points of contact between parasite and host in the host tissues and the general reactions of the host which arise without apparent direct intervention of the parasite. These points are considered below in regard to *Plasmodia* and *Entamoebae*. In considering the pathogenicity of plasmodia, the complicating and vital factors introduced by vector transmission are not discussed.

Analysis of the information available regarding the pathogenicity of protozoa brings to light certain general principles (Maegraith, 1954*a*). Although parasites obtain the energy for growth and development from the host, the anticipated competition between parasite and host for nutrients and basic requirements such as oxygen is not evident in any protozoan condition so far studied. It is presumed, however, that the metabolic and environmental demands of a given parasite determine the ultimate sites of successful distribution and development in the host, or, as with the entamoebae, the site (in this case the lumen of the large gut) in which infection can be maintained before invasion. This is equally true whether the parasite is vector-transmitted or not. Moreover, in some instances a particular phase of parasitic development may be required to invade a given environment. For example, in mammalian plasmodial diseases, sporozoites inoculated by the vector develop not in the tissues or blood into which they are injected, but in remote tissue cells from which new parasite forms eventually emerge to invade the erythrocytes. In this case, the highly selective invasion of tissue is specific to the particular phase of the parasite. It can be concluded that the local biochemical and nutrient environment required by the parasite in a particular stage of its development must be of fundamental import-ance in determining the invasion of the host tissue. There is little doubt, however, that successful invasion also depends to some extent on the host and the conditions obtaining in the host tissues at the time of contact with the parasite. It thus becomes clear that the success or otherwise of an invasion may be largely fortuitous, even though the pathogenic potentiality exists in the parasite concerned and the host is suitable. An example of this, as we shall see, is the common failure and occasional success of invasion by metastatic amoebae in the liver tissue.

Other host factors may influence parasitic development in the host and thus the effective pathogenicity of the particular parasite con-cerned. One of the most important of these, as is clearly demonstrable in mammalian plasmodial diseases, is the nutritional status of the host. Another is the development of acquired immunity or tissue sensitivity, illustrated respectively by the specific phagocytosis acquired in malaria and by the development of amoebic hepatic lesions in amoebiasis.

The growth and development of a parasite in a host usually leads to some metabolic disturbances in the host, arising either from direct in-vasion by the parasite—for example, the cellular reactions initiated by *Leishmania*—or from the general physiological effect of local changes, not necessarily directly attributable to the presence of the parasites, in active organs such as the liver or adrenals. It is important to realize that the clinical picture in some cases may thus be dominated by func-tional and morbid changes such as fever, medical shock, or hepatic and renal dysfunction, which have arisen indirectly and not directly from the invasion. On the other hand, some of these changes may depend essentially on inherent characteristics of the invading organism. Thus, although changes in carbohydrate metabolism in malaria probably arise from general effects initiated in some way by the plasmodia and involving the liver, adrenals and other organs, those in certain forms of trypano-somiasis appear to run parallel to the presence or otherwise of heavy-metal catalysts in the invading trypanosome.

The results of invasion of the host by the parasite—that is, the pathogenic effects of the invasion—are clearly conditioned both by the parasite and the host. The invasion, once established, can lead to local effects on the invaded tissues and remote effects on the host tissue as a whole. What initiates and maintains these processes is at present unknown. No extract or metabolic product of any protozoa have so far been identified capable of reproducing the physiological and pathological effects of invasion. Certain effects are probably specific to the invading parasite, but it appears that the more striking non-specific general effects, such as fever, shock and renal failure, are in fact common not only to many protozoan diseases but also to other pathological conditions. It can be reasonably assumed that many of these effects arise from similar physiological origins in the conditions in which they appear. Some of them—for example, fever—may well derive, as in certain bacterial conditions, from the activity of physiologically active non-specific soluble substances, search for which has not yet been made in protozoan conditions.

No attempt is made to do more than cover a few of the points discussed above. It is hoped, however, that the information and arguments presented will be of interest and will stimulate controversy and—who knows?—lead to research in a field hardly yet explored.

THE PATHOGENICITY OF PLASMODIA

The pathological effects of plasmodial invasion and the clinical responses of the host are complex and protean, and may be clearly defined or intricately mixed in the same individual host. In the evolution of an attack of *falciparum* malaria, for instance, functional and structural changes in the tissues may lead to a bewildering range of clinical signs and symptoms, involving the circulation, the central nervous system, or organs such as the kidneys, the liver and the adrenals.

The pathogenic effects of plasmodia are taken here to include the whole range of such functional and pathological changes induced in the host, and the basic pathogenic processes that determine them, whether these originate directly or indirectly from the invasion of the erythrocytes.

Consideration of the pathogenicity of plasmodia thus covers the study of significant host-parasite relationships arising directly from the invasion of the erythrocyte, of general host responses which arise remotely as a result of the invasion but are not directly dependent on it, and of the factors which initiate and maintain the complicated processes which determine the clinical and pathological responses of the host. These problems have been discussed in detail elsewhere (Maegraith, 1948). In the space available here only representative features are considered.

Some parasite-host relationships
(a) Invasion of the erythrocyte

It is generally agreed that the tissue forms of the parasite have no great direct pathogenic effect, other than local, on the tissues of the host. The evidence indicates that the blood phase (E forms) is the essential pathogenic form of the parasite. The absence of any direct evidence of activity originating in the extra-erythrocytic parasitic forms, does not, however, exclude the possibility that these forms may have some indirect influence on the pathogenicity of the E forms or on the bodily responses; to this extent, experimental work based solely on artificial blood infections may need to be accepted with some caution.

It might be argued that the original acceptance of the parasite by the tissue cells (and vice versa) and its development therein constitutes the earliest indication of parasitic pathogenicity. Broadly speaking, however, it is legitimate to consider that the pathogenic activity of plasmodia begins with the invasion of the erythrocytes and the initiation of the asexual cycle therein.

The successful invasion of the erythrocyte presumably depends on the existence within it of a suitable environment. Thus, the chemical make-up of the erythrocyte may represent an inherent factor of considerable importance in determining the 'take' or otherwise of the infection. It is interesting, for instance, to note that plasmodia in general survive and multiply in erythrocytes which possess a high K/Na ratio, whereas other erythrocyte-living parasites—for example, *Babesia canis*—infect cells with a low K/Na ratio. There are no doubt many other factors of a similar nature, particularly the availability of nutrients and essential substances to the parasite within the cell which has been invaded. Some of these substances are held within the cell, others can be supplied from without—for example, from the plasma. How far this nutritive environment is essential to the parasite and important in its acceptance of the red cell as a host is difficult to say.

The interpretation of the results of *in vitro* studies of the nutrient and metabolic requirements of the parasite is limited by the present technical impossibility of differentiating between the activity of the parasite and its host cell. Nevertheless, some useful information has been obtained and the plasmodium has been found on the whole to behave in the same way as the host, possessing similar enzymes and using the same metabolic pathways. It is surprising that an intracellular specialized parasite should be so relatively independent of the host in regard to its metabolic requirements and yet so similar in these respects to its environment. It might be expected, indeed, that there might be some direct competition between parasite and host for nutrient substances (enzymes, oxygen and so forth, and that this competition might constitute an important pathogenic factor. There is, however, no indication that this is so (Lwoff, 1951).

There is abundant evidence to show that the nutritional status of the host is important to the invading parasite. For instance, *in vivo* experiments with mammalian malaria, in which animals have been starved either during a malaria infection or at the time of infection, have indicated that so long as starvation is continued growth and multiplication of the parasites is retarded. Restoration of an adequate diet, or the addition of methionine or *p*-aminobenzoic acid, reverses the effect. The relation between the deficient host and the parasite so far as methionine and *p*-aminobenzoic acid are concerned is indicated by the fact that this reversal can occur at a time when the concentration of these substances in the free state in the plasma is higher than normal (Lwoff, 1951).

The recent demonstration that a milk diet produces a suppressive effect on mammalian parasite growth and multiplication is a further illustration of the importance of the nutritional state of the host in regard to the parasite (Maegraith, Deegan & Jones, 1952). The effect of the milk diet is immediate and striking in *Plasmodium berghei* and *P. knowlesi* infections, both of which are very sensitive to sulphonamides. It is evident but less pronounced in *P. vivax* infection in man. The incomplete reversal of milk suppression by the addition of *p*-aminobenzoic acid (Hawking, 1954), however, suggests that some more complex process is involved than mere withdrawal of this amino-acid. Some reversal follows the addition of methionine and certain other substances to the host diet.

As already explained, the measurement of oxygen requirements of the parasite is technically difficult because of the development of the parasite in the specialized environment of the erythrocyte, which may not itself be metabolically inert, and the metabolism of which may or may not itself be influenced by the presence of the parasite (Jones, Maegraith & Gibson, 1953).

Nevertheless, with all the imperfections of present techniques allowed for, the evidence indicates that the demands of the parasite on the oxygen contained in the oxyhaemoglobin within the erythrocyte and that dissolved in the plasma are inconsiderable in relation to the requirements of the host.

(b) Changes in the host

Although there is no evidence of direct biochemical competition between the parasite and host the profound physiological changes induced in the host by the parasite may in themselves ultimately affect both the parasite and the cell containing it. It would appear therefore that in discussion of the pathological effects, of plasmodia on the host, consideration should be given to the possible reaction of such changes on the parasite itself. Unfortunately, the conception of the changing parasite in a changing environment is one to which our existing techniques cannot adequately contribute. At this stage we must largely confine ourselves to the examination of the mechanisms involved in the production of some of the more obvious changes in the host. Details of the physiological and pathological results of parasitic infection have been considered in detail elsewhere. Here we can deal with only a few which indicate certain features of a remarkably complex process.

Blood pigments. The parasite maturing in the erythrocytes uses haemoglobin as a metabolite. Successful invasion of the cell must therefore presuppose the acceptability of the contained haemoglobin for the particular parasite concerned. This may be as important to successful invasion as, for instance, the prevailing ionic balance between potassium and sodium already mentioned.

The total haematin of the infected cell remains unchanged during invasion, although the content of haemoglobin itself falls as the pigment is split by the metabolizing parasite and the haematin-containing malarial pigment (haemozoin) is formed. Early erythrocytic stages of plasmodia and parasites in tissue cells or tissue culture do not produce pigment. Some disappearance of haemoglobin from the infected erythrocyte can, however, be detected even in the early stages of the E cycle. Pigment formation as such thus appears to be a late event in the asexual development of the parasite and may be concerned with keeping the excess haematin, which would otherwise be toxic to host and parasite alike, out of solution. The mechanism of the production of haemozoin is not understood. Most authors have concluded that haemozoin is haematin split from the haemoglobin, probably by enzymes themselves synthesized by the growing parasite. Recent work, however, indicates that the pigment is not haematin itself but haematin combined firmly with some heavier nitrogenous molecule (Deegan, 1955).

The fate of haemozoin on release into the plasma at the rupture of the schizont is not fully known. Much of it is taken up by phagocytes in which it remains for long periods. Since haemozoin contains haematin in some form, in a heavy infection it may represent a considerable fraction of the total body iron. It is important, therefore, to discover something of the availability of the iron locked up in the pigment. Surprisingly little interest has been taken in this problem. Rigdon (1945) has suggested on histological evidence that haemozoin in birds might be slowly changed to haemosiderin so that the iron eventually became available for haemoglobin regeneration, but no attempt seems to have been made until recently to measure the effect of haemozoin production on the host iron reserves. Recently, however, in our laboratories it has been shown that in mammalian malaria iron is in fact removed from the circulation during the formation and deposition of malarial pigment, and that this iron is not readily or immediately available for the resynthesis of haemoglobin. It is apparent, therefore, that in animals in which the iron stores are depleted, the access of malaria may have a serious effect on the haemoglobin content of the blood. In the long run, in several infections in which haemolysis is continuous, this loss of available iron might indeed become an important pathogenic factor.

Haemozoin appears to be the only inert haematin-containing pigment formed in the invaded cell during parasitic growth. There is no evidence of methaemoglobin production. The unconverted haemoglobin in the cell is apparently unchanged so far as its respiratory functions are concerned, oxygen association and dissociation remaining normal within the limits of changes occurring in the plasma.

The haemoglobin of the uninvaded erythrocytes also remains unchanged. Its respiratory functions as measured *in vitro* are normal so long as the plasma environment is kept within physiological limits. It appears therefore that the oxygen-carrying capacity of the blood in malaria, other things being equal, is, as in normal blood, a function of the total haemoglobin content.

Oxygen dissociation curves calculated by the Haldane method on malarial infected blood may show a false shift to the right due to absorption of some of the oxygen during the time necessary for equilibration. Determination made with the Roughton-Scholander syringe technique indicates, however, that in *P. berghei* infections in rats and *P. knowlesi* infections in monkeys the curves are normal. Jones & McGregor (1954) recently observed a slight shift to the right in *P. falciparum* infections in children in the Gambia associated with small deviation in the pH of the plasma. Considerable shift to the right, probably arising from changes in the plasma, has also been reported in dissociation curves for duck blood in *P. gallinaceum* infection (Rostorfer & Rigdon, 1946).

The haemoglobin liberated into the plasma during haemolysis

apparently remains unchanged in animals other than primates, in which part of it is converted by some unknown process into haematin-albumin (Fairley, 1939). It is not known how the transfer of the haematin from globin to albumin takes place in primates, but it is generally agreed that free haematin does not appear in the plasma. This is important in view of the toxic action of haematin on both parasite and host. Haemoglobin which reaches the plasma is removed rapidly. A small fraction may pass the glomeruli and, if the threshold is exceeded, appear in the urine. Most of the remainder is apparently broken down and the iron is either stored in tissue and phagocytic cells in the easily available form of haemosiderin, or used immediately for re-synthesis of haemoglobin. The fate of the iron contained in the heavy molecule of haematin-albumin has not yet been determined, but it is presumed that this molecule is eventually disintegrated and the iron made available.

The indications are therefore that the removal of iron from the circulation in malaria largely depends on the formation of haemozoin, and that this is likely to be important to the economy of the host only when the initial iron reserves are low, although it may possibly become significant in very heavy infections.

Haemolysis. In addition to the erythrocytes destroyed as a direct result of maturation of parasites within them, uninfected erythrocytes are also lost from the circulation in malaria. This loss can be attributed to the processes of intravascular haemolysis and specific phagocytosis.

So far no explanation of the haemolysis has been entirely satisfying. There is evidence that both the erythrocyte and its environment may be concerned, but the mechanisms involved are obscure.

Very little is known about the properties of the surface of either the infected or the uninfected erythrocytes in malaria. There appears to be no significant change in the fragility of erythrocytes in saline. Foy & Kondi (1943) have reported increased fragility to lysolecithin in black-water fever, but there is no comparable finding in malaria. Overman (1951) has recently measured the ionic exchange of unparasitized erythrocytes and found that sodium moves into the cell and potassium moves out.

There is very little evidence of changes of erythrocyte shape or volume in malaria. Reports on measurements of mean cellular volume vary. Some workers have reported no change in blackwater fever or long-standing malaria, others have found it increased. Spherocytosis has been described by Foy & Kondi (1943). It has not been reported in *P. vivax* malaria, although it has been found that the density of infected cells enables their easy separation from uninfected erythrocytes by centrifugation. The same thing is true in *P. berghei* malaria. If clearly demonstrated, spherocytosis would be of some significance, because such a change in volume and diameter-thickness ratio is commonly a prelude to lysis. Separation of cells and plasma followed by their re-combination is said to give rise to spherocytosis and thus be favourable to lysis. Vint (1941), has suggested that this may occur in the spleen in malaria, but this view depends on the acceptance of a type of splenic circulation which is still in doubt.

Laser (1946) demonstrated the presence of a lytic substance, which he believes to be an unsaturated monocarboxylic fatty acid, in normal human serum and found the same substance in greater quantity in infected monkey erythrocytes. This substance lyses normal erythrocytes, the effect being accelerated by haematin. Laser suggests that this fatty acid accumulates in the parasitized cell and may be the cause of its rupture at sporulation.

Various suggestions have been made regarding possible haemolytic mechanisms involving the environment of the erythrocytes. There is little evidence that the physico-chemical environment of the erythrocytes is sufficiently altered in malaria to cause haemolysis. Recorded changes in plasma pH, for instance, have been relatively insignificant or of late occurrence. Ponder (1948) has suggested that lysis may result from changes in plasma content of cholesterol, protein and possibly lecithin. Normal animal tissues have been shown to possess lytic properties under certain conditions which are inhibited by normal plasma; the lytic effect may be enhanced by extracts of haemolysed cells. It has been suggested that lysis in malaria may result from inhibition of the factors which themselves normally inhibit these tissue lytic effects. Ponder has suggested that the tissue lytic agent responsible may be lysolecithin.

Gear (1946) has suggested that the haemolysis may be the outcome of antigen-antibody reactions. It is possible that the parasitic invasion may make the erythrocyte auto-antigenic, so giving rise to auto-anti-bodies which precipitate lysis in the presence of red cells and complement. The experiments of Foy & Kondi on the fate of transfused cells in blackwater fever and in normal circulations could be explained on this basis. The presence of antibodies of several kinds, including agglutinins, complement-deviating bodies and opsonins, and also the change in globulin pattern all give support to the general idea that some antibody-antigen reaction may be involved. Haemozoin liberated at sporulation is inert so far as haemolysis is concerned. The accumulation of products of incomplete parasite metabolism, such as lactic acid or pyruvate, is also considered not to have any direct effect.

216   B. G. MAEGRAITH

Coagulation time is little altered in human malaria. Information about the fibrinogen content of plasma is equivocal. Prothrombin values are normal. A slight reduction in platelets has been described during the paroxysm in *P. vivax* malaria.

Some light may be thrown on the mechanisms of lysis in malaria by the recent studies of the very similar lysis which occurs in canine babesiasis (Maegraith, 1953). Evidence obtained by the study of the fate of normal erythrocytes (labelled with radio-isotopes) and by examination of *in vitro* lysis during shaking has indicated that in babesiasis both the red cells and their environment, in this case the plasma, may be concerned in the lysis. One factor of great importance is time. For instance, during the lytic phase of babesiasis, erythrocytes from the infected animal are readily lysed in whole blood, or after washing and resuspension in saline or plasma from either normal or infected animals in the pre-lytic stage. Erythrocytes taken before the lytic phase, or from normal animals, are resistant to lysis under similar circumstances. Normal erythrocytes, however, lyse readily in plasma taken from an animal in the lytic phase. These results indicate that the erythrocytes of the infected animal become unusually labile during the lytic phase, and that the plasma during this phase, but not before, acquires lytic properties towards erythrocytes from both normal and infected animals. Work of a similar nature to this would be profitable in malaria. The existence of a biphasic lytic reaction of this sort involving both erythrocytes and their environment would certainly help to explain some of the inconsistent results of workers to date.

(c) Some general effects

Anoxaemia and anoxia. The destruction and phagocytosis of parasitized and unparasitized cells may lead to severe anaemia if the rate of erythrocyte loss exceeds that of replacement, as may happen in *P. falciparum* and *P. knowlesi* malaria. Reduction in red cell numbers may not, however, be a prominent feature even in severe malaria, the worst effects of which may arise with relatively little anaemia. Moreover, considerable anaemia may exist without prominent clinical or pathological effects. Furthermore, as we have seen, the parasitic invasion does not appear directly or indirectly to affect oxygen acceptance or discharge by haemoglobin. Except in very severe cases, therefore, it appears unlikely that the anaemia can seriously affect the reserve oxygen-carrying capacity of the blood. Anaemia and associated anoxaemia are thus unlikely to be direct pathogenic factors in the development of malaria (Maegraith, 1951).

Measurement of the oxygen content of the circulating blood in malaria indicates that the oxygenation of erythrocytes in the lungs proceeds satisfactorily, at any rate until the late stages of lung involvement. This ready oxygenation plus the apparently normal physiological behaviour of the haemoglobin leads us to the conclusion that the tissues of the host, in the absence of any large claim by the parasite, should be adequately supplied with oxygen during the infection.

Nevertheless, there is considerable evidence of the existence of tissue anoxia, possibly of a histotoxic type. Two explanations of this are apparent. First, there may be some change in the delivery or acceptance of oxygen at the tissue face, and secondly, the changes in the tissues may be secondary to changes in the local blood flow. The second point is considered below. So far as the first is concerned, there is no evidence that any change in the dissociation of oxyhaemoglobin at low oxygen tensions occurs in malaria, nor is there any indication that the oxygen demands and uptake of parasites at low tensions are significantly greater in proportion than those of tissue. There is left the possibility that the oxygen acceptance by the tissue cells may be at fault, allowing a state of anoxia to develop in the presence of adequate supplies of well-oxygenated blood and normal oxyhaemoglobin dissociation. We have as yet practically no information concerning the acceptance of oxygen by tissue in malaria or any other disease state. Investigation of this point might be highly rewarding.

The effects of fever and general circulatory changes

The physiological effects of fever presumably play a role in plasmodial diseases. The raised temperature and the heightened cellular metabolism and changes in heart rate and output and of blood flow associated with it, are not, however, in themselves apparently very important to the host so far as pathological processes are concerned. In some cases in which the fever is high and persistent, the changes in the cardio-vascular system may provoke myocardial failure; in others hyperpyrexia may develop and determine its own pathological effect. The commonest circulatory disturbance, however, is the appearance of medical shock, with associated loss of circulating blood volume and resultant haemoconcentration.

It is important to realize that shock in itself creates a serious potential pathological state (Moon, 1938). Malaria in which shock has developed must, in fact, be regarded as malaria plus shock, so that the pathological pattern in a given case may be compounded of the effects of the parasitic invasion plus those of vascular failure. The recognition of this point is a recent development which has helped greatly to explain the appearance of seemingly identical physiological and pathological changes in so many aetiologically differing conditions. Examples of this are the appearance of hepatic centrilobular necrosis or renal anoxia in conditions as distinct as heat hyperpyrexia and blackwater fever, in which the important element of time is also clearly established, because the pathological picture depends to some extent on the duration of the vascular collapse (see later). In malaria, as in so many other conditions in which shock may develop, we are ignorant of the factor that initiates the vascular failure.

Changes in local tissue may be partly the reflexion of general processes initiated, for instance, by fever or by vascular failure, but the pattern of change in an organ depends very largely on local conditions and factors, paramount among which is the blood flow. Changes in local circulation may arise in response to general circulatory changes or may develop independently of them. In either event, they probably exert a profound effect on the development of local physiological or pathological disturbances which, in turn, may have generalized effects upon the host. To some extent local circulatory responses may depend on the anatomical structure of the tissue concerned. For instance, circulation through sinusoids may be affected when other types of circulation are not. Again, changes in the lumen of blood vessels arising from swelling or separation of the endothelial lining cells, accumulation of macrophages or parasitized or sludged cells may lead to local physical obstruction to blood flow. On the whole, however, with a few notable exceptions, such mechanical effects are of minor importance. Two other processes are dominant in determining the circulatory reaction— namely, dynamic changes in local blood vessels arising probably from certain vascular reflexes, and local and general effects initiated by humoral substances, such as adrenalin, often themselves secreted in response to changed circulation in the endocrine organ concerned. The view that pathological or functional changes in the tissues may largely depend on local changes in blood flow is, I believe, one of the most important concepts in the study of the pathogenesis of disease processes. The circulation should not be regarded as a vascular system comprising a complex of physiologically similar channels conveying blood to the tissues. On the contrary, the vessels of a given tissue or organ should be regarded as specific to it in just the same way as its secreting tissue. Appreciation of the point that the vessels of one organ may differ basically from those of another in regard to the properties of the endothelium or in dynamic activity in response to humoral or nervous control, helps to clarify much of the genesis of local tissue lesions.

Hepatic lesions

Disturbances of hepatic function, based on the results of so-called hepatic-function tests, have been demonstrated in many forms of malaria, with and without concomitant structural changes. Many authors incline to the view that some deviation in hepatic function occurs in all mammalian malaria. The truth of this of course depends on the intrinsic value of the battery of function tests examined. For instance, changes in plasma protein cannot be entirely interpreted in terms of liver function, and probably reflect additional reticulo-endothelial dysfunction. Nevertheless, the evidence strongly supports the contention that hepatic function is frequently disturbed, especially in the severe forms of mammalian malaria (Maegraith, 1948). In many instances deviations of hepatic function have been identified in the absence of any notable structural change in the liver, but in severe infections the pattern of tissue change varies from lobular congestion to centrilobular degeneration and necrosis, a picture which is essentially similar to that occurring in many other conditions ranging from shock to pernicious anaemia and canine babesiasis. The underlying pathogenic process involved in the production of these changes is probably a circulatory one, whereby the blood flow to the central regions of the lobule is impeded to the extent of creating a state of stagnant anoxia which, depending on the time over which it acts, eventually leads to cellular damage. The impedance of blood flow to the centre of the lobule could arise either mechanically or dynamically. Some physical obstruction to flow could come from endothelial swelling, hypertrophy of the Kupffer cells, or the formation of sludge, or from swelling of the polygonal cells and consequent obstruction to the sinusoidal flow, such as occurs in carbon tetrachloride poisoning (Himsworth, 1947).

Although some swelling of epithelial cells has recently been demonstrated in *P. vivax* malaria (Loomis, Heller, Hall & Zimmerman, 1954), mechanical obstruction appears to be less important than dynamic effects in impeding the lobular flow in malaria, and in the many other conditions in which centrilobular changes occur. There is some evidence that centrilobular flow may be reduced because of constriction of radicles of the hepatic venous tree. The ability of the hepatic venous tree to constrict in this manner has not yet been demonstrated in man. Nevertheless, recent research on the hepatic blood flow strongly supports the view that in certain animals the hepatic venous tree is capable of independent constriction, and that this constriction can be brought about by the action of certain drugs and by certain physiological states including shock (Andrews & Maegraith, 1951). The degree of cellular change in the central region produced by impedance of the circulation depends partly on the time over which the reduction of flow is maintained (Delorme, 1951).

It is suggested that two of the factors concerned in hepatic disturbances in malaria are mechanical or dynamic impedance of lobular blood flow, and cellular anoxia resulting from it. With regard to anoxia, it may fairly be said that, despite occasional adverse comment, the existence of an anoxic element (using the term anoxia in its widest sense) in the pathogenesis of these lesions and many others in malaria is established. The points at issue are whether the hepatic lesions arise from mechanical impedance of the circulation or from dynamic changes in the vessels (or both), and what factors control these vascular responses. Here, indeed, is a fruitful field for research.

Renal changes

Acute renal failure with anuria and uraemia is a common terminal event in blackwater fever and occurs sometimes in severe *P. falciparum* malaria and in other disease states in many of which anaemia, haemolysis and haemoglobinuria are absent (Maegraith, Havard & Parsons, 1945). It is now widely held that the clinical picture and pathological findings in such cases can best be explained in terms of some change or redistribution of renal blood flow leading to renal ischaemia which may differentially involve the cortex. It is assumed that the diminution of blood flow eventually leads to failure of filtration across the glomerular membrane and so to reduction in urinary secretion. Reduction of total renal blood flow has been demonstrated in traumatic shock in man and experimentally in other instances of vascular failure (Lauson, Bradley, & Cournand, 1944). It seems reasonable to assume that shock arising from causes other than trauma, in this instance from malaria, may initiate similar changes in renal blood flow. The acute renal failure in malaria may thus arise, as in other acute pathological states, from reduction, general or selective, in renal blood flow. This hypothesis helps to explain the often surprisingly rapid failure of urinary flow, and the accompanying tubular epithelial degeneration, and the reversibility of the syndrome.

In the renal lesions we thus have a good example of changes which can be adequately explained in terms of vascular activity within the organ. Under certain circumstances, the renal blood flow may be reduced to a point at which glomerular filtration stops. Coincidentally the blood flow to the tubules is reduced and, with time, the function and eventually the structure of the tubular cells become affected. We do not yet know how this change in blood flow is initiated in man. It has been shown in some animals to follow, probably reflexly, both extrarenal and intrarenal stimuli (Trueta, Barclay, Franklin, Daniel & Prichard, 1947).

This renal syndrome, which appears in the literature under a variety of labels, is an excellent illustration of the importance of the specific responses of local blood vessels. Study of the pathological changes arising in the host as a remote result of plasmodial invasion reveals others, but consideration of these must be omitted here and we must pass to another aspect of vascular activity which may have a very considerable effect on the reactions of the host—namely, changes in the circulation through certain organs, notably the endocrine glands, the secretion of which have powerful general physiological effects.

Adrenals. There are many features of a severe malarial attack in mammals which suggest adrenal involvement. For instance, the clinical picture of algid *P. falciparum* malaria—that is, malaria associated with shock—is very similar to that of acute adrenal insufficiency. Moreover, many workers have described extensive adrenal lesions in both human (*P. falciparum*) and simian malaria, the pattern combining changes in both cortex and medulla with vascular disturbances, including congestion and haemorrhage.

It is not surprising therefore that attempts have been made to incriminate the adrenal in the pattern of changes wrought by the parasite in the host. The evidence for this, however, is not complete. In the first place, algid malaria in man or severe *P. knowlesi* malaria in monkeys may be present without pathological change in the adrenals. The high potassium and low sodium content of plasma during the febrile stages of human, monkey and bird malaria are also observed after adrenalectomy; on the other hand, the increased urinary excretion of potassium, and decreased excretion of sodium and chloride reported by some authors in malaria, are the reverse of what might be expected in adrenalectomy. Overman (1951) has recently pointed out that the ionic anatomy of malaria fits the pattern produced by excessive dosage with desoxycorticosterone rather than that caused by overall adrenal failure, and has suggested that the disturbances of ionic balance in malaria may be concerned more with an imbalance of the various adrenal hormones. There are, however, many other factors involved in water/salt balance which confuse the issue, including the effects of dehydration, vomiting, diarrhoea, changes in plasma volume and disturbances of renal function and of carbohydrate metabolism. Moreover, the destruction of erythrocytes may account for a considerable proportion of the rise in plasma potassium.

The problem with regard to the adrenals in malaria is thus to decide what part dysfunction, with or without obvious pathological origin, plays as a pathogenic factor. Shock and associated phenomena, the pictures of which are closely similar to those of adrenal insufficiency, may arise in pernicious malaria independent of apparent adrenal damage. On the other hand, shock, in which the adrenal blood flow may be reduced, may itself give rise to humoral changes similar to those of adrenal insufficiency, and eventually to pathological changes in the adrenal glands. There is some evidence, moreover, that changes in the adrenal circulation and the associated disturbances, which are at first functional but may eventually become pathological, can have other causes, including extremes of anoxic anoxia. It appears therefore that disturbance of adrenal secretion, which may affect the whole bodily economy, can arise primarily from local changes in blood flow, which may or may not be associated eventually with local tissue changes.

It is not possible here to deal with the many other factors involved in the physiological and pathological reactions of the host to malaria. Mention must, however, be made of the time factor. Changes in tissue require time to develop and to exert their local and general effects. The final pathological picture largely depends on the duration of these effects in which, as in other protozoal infections, the opposing forces of dysfunction and destruction and of regeneration are continually active.

PATHOGENICITY OF *ENTAMOEBA HISTOLYTICA*

Discussion of the pathogenicity of *Entamoeba histolytica* raises certain problems which differ from those in malaria. In amoebic infections, for instance, more attention must be paid to the site and mode of invasion of the host. In malaria, introduced as it is by a vector, the initial take depends on extremely complex factors which demand exactly the right set of circumstances for each stage of the invasion. In invasion by *E. histolytica*, on the other hand, the parasite, in the absence of a vector, must make its own entry into the host, a process which is in some ways considerably easier to follow than in malaria.

Of the factors involved in the invasion of the host by amoebae, only a few can be mentioned here. We shall refer to three: factors governing (i) the initial invasion, (ii) the local spread in the tissues of the host, and (iii) the extra-intestinal spread in the host, especially in relation to the development of hepatic amoebiasis.

(i) *The initial invasion*

There are undoubtedly factors inherent in both parasite and host which govern the acceptance or otherwise of the parasite by the host, but this acceptance is nevertheless considerably influenced by chance. This is well illustrated by the fact that the parasite can become established in the contents of the large gut in a wide group of hosts provided the physico-chemical environment is suitable for its growth and multiplication. Establishment of the same organism in the same group of hosts can, however, be made more difficult by changing the characteristics of the lumen contents, for example, by altering the host diet. Thus, the growth of *E. histolytica* in the large bowel is restricted in dogs by a milk diet and accelerated by a diet of salmon (Taylor, Greenberg & Josephson, 1952).

There is good evidence that the establishment of growing amoebae in the gut lumen is not necessarily followed by invasion of the intestinal wall. Many other factors are involved in determining this invasion, such as the numbers of parasites available and the ease and duration of contact between parasite and host epithelium. Factors inherent in the parasite are probably also of importance. It is possible, for instance, to reduce the percentage take in a given species of host by long-continued cultivation of the parasite *in vitro*; the take can sometimes be increased in the same organism by rapid animal passage. Such changes in the invasive powers of the amoeba may be only apparent, and reflect some unrecognized extraneous factor, but there is some evidence that these effects may sometimes result from changes in factors actively concerned with epithelial penetration.

The possibility that amoebae penetrate the gut epithelium at least in part through the agency of some lytic factor is indicated by the recorded speed of tissue invasion in experimental animal infections. Tissue invasion may commence, for instance, within a few hours of feeding *E. histolytica* cysts to puppies; well-developed intestinal lesions have been reported within 24 hr. of feeding cysts to dogs or infecting guinea-pigs intra-caecally with amoebae. It has been pointed out, however, that experimental evidence of this sort obtained in artificial infections in unnatural hosts may not apply to natural infections, since cytolysins produced by an amoebic strain under such conditions may be active in the one host and inactive in others.

The existence under laboratory conditions of lytic agents in strains of *E. histolytica* has been demonstrated on several occasions. For instance, Craig (1927) made an alcoholic extract of amoebic cells and demonstrated both haemolysins and tissue lysins therein. The haemolysin was not present in the supernatant fluid of cultures, but only in extracts of living organisms. It was probably non-specific and similar to other lysins, which have been described in many tissues and cells (Ponder, 1948). The cytolytic action of the extract was, however, suggestive evidence of the presence of some proteolytic factor in the living growing amoebic cells. In 1938 Morita demonstrated destruction of epithelial cells suspended in culture media following incubation with amoebae.

These experiments have been confirmed and extended recently in our laboratories. Harinasuta & Maegraith (1954) succeeded in demonstrating an agent capable of lysing gelatin in living *E. histolytica* cells and in extracts obtained from them after freezing and thawing. It is believed that this activity represents the presence of proteolytic enzymes, some of the properties of which have been studied. The agent concerned works within the pH range of the trypsin group of enzymes, which would enable it to function in the lumen of the large gut, in the faeces, or in liver tissue. One interesting fact which has emerged, and which might have some bearing on the relation of this lytic agent to the invasion of the host epithelium, is the observation that the proteolytic activity is strongly inhibited by the presence of soluble protein. For instance, amoebic cells suspended in culture medium containing serum are inactive. The same organisms washed and resuspended in saline are actively proteolytic. The addition of horse serum to the suspension or to an active extract prepared by freezing and thawing amoebic cells inhibits the activity.

It has yet to be shown that the existence of proteolytic agents in amoebic cells is a factor in determining the invasive properties or otherwise of a particular strain of parasite, but it is interesting to note that some strains possess this lytic property and others do not. Moreover, it has been shown that the percentage take after intra-caecal injection into guinea-pigs of a given strain of *E. histolytica* cultivated in Locke egg-serum medium is considerably higher if the cells are washed free of medium before introduction. It is possible that further examination may show that this effect results from the inhibitory effect of the serum contained in the medium upon the proteolytic activity of the amoebic cell. In any case, it serves very well to illustrate the point made above, namely that the 'pathogenicity' of a given strain at a given time may depend on the circumstances of parasite-host contact and not primarily on any inherent qualities of either (Maegraith, 1954b).*

* Miles (pp. 14–15) proposes that 'pathogenicity' should be applied to the attribute of a group and the term 'virulence' used to denote the outcome of a particular host-parasite encounter. (Editor.)

(ii) *Invasion of the tissues*

The migration of the amoeba in the deeper tissues depends partly on mechanical factors, such as intestinal muscular contractions and tissue-fluid movement, and partly on the activity of the parasite itself.

The mechanism of spread is not understood. Many authors have suggested that there may be some cytolytic process at work. The histological picture of 'haloes' around embedded parasites supports the view that connective tissue may be under process of attack by lytic enzymes possibly similar to hyaluronidase, which may be either present in the parasite cells or produced by them. *E. histolytica* grown in the usual culture media does not possess hyaluronidase. Suspensions of washed amoebae obtained from artificially produced liver lesions in hamsters have, however, recently been found to have strong action on potassium hyaluronate. Once the enzyme has been produced by a given strain in this way, it survives several cultures *in vitro* but is eventually lost. It can then be reproduced after further liver passage. It thus appears that hyaluronidase can be synthesized under certain conditions by amoebae (Bradin, 1953). It has not yet, however, been determined whether this enzyme is present and active during tissue invasion in the natural host. It is possible, of course, that, even if it is present, it may be naturally inhibited by antihyaluronidases in the tissues.

Tissue invasion by *E. histolytica* is influenced very considerably by the reaction of the host. In infections of the natural host the local cellular response is usually minimal. This does not necessarily indicate failure on the part of the host so much as demonstrate that resistance may be achieved by processes other than cellular defence.

The mode of action of host resistance is not understood. It is possible that the conditions of pH and oxidation-reduction potential prevailing in the tissues are unsuitable for the parasite. In the ordinary course of events parasites presented with such an environment would presumably perish. Alteration in local physiological conditions might, however, lead to survival of the parasite and its ultimate development and multiplication. Thus, for instance, changes in local circulation or metabolism might lead to local conditions of low pH and negative oxidation-reduction potential suitable for amoebic growth. Survival in tissues may thus depend not only on the amoebic cell but on the environment in which it exists. The significance of this assumption is clearly seen in the fate of amoebae distributed metastatically to tissues remote from the intestinal lesion.

(iii) *Extra-intestinal amoebiasis*

In naturally acquired *E. histolytica* infections parasites reach the tissues almost always through the mucosa of the large intestine. Spread of amoebic processes to other organs is regarded as secondary to their establishment, temporary or otherwise, in the intestinal tissues, and occurs either by contiguous extension or by metastasis via lymphatic or blood vessels.

Extension to neighbouring tissues is the result of the progress of the invasive processes already mentioned and is associated with existing active intestinal lesions. Abdominal complications of amoebic infection such as local peritoneal reactions and the development of amoebic granulomata (amoebomata) are mostly of this nature.

Viscerotropic strains of *E. histolytica* have not been described. The spread of infection to remote organs is presumed to be metastatic, the original focus of infection being in the intestinal tissues. But lesions in tissues other than the gut are not always associated with contemporaneous active gut lesions and the development of the extra-intestinal lesions, once they are established, is probably independent of the intestinal lesions. It is possible that even in minor gut lesions which subsequently heal, a vessel may be invaded and amoebae may be transported to other sites.

Metastatic distribution of amoebae arising from invasion of lymph or blood vessels in intestinal lesions is considered by some workers to be much commoner than is indicated by the incidence of remote lesions. It appears, if this is so, that the chance of survival at the site of parasitic arrest is small and that survival and subsequent multiplication of metastatic amoebae presumably depend largely on the conditions prevailing in the tissues concerned.

Metastatic lesions occur most frequently in the liver. There is evidence that in human and experimental hepatic amoebiasis the initial lesion is commonly an infarct caused by embolism of a branch of the portal vein. The further spread of the amoebic lesion into the liver tissue apparently occurs by direct extension. It may be accompanied by centrilobular degeneration in the immediately adjacent lobules.

Experimental extra-intestinal amoebiasis

Attempts to produce amoebic liver lesions have been made in kittens, cats, dogs, hamsters, rats and guinea-pigs. Abscesses have occasionally developed spontaneously in the course of experimental intestinal amoebiasis in animals, and abscesses or 'hepatitis' have also been produced by direct injection of infective material into the liver substance. Injection of amoebae into the mesenteric or portal veins of these animals has not been followed by the establishment of abscesses containing amoebae.

Spontaneous development of amoebic abscess has not been demonstrated in artificially induced intestinal amoebiasis in guinea-pigs, but from these and other animals amoebae have been cultured from apparently unchanged liver tissue during such infections, and scattered minute bacterial abscesses have been described. Recently, however, abscesses containing amoebae and associated bacteria have been produced by the inoculation of suspension of artificially cultivated amoebae into the portal vein (Maegraith & Harinasuta, 1953). The abscesses (often single) develop consistently in one of the right lobes of the liver, supporting the generally accepted view that metastatic transplantation through the portal vein occurs along certain stream-lines. In otherwise normal animals abscesses produced in this way progress for only a few days and then regress rapidly and are replaced by fibrous tissue. In animals in which long-continued or 'chronic' intestinal amoebic lesions have been set up by alternate intra-caecal infection and partial treatment, artificially produced abscesses containing amoebae persist for much longer. Prolonged abscess formation can also be induced by intra-portal injection of amoebae in animals 'sensitized' by repeated intra-muscular injection of 'antigens' or extracts of homologous amoebae made by freezing and thawing washed parasites. In animals so 'sensitized' and in animals with induced 'chronic' intestinal lesions intra-dermal injection of the antigen was followed by vigorous skin reactions. These experiments suggest that survival of metastatic amoebae reaching the liver may be prolonged by some sort of 'preparation' of the tissue. It is interesting to note here the recent demonstration of local impedance of liver circulation after injection of antigen into the surface of the canine liver following sensitization of the dog to horse serum (Maegraith, Andrews & Wenyon, 1949). Some such interference with flow might conceivably be set up by amoebae in organs 'sensitized' by gut infection or by artificially prepared antigens and lead to local conditions of oxidation-reduction potential and pH which would support amoebic growth and multiplication within the liver and so permit the parasite to become established. Reactions of this sort, depending on changes in the tissues arising from 'sensitization' by previous or prevailing parasitic invasion, may well be important in the creation of lesions in many conditions besides amoebiasis. They offer a wide and interesting field for research.

228   B. G. MAEGRAITH

REFERENCES

ANDREWS, W. H. H. & MAEGRAITH, B. G. (1951). Studies on the liver circulation.
III. The vascular responses of the perfused canine liver to adrenaline and
acetylcholine. *Ann. trop. Med. Parasit.* **45**, 255.
BRADIN, J. L. (1953). Studies on the production of hyaluronidase by *Entamoeba
histolytica. Exp. Parasit.* **2**, 230.
CRAIG, C. F. (1927). Observations of the hemolytic, cytolytic and complement-
binding properties of extracts of *Entamoeba histolytica. Amer. J. trop. Med.* **7**,
225.
DEEGAN, T. (1955). Nature of Haemozoin. *Trans. R. Soc. trop. Med. Hyg.* **49**
(in the Press).
DELORME, E. J. (1951). Arterial perfusion of the liver in shock: an experimental
study. *Lancet*, no. 260, p. 259.
FAIRLEY, N. H. (1939). Methaemalbumin in man (pseudo-methaemoglobin). *Proc.
R. Soc. Med.* **32**, 1278.
FOY, H. & KONDI, A. (1943). Lysolecithin fragility in blackwater fever. *Trans. R.
Soc. trop. Med. Hyg.* **36**, 197.
GEAR, J. (1946). Autoantigens and autoantibodies in the pathogenesis of disease
with special reference to blackwater fever. *Trans. R. Soc. trop. Med. Hyg.* **39**,
301.
HARINASUTA, C. & MAEGRAITH, B. G. (1954). Experimental amoebiasis in the
guineapig. (Demonstration.) *Trans. R. Soc. trop. Med. Hyg.* **48**, 7.
HAWKING, F. (1954). Milk, *p*-aminobenzoate and malaria of rats and monkeys.
Brit. med. J. **2**, 853.
HIMSWORTH, H. (1947). *Lectures on the Liver and its Diseases.* Oxford: Blackwell
Scientific Publications.
JONES, E. S. & McGREGOR, I. A. (1954). Pathological processes in disease, V: Blood
physiology of Gambian children infected with *Plasmodium falciparum. Ann.
trop. Med. Parasit.* **48**, 95.
JONES, E. S. MAEGRAITH, B. G. & GIBSON, Q. H. (1953). Pathological processes in
disease, IV. Oxidations in the rat reticulocyte, a host cell of *Plasmodium
berghei. Ann. trop. Med. Parasit.* **47**, 431.
LASER, H. (1946). A method of testing the antimalarial properties of compounds
in vitro. Nature, Lond., **157**, 301.
LAUSON, H. D., BRADLEY, S. E. & COURNAND, A. (1944). Renal circulation in
shock. *J. clin. Invest.* **23**, 381.
LOOMIS, G. W., HELLER, P., HALL, W. H. & ZIMMERMAN, H. J. (1954). The
pattern of hepatic dysfunction in malaria. *Amer. J. med. Sci.* **227**,
408.
LWOFF, A. (1951). *Biochemistry and Physiology of Protozoa.* New York: Academic
Press Inc.
MAEGRAITH, B. G. (1948). *Pathological Processes in Malaria and Blackwater Fever.*
Oxford: Blackwell Scientific Publications.
MAEGRAITH, B. G. (1951). Physiological approach to the problems of malaria.
Brit. med. Bull. **8**, 28.
MAEGRAITH, B. G. (1953). Some problems of pathology and pathogenesis in malaria
and blackwater fever. *Rapports V Congrès Internat. Med. Trop. Paludisme,* **1**,
50.
MAEGRAITH, B. G. (1954a). Physiological aspects of protozoan infection. *Ann. Rev.
Microbiol.* (in the Press).
MAEGRAITH, B. G. (1954b). Discussion on immunity in protozoal infection. *Proc.
R. Soc. Med.* (in the Press).

MAEGRAITH, B. G., ANDREWS, W. H. H. & WENYON, C. E. M. (1949). Studies on the liver circulation, I. Active constriction of the hepatic venous tree in anaphylactic shock. *Ann. trop. Med. Parasit.* **43**, 225.

MAEGRAITH, B. G., DEEGAN, T. & JONES, E. S. (1952). Suppression of malaria (*P. berghei*) by milk. *Brit. med. J.* **2**, 1882.

MAEGRAITH, B. G. & HARINASUTA, C. (1953). Experimental amoebiasis in the guineapig. *Trans. R. Soc. trop. Med. Hyg.* **47**, 582.

MAEGRAITH, B. G., HAVARD, R. E. & PARSONS, D. S. (1945). Renal syndrome of wide distribution induced possibly by renal anoxia. *Lancet*, no. 249, p. 293.

MOON, V. H. (1938). *Shock and Related Capillary Phenomena.* London: Cumberlege.

MORITA, Y. (1938). Investigations on amoebic dysentery XII—Toxicological studies of the extracts made from cultured dysenteric amoebae. *J. orient. Med.* **28**, 37.

OVERMAN, R. R. (1951). Sodium, potassium and chloride alterations in disease. *Physiol. Rev.* **31**, 285.

PONDER, E. (1948). *Haemolysis and Related Phenomena.* New York: Grune and Stratton.

RIGDON, R. H. (1945). Malarial pigment. A consideration of the mechanism of elimination from the duck. *Amer. J. clin. Path.* **15**, 489.

ROSTORFER, H. H. & RIGDON, R. H. (1946). A study of oxygen transport in the blood of young and adult domestic ducks. *Amer. J. Physiol.* **146**, 222.

TAYLOR, D. J., GREENBERG, J. & JOSEPHSON, E. S. (1952). The effect of two different diets in experimental amoebiasis in the guineapig and in the rat. *Amer. J. trop. Med.* **1**, 559.

TRUETA, J., BARCLAY, A. E., FRANKLIN, K. J., DANIEL, P. M. & PRICHARD, M. M. L. (1947). *Studies of the Renal Circulation.* Oxford: Blackwell Scientific publications.

VINT, F. W. (1941). Some recent researches on the spleen and their possible relationship to blackwater fever. *E. Afr. med. J.* **18**, 162.

HOST-PARASITE RELATIONS AND PATHOGENESIS IN INFECTIONS WITH *ENTAMOEBA HISTOLYTICA*

C. A. HOARE AND R. A. NEAL

Wellcome Laboratories of Tropical Medicine, London

Among the five intestinal amoebae occurring in man, *Entamoeba histolytica* is the only one which is pathogenic, being responsible for amoebic dysentery and other symptoms of amoebiasis. Since the first description of this disease 70 years ago (Lösch, 1875), a vast literature has accumulated, dealing with its clinical course and histopathology, and diverse hypotheses have been advanced to explain the pathogenesis of infections with this parasite, but since none of these views is supported by conclusive experimental evidence, it must be admitted that this question is still unsolved. The most that can be done at the present stage of our knowledge of the pathogenesis of amoebiasis is to consider the conditions under which the pathological action of *E. histolytica* is revealed, and to review the different hypotheses in the light of the available data regarding its biology and host-parasite relations.

HOST-PARASITE RELATIONS

The pathogenesis of *E. histolytica* cannot be properly understood without a consideration of its normal behaviour in the host. Though some observers still regard it as an obligatory pathogen which invariably attacks the intestinal wall with the production of lesions and clinical symptoms, it has now been conclusively established (Hoare, 1952) that in the great majority (about 80 %) of infected human beings—as well as in all macaque monkeys—*E. histolytica* inhabits the lumen of the large bowel without injuring its wall or producing symptoms of disease. In fact, in most human carriers *E. histolytica* lives as a commensal, like its non-pathogenic congener, *E. coli*. In the lumen of the gut amoebae of both these species multiply and produce cysts, which are discharged with the faeces and serve to propagate the infection to new hosts. They both feed at the expense of the gut contents, ingesting bacteria and other formed elements, but, whereas the nutrition of *E. coli* is exclusively phagotrophic, *E. histolytica* also feeds saprozoically by absorbing fluid matter through its body. Another distinction between these two species is that *E. coli* always leads a commensal existence, whereas *E. histolytica* is capable, under certain conditions, of invading the intestinal wall and giving rise to clinical symptoms of amoebiasis. This change of habitat is correlated with changes in the food habits of *E. histolytica*, the tissue forms of which, in addition to saprozoic nutrition, now feed on erythrocytes and tissue elements, but no longer ingest bacteria. It is thus seen that although *E. histolytica* is a pathogenic parasite, in the sense that it is capable of causing disease, its virulence or noxiousness is not always evident, for at times it may behave like a harmless commensal. During such periods *E. histolytica*—though potentially pathogenic—is not virulent, but when its virulence is manifested, it is determined by the degree of invasiveness, which can be measured by a scoring system based on the severity of ulceration in the gut (cf. Neal, 1951*a*).

FACTORS AFFECTING PATHOGENICITY
Parasitic factors

We may now consider the factors governing the virulence and invasive power of *E. histolytica*. From the foregoing comparison of the two closely related entamoebae—the commensal *E. coli* and the pathogenic *E. histolytica*—which normally occupy the same habitat, it is seen that *E. histolytica* alone is endowed with invasive properties, whereas *E. coli* does not possess them in any circumstances. It is therefore evident that one of the factors in the pathogenesis of *E. histolytica* is inherent in its genetic make-up. Though this is admittedly an explanation of *ignotum per ignotius*, its validity is borne out by the fact that the pathogenicity of *E. histolytica* can be readily demonstrated for most strains, even when their virulence is dormant (as in symptomless carriers), by experimental infection of such highly susceptible animals as kittens, in which the infection usually assumes an acute course.

There is also some evidence that strains from different geographical areas and from different hosts differ in virulence. Thus Meleney & Frye (1933, 1935) and Burova & Kakabadse (1941) have shown that strains from different localities—in the United States and the Caucasus respectively—vary in their virulence for kittens. A considerable amount of work has also been done on the virulence for experimentally infected animals of strains isolated from patients with different types of amoebiasis. The earlier results obtained with kittens were contradictory, for some observers found that strains from acute cases were more virulent than those from carriers (e.g. Dale & Dobell, 1917), whereas others found no difference between such strains (Kessel, 1928; Meleney & Frye, 1933, 1935, 1937; Ter-Matevossian, Sarkissian & Zaturian, 1936; Sarkissjan, 1938). This discrepancy is due to the employment of kittens, whose susceptibility and vulnerability is exceptionally high. However, with the introduction of rats as experimental animals, this question could be studied under more natural conditions, because the course of amoebic infection in rats is more comparable to that in man. One of us (Neal, 1951 *a*, *b*; Neal & Vincent, 1955) has carried out numerous experiments in which rats were infected with strains from symptomless human carriers and from acute cases of amoebiasis. The results have demonstrated conclusively that strains from acute cases were invasive to the tissues of the caecum, whereas those from carriers failed to invade them. There was thus a good correlation between the virulence of *E. histolytica* in the rat and the course of infection in the human donor. These experiments provided evidence of the existence of strains of *E. histolytica* differing in virulence, but it is still unknown whether these differences are innate in strains. In fact, some observations seem to indicate that enhanced virulence might be acquired by a strain as the result of adaptation to life in the tissues (Reichenow, 1931). In this connexion it may be noted that some authors claim to have increased the virulence of *E. histolytica* by serial passages through experimental animals (Faust & Swartzwelder, 1935; Meleney & Frye, 1937). On the other hand, Westphal (1950) believes that prolonged sojourn in the lumen of the gut may reduce the invasiveness of *E. histolytica*. The effect upon the invasive power of the parasite of conditions previously experienced by it in the host might explain the occurrence of virulent strains in the tropics, where amoebic dysentery is more common, and the predominance of avirulent ones in temperate regions, where amoebiasis is usually symptomless. It is possible, however, that the behaviour of different strains is not always due to innate or acquired peculiarities of the amoeba itself, but might be influenced by some of the factors discussed below.

It has also been suggested that cyst production may be one of the factors producing variation in the virulence of *E. histolytica*. Some observers (Deschiens, 1939, 1941; Chang, 1945) maintained that the infectivity of *E. histolytica* for kittens diminished after prolonged cultivation in the trophic stage but was restored after the amoebae were allowed to encyst. However, one of us (Neal, 1954) demonstrated that the infectivity and invasiveness of avirulent strains for rats was not altered by inducing their encystation. Invasiveness is therefore independent of encystation.

Bacterial factors

It is well known that bacteria play an essential role in the life of *E. histolytica*, both as a source of food and by providing some unknown growth factors. Numerous *in vitro* studies conducted during the last

25 years have shown conclusively that bacteria are indispensable to the amoebae in culture, some species promoting, others inhibiting their development and life cycle (cf. Dobell & Neal, 1952). Likewise *in vivo* the intestinal flora not only serve to supplement the food supply of the lumen-dwelling amoebae, but also appear to influence the course of the amoebic infection. The general effect of bacteria was recently demonstrated by Luttermoser & Phillips (1952), who found that *E. histolytica* in bacteria-free cultures (with a trypanosome associate) had a low degree of infectivity for rabbits. However, when associated with a single species of bacteria it produced acute ulcerative infection in half of them, and in the majority of animals when accompanied by the mixed concomitant flora. Furthermore, the virulence of the pure culture was restored after addition of the bacteria. Others have shown that the addition of certain micro-organisms to cultures of *E. histolytica* increased its virulence for experimental animals. This effect was produced with bacteria of the enteric group (Deschiens, 1936) and with *Bacterium* (= *Escherichia*) *coli* (Deschiens, 1937, 1938 *a*; Nauss & Rappaport, 1940). On the other hand, Frye & Shaffer (1948) claimed that the pathological effect of mild and virulent strains of *E. histolytica* for kittens was not altered by an exchange of their flora, and that the addition of virulent haemolytic streptococci failed to augment the invasiveness of the amoebae. Some circumstantial evidence of the part played by bacteria was provided by Stewart (1947, 1948), who compared the bacteriological findings in acute human amoebiasis with those in healthy persons. He showed that in the diseased group paracolon bacilli and *Streptococcus faecalis* were considerably more numerous, and maintained that this difference was statistically significant.

The influence of the intestinal flora on the course of amoebiasis has also been the subject of many investigations in the human host. Some observers (Westphal, 1937, 1938 *a*, *b*; Deschiens, 1938 *b*; Mathis, 1950) believe that bacteria play a major role in the pathogenesis of this disease. According to this view, in healthy carriers with a normal intestinal flora the mucosa of the gut wall is able to resist penetration by the amoebae, but when it is injured by virulent bacteria and their toxins, the amoebae gain access to the tissues, producing in them the characteristic lesions. An interesting experiment supporting this view was carried out by Westphal (1937), who infected himself with bacteria-free cysts of *E. histolytica*, isolated from a patient cured of the clinical symptoms of amoebic dysentery. The infection ran a symptomless course for 8 months, during which the author harboured the commensal forms of the amoebae. He then super-infected himself with the bacteria separated from another case of amoebic dysentery, and developed acute symptoms of this disease, with haematophagous amoebae in his stools. Since similar symptoms were produced in a control, who was infected with the same flora but did not harbour *E. histolytica*, it was concluded that the clinical and parasitological manifestations of dysentery were caused primarily by bacteria, among which Flexner-Y dysentery bacilli were identified. Further support to the view that amoebic dysentery is preceded by damage to the gut wall caused by dysentery bacilli came from the same author's observations in North Africa (Westphal, 1948), which indicated that, when amoebic carriers contracted bacillary dysentery, the lumen forms of *E. histolytica* were transformed into haematophagous amoebae. That virulent bacteria are capable of producing dysenteric symptoms, indistinguishable from those in amoebic dysentery, was also demonstrated in parallel infections of kittens with bacteria—*Escherichia coli* and haemolytic streptococci—(*a*) in association with amoebae and (*b*) without amoebae (Deschiens, 1937, 1938*a*; Westphal & Marschall, 1941).

Thus, according to the named observers, the invasive powers of the commensal lumen-dwelling amoebae are only activated after the gut wall is damaged by pathogenic bacteria, which pave the way for the amoebae. Other authors (Faust & Kagy, 1934; Craig, 1944), while admitting the part played by bacteria in producing the pathological changes in amoebiasis, regard the micro-organisms as secondary complicating factors. Though there can be no doubt that bacteria influence the course of amoebic infection, the exact part played by them in the pathogenesis of amoebiasis has not been conclusively established.

Other factors

Other conditions which may influence the pathological manifestations of amoebiasis will be only briefly considered. In addition to bacteria, it has been suggested that other causes of functional disturbance may affect the structural integrity of the intestine and thus expose it to invasion by the amoebae. Examples of these causes are: abnormal secretory function, temperature fluctuation, and irritant foodstuffs (Westphal, 1938*b*); inflammatory and erosive processes like alimentary and toxic colitis (Deschiens, 1950*a*); and possibly psychosomatic disorders like colon neurosis (Paulley, 1950). The prevalence of amoebic dysentery in the tropics and its rarity in temperate regions raises the question of the effect of climate, but since in hot countries the gastrointestinal system is particularly vulnerable to the effect of both bacterial and functional factors, all of which tend to lower the host's resistance.

it is doubtful if climate *per se* is a deciding factor in the pathogenesis of amoebiasis. As regards the resistance of the human host, the classical experiments of Walker & Sellards (1913) have clearly demonstrated the existence of individual variation in the susceptibility to infection with *E. histolytica*.

It is also conceivable that diet may be a predisposing factor in amoebiasis. It is well known that infection with intestinal protozoa in general is promoted by a diet poor in protein. In a series of papers, Elsdon-Dew (1946, 1953) has shown that a particularly severe form of amoebic dysentery is prevalent in Natal among Africans, whose diet—consisting mainly of maize—is protein-deficient, whereas among the Indian and European inhabitants, whose diets have a higher protein level, the infection runs a mild course. However, Carrera, Sadun & Faust (1952) failed to detect any difference in the infectivity rate and histopathological changes between experimentally infected guinea-pigs fed on adequate diets, and on diets qualitatively or quantitatively deficient in protein. Likewise, one of us (R.A.N.) found that, in rats infected with an avirulent strain of *E. histolytica*, a diet deficient in protein did not promote caecal ulceration. Some work has also been done on the effect of vitamins in experimental amoebiasis. Sadun, Bradin & Faust (1951) demonstrated that in guinea-pigs fed on a diet deficient in ascorbic acid the amoebic infection ran a more severe course than in those receiving an adequate supplement of this vitamin. Similar observations were carried out in dogs by Larsh (1952), who showed that in animals kept on a diet deficient in nicotinic acid the infectivity of *E. histolytica* and the degree of ulceration produced by it were higher than in the controls, whose food was supplemented with this vitamin.

MECHANISM OF INVASION

We can now consider the mechanism of tissue invasion by *E. histolytica*, which is the expression of its pathogenicity. Since metastatic amoebic infection of the liver is more fully dealt with in another communication to this Symposium (Maegraith, p. 207), we shall restrict ourselves in this paper to intestinal amoebiasis. Even if it is correct—and it is no more than a hypothesis—that the ground for invasion by the amoebae is prepared by some structural damage to the mucosa produced by other agencies, such as bacteria and functional disturbances, the actual penetration of the tissues by the amoebae is an established fact. Some light is thrown on this problem by the character of the intestinal lesions in amoebiasis.

Lesions

In the fully developed intestinal ulcers of amoebiasis, it may be difficult to distinguish between the pathological effects produced by bacteria
and those produced by the amoebae, but histological sections of early
lesions reveal the amoebic infection in its pure form without any
complicating bacterial infection. After penetration of the mucosa by the
amoebae, the first lesion to appear is an abscess filled with fluid produced
by histolysis of the tissues, the amoebae being in contact with the sound
tissue along the periphery and base of the lesion, where they feed mainly
saprozoically but also by ingestion of red blood corpuscles. The amoebae
continue to penetrate deeper into the tissues, which are gradually eroded
by histolysis but show no signs of any inflammatory reaction or necrosis.
As the tissues are destroyed the lesion extends in all directions, until it
opens into the lumen of the gut, giving rise to a typical ulcer. The lesion
is now exposed to secondary invasion by the intestinal bacteria, which
produce in it the histopathological changes characteristic of bacterial
infections: necrosis, suppuration and cellular infiltration (Walker &
Sellards, 1913; Dobell & O'Connor, 1921; James, 1927; Deschiens,
1938b; Westphal, 1938a; Craig, 1944; Brumpt, 1949).

Methods of invasion

There has been much speculation regarding the actual method by
which E. histolytica penetrates into the gut wall of its host. The appearance of the early lesions, showing histolysis of the tissues, upon which
the saprozoic nutrition of the amoebae depends, indicates that the
parasites elaborate a substance which destroys the tissues. Some authors
(Rees, 1929; Meleney, 1944; Frye & Shaffer, 1948) regard this secretion
as a toxin, but, as pointed out by Westphal (1938a, b), there are no
signs of toxic effects (e.g. necrosis) in aseptic amoebic lesions, and
rabbits inoculated with extracts of cultures of E. histolytica do not
manifest symptoms of intoxication.

Most authorities are agreed that invasion of the tissues by E. histolytica and its pathological effect are due primarily to fermentative action,
and attempts have accordingly been made to identify the enzymes
responsible. Craig (1927) was the first to demonstrate the existence, in
extracts of E. histolytica in culture, of a haemolytic and histolytic substance. When scrapings of the mucosa of a kitten's large bowel were
exposed to the action of 'cytolysin'—as this substance was named—the
epithelial cells were completely destroyed. Later, Morita (1938) demonstrated the cytolytic action of living E. histolytica upon cells of the

mucous membranes of different animals suspended in amoebic cultures. Other observations on cultures (Deschiens, 1950b) also indicate that this amoeba is capable of hydrolysing proteins present in the medium—for example, the coagulated horse serum or egg white in the solid phase. In none of these cases was the exact nature of the enzymes determined, but Rees, Baernstein, Reardon & Phillips (1953) claim to have detected the production of gelatinase by *E. histolytica* in culture. Quite recently Bradin (1953) discovered the presence of hyaluronidase in strains of *E. histolytica* from induced liver abscesses in hamsters, but this enzyme disappeared when the amoebae were maintained in culture. This author regards hyaluronidase as a possible factor in the pathogenesis of amoebiasis, but DeLamater, Michaelson, Hallman & Blumenthal (1954), who repeated these experiments, were unable to detect the presence of this enzyme in *E. histolytica*.

It is thus seen that the evidence regarding the nature of the enzymes promoting the invasiveness of *E. histolytica* is still fragmentary and conflicting. However, most observers are agreed that this amoeba produces a proteolytic enzyme, which liquefies the intestinal mucosa, thereby enabling it to penetrate into the tissues, which continue to break down by histolysis as the amoebae multiply and extend through the lesion. It is also possible that their spread within the tissues is facilitated by the hydrolytic action of hyaluronidase upon the intercellular ground substance.

In addition to this fermentative process, there can be no doubt that the progress of the amoebae into and through the tissues is aided by their locomotion. Though some observers (e.g. Dobell & O'Connor, 1921) doubted this, it is inconceivable that this motile amoeba, which is so active when observed *in vitro*, should remain passive *in vivo*.

CONCLUSIONS

From the foregoing review it is evident that the available data do not afford a clear-cut solution to the problem of pathogenesis in infections with *Entamoeba histolytica*. However, they have thrown light on the complexity of the factors affecting the host-parasite relations in amoebiasis, and have provided indications of the course to be pursued in further investigations on this subject.

At this stage it will be useful to summarize the present state of our knowledge regarding the pathogenesis of amoebiasis. It has been clearly demonstrated that about 80 % of persons harbouring *E. histolytica* are symptomless carriers of the infection, in whom the amoebae lead a commensal existence, without damaging the gut. However—unlike *Entamoeba coli*—*E. histolytica* is a facultative pathogen, which under certain conditions manifests its dormant virulence by invading the intestinal wall, with the production of the well-known clinical symptoms and lesions. Because of the innocuousness of this parasite in the great majority of infections, it would seem that it is incapable of penetrating the intact mucosa, and that its invasiveness is activated in some way by extraneous factors affecting the host's health. These factors have not been fully elucidated, but there is considerable evidence that certain pathogenic bacteria may play an important part in the pathogenesis of amoebiasis, by injuring the surface of the gut wall and thereby paving the way for penetration of the mucosa by the amoebae, the invasiveness of which probably varies with different strains. Since the primary lesion may be aseptic, it would seem that the amoebae alone are responsible for its production and extension, which proceed by histolysis of the tissues. The histolytic changes in the lesions point to the elaboration by the amoebae of proteolytic enzymes, and possibly hyaluronidase as well. These enzymes are the essential factors in the mechanism of invasion of the tissues, within which the amoebae progress actively with the aid of their pseudopodia.

The correctness of this interpretation can only be established by further researches on the physiology of *E. histolytica* and the host-parasite relationship in amoebiasis. Among the problems awaiting solution are the detection and identification of the parasitic enzymes, and the exact determination of the part played by bacterial factors in the pathogenesis of amoebiasis. Hitherto, most of the investigations on this subject were carried out either by parasitologists or by clinicians, who—however competent—cannot be expected to deal with the aspects of pathogenesis in amoebiasis which are outside their own field. A satisfactory solution of this question can only be expected from a close co-operation between protozoologists, bacteriologists, biochemists, and pathologists.

REFERENCES

BRADIN, JR. J. L. (1953). Studies on the production of hyaluronidase by *Endamoeba histolytica*. *Exp. Parasitol.* **2**, 230.

BRUMPT, E. (1949). *Précis de Parasitologie*, 6th ed., **1**, 209. Paris: Masson et Cie.

BUROVA, L. F. & KAKABADSE, M. G. (1941). [Experimental study of strains of *Entamoeba histolytica*.] *Trav. Acad. milit. Méd.* (Leningrad), **25**, 360. [In Russian.]

CARRERA, G. M., SADUN, E. H. & FAUST, E. C. (1952). The effect of protein deficient diets on the susceptibility of guinea pigs to infection with *Endamoeba histolytica*. *Amer. J. trop. Med. Hyg.* **1**, 966.

CHANG, S. L. (1945). Studies on *Entamoeba histolytica*. V. On the decrease in infectivity and pathogenicity for kittens of *E. histolytica* during prolonged *in vitro* cultivation and restoration of these characters following encystment and direct animal passage. *J. infect. Dis.* **76**, 126.

CRAIG, C. F. (1927). Observations upon the hemolytic, cytolytic and complement-binding properties of extracts of *Endamoeba histolytica*. *Amer. J. trop. Med.* **7**, 225.

CRAIG, C. F. (1944). *The Etiology, Diagnosis and Treatment of Amoebiasis*. Baltimore: Williams and Wilkins Co.

DALE, H. H. & DOBELL, C. (1917). Experiments on the therapeutics of amoebic dysentery. *J. Pharmacol.* **10**, 399.

DeLAMATER, J. N., MICHAELSON, J. B., HALLMAN, F. A. & BLUMENTHAL, H. (1954). An investigation into hyaluronidase as a factor in the mechanism of tissue invasion by *Endamoeba histolytica*. *Amer. J. trop. Med. Hyg.* **3**, 1.

DESCHIENS, R. (1936). Modifications expérimentales du pouvoir pathogène de l'amibe dysentérique. *C.R. Soc. Biol., Paris*, **123**, 783.

DESCHIENS, R. (1937). Rôle de la flore microbienne associée à l'amibe dysentérique dans l'étiologie de l'amibiase expérimentale. *C.R. Soc. Biol., Paris*, **125**, 1017.

DESCHIENS, R. (1938*a*). Nouvelles données sur le rôle de la flore associée à l'amibe dysentérique dans l'amibiase expérimentale. *C.R. Soc. Biol., Paris*, **127**, 1076.

DESCHIENS, R. (1938*b*). Le rôle de la flore bactérienne, associée à l'amibe dysentérique, dans l'amibiase. *Ann. Inst. Pasteur*, **61**, 5.

DESCHIENS, R. (1939). Le pouvoir pathogène des amibes dysentériques en culture, ses relations avec l'enkystement. *Bull. Soc. Path. exot.* **32**, 923.

DESCHIENS, R. (1941). Nouvelles données sur la relation existant entre l'enkystement et la conservation du pouvoir pathogène des amibes dysentériques, en culture. *Ann. Inst. Pasteur*, **67**, 468.

DESCHIENS, R. (1950*a*). La biologie de l'amibe dysentérique dans ses relations avec l'amibiase. *Gaz. méd. Fr.* **57**, (16), 829.

DESCHIENS, R. (1950*b*). La nutrition de l'amibe dysentérique. *Biol. méd.* **39**, 57.

DOBELL, C. & O'CONNOR, F. W. (1921). *The Intestinal Protozoa of Man*. London: J. Bale, Sons and Danielsson.

DOBELL, C. & NEAL, R. A. (1952). Researches on the intestinal protozoa of monkeys and man. XII. Bacterial factors influencing the life history of *Entamoeba histolytica* in cultures. *Parasitology*, **42**, 16.

ELSDON-DEW, R. (1946). Some aspects of amoebiasis in Africans. *S. Afric. med. J.* **20**, 580 and 620.

ELSDON-DEW, R. (1953). The pathogenicity of *Entamoeba histolytica*. *S. Afric. med. J.* **27**, 504.

FAUST, E. C. & KAGY, E. S. (1934). Studies on the pathology of amebic enteritis in dogs. *Amer. J. trop. Med.* **14**, 221.

FAUST, E. C. & SWARTZWELDER, J. C. (1935). Effect of continuous passage of *Endamoeba histolytica* through experimental dogs. *Proc. Soc. exp. Biol., N.Y.*, **32**, 954.

FRYE, W. W. & SHAFFER, J. G. (1948). Experimental pathology of amebiasis. *Proc. 4th int. Congr. trop. Med. Malaria*, Washington, **2**, 1075.

HOARE, C. A. (1952). The commensal phase of *Entamoeba histolytica*. *Exp. Parasitol.* **1**, 411.

JAMES, W. M. (1927). Some observations on intestinal amoebiasis due to infection with *Entamoeba histolytica*. *Ann. Rep. Unit. Fruit Co. Med. Dep.* (Boston), **16**, 185.

KESSEL, J. F. (1928). Amoebiasis in kittens infected with amoebae from acute and 'carrier' human cases and with tetranucleate amoebae of the monkey and of the pig. *Amer. J. Hyg.* **8**, 311.

LARSH J. E. JR, (1952). The effect of a blacktongue-producing diet on experimental amebiasis in dogs. *Amer. J. trop. Med. Hyg.* **1**, 970.

Lösch, F. (1875). Massenhafte Entwickelung von Amöben im Dickdarm. *Arch. path. Anat.* **65**, 196.

Luttermoser, G. W. & Phillips, B. P. (1952). Some effects of cultural associates on the infectivity of a strain of *Endamoeba histolytica* for the rabbit. *Amer. J. trop. Med. Hyg.* **1**, 731.

Mathis, C. (1950). Considérations générales sur 'l'amibiase'. *Gaz. méd. Fr.* **57** (16), 731.

Meleney, H. E. (1944). The relationship of clinical amoebiasis to various strains and growth requirements of *Endamoeba histolytica*. *Puerto Rico J. publ. Hlth trop. Med.* **20**, 59.

Meleney, H. E. & Frye, W. W. (1933). Studies of *Endamoeba histolytica* and other intestinal protozoa in Tennessee. V. A comparison of five strains of *E. histolytica* with reference to their pathogenicity for kittens. *Amer. J. Hyg.* **17**, 637.

Meleney, H. E. & Frye, W. W. (1935). Studies of *Endamoeba histolytica* and other intestinal protozoa in Tennessee. IX. Further observations on the pathogenicity of certain strains of *E. histolytica* for kittens. *Amer. J. Hyg.* **21**, 422.

Meleney, H. E. & Frye, W. W. (1937). The pathogenicity of four strains of *Endamoeba histolytica* from Chicago. *Amer. J. dig. Dis.* **4**, 37.

Morita, Y. (1938). Investigations on amoebic dysentery. *J. orient. Med.* **28**, 35. [Quoted from *Bull. Inst. Pasteur*, **36**, 1938, 709, and from Anderson *et al. Amebiasis.* 1953, pp. 80–1.]

Nauss, R. W. & Rappaport, I. (1940). Studies on amebiasis. I. Pathogenesis of mucosal penetration. *Amer. J. trop. Med.* **20**, 107.

Neal, R. A. (1951 a). Some observations on the variation of virulence and response to chemotherapy of strains of *Entamoeba histolytica* in rats. *Trans. R. Soc. trop. Med. Hyg.* **44**, 439.

Neal, R. A. (1951 b). The duration and epidemiological significance of *Entamoeba histolytica* infections in rats. *Trans. R. Soc. trop. Med. Hyg.* **45**, 363.

Neal, R. A. (1954). The influence of encystation upon the virulence of *Entamoeba histolytica* in rats. *Trans. R. Soc. trop. Med. Hyg.* **48**, 533.

Neal, R. A. & Vincent, P. (1955). Strain variation in *Entamoeba histolytica*. I. Correlation of invasiveness in rats with the clinical history and treatment of the experimental infections. *Parasitology* (in the Press).

Paulley, J. W. (1950). Amoebiasis and personality. *Brit. med. J.* ii, 525.

Rees, C. W. (1929). Pathogenesis of intestinal amebiasis in kittens. *Arch. Path.* **7**, 1.

Rees, C. W., Baernstein, H. D., Reardon, L. V. & Phillips, L. (1953). Some interactions *in vitro* of *Endamoeba histolytica* and single species of microbial symbionts. *Amer. J. trop. Med. Hyg.* **2**, 1002.

Reichenow, E. (1931). Die pathogenetische Bedeutung der Darmprotozoen des Menschen. *Zbl. Bakt.* (I. Orig.), **122** (Ber. 14. Tag. Deutsch. Ver. Microbiol. p. *195).

Sadun, E. H., Bradin, Jr., J. L. & Faust, E. C. (1951). The effect of ascorbic acid deficiency on the resistance of guinea-pigs to infection with *Endamoeba histolytica* of human origin. *Amer. J. trop. Med.* **31**, 426.

Sarkissjan, M. A. (1938). Pathogéneité des souches d'*Entamoeba histolytica* provenant de porteurs sains pour les chatons. *Med. Parasitol.* (Moscow), **7**, 123.

Stewart, G. T. (1947). Added bacterial infection in amoebiasis and post-dysenteric colitis. *Trans. R. Soc. trop. Med. Hyg.* **41**, 75.

Stewart, G. T. (1948). The role of bacteria in intestinal amoebiasis in man. *Ann. trop. Med. Parasit.* **42**, 198.

Ter-Matevossian, C., Sarkissian, M. & Zaturian, A. (1936). Rôle pathogène de différentes souches d'*Entamoeba histolytica* rencontrées en Arménie. *Med. Parasitol.* (Moscow), **5**, 108.

WALKER, E. L. & SELLARDS, A. W. (1913). Experimental entamoebic dysentery. *Philipp. J. Sci.* **8B**, 253.

WESTPHAL, A. (1937). Betrachtungen und experimentelle Untersuchungen zur Virulenz der *Entamoeba histolytica* beim Menschen. *Arch. Schiffs- u. Tropenhyg.* **41**, 262.

WESTPHAL, A. (1938*a*). Die Pathogenese der Amöbenruhr bei Mensch und Tier. I. Das Wesen der pathogenetischen Wirksamkeit der Ruhramöbe. *Arch. Schiffs- u. Tropenhyg.* **42**, 343.

WESTPHAL, A. (1938*b*). Die Pathogenese der Amöbenruhr bei Mensch und Tier. II. Die Pathogenese der Amöbenruhr beim Menschen. *Arch. Schiffs- u. Tropenhyg.* **42**, 441.

WESTPHAL, A. (1948). Zur Epidemiologie und Pathogenese der Amöbenruhr in Nordafrika 1941/42. *Z. Hyg.* **128**, 73.

WESTPHAL, A. (1950). Die Amöbenruhr. In Gundel's *Die ansteckenden Krankheiten*, 4th ed. **1**, 602.

WESTPHAL, A. & MARSCHALL, F. (1941). Amöbenruhr bei Katzen auf bakterieller Grundlage. *Virchows Arch.* **308**, 22.

PATHOGENICITY OF FUNGI IN MAN AND ANIMALS

G. C. AINSWORTH

Department of Botany, University College, Exeter

Although the first pathogenic fungi to be recognized were parasites of animals and man, fungi are characteristically parasites of plants, and the relatively few fungi known to attack man and higher animals show certain significant contrasts both to the many which parasitize plants and to bacteria pathogenic for animals. With one or two possible exceptions, there are no obligate fungal parasites of higher animals but many of plants, and the obligate parasites of plants comprise several of the major and ubiquitous orders of Fungi. The nutritional requirements of the fungi which parasitize warm-blooded animals are not unduly specialized. In contrast to pathogenic bacteria, the most highly pathogenic fungi have less exacting nutritional requirements than have certain well-adapted parasites of low pathogenicity, and some saprophytes. These facts are in line with what is perhaps the most important recent development in medical and veterinary mycology—namely, the growing appreciation that fungi are only incidentally pathogens of man and animals. In other words, the pathogenic state of these fungi is probably the exception to a normally saprophytic phase. The full implications of this realization are not yet apparent, but it has already led to a better understanding of the epidemiology of several important mycoses and to the development of more rational measures for their control.

A saprophytic phase had long been postulated for the ringworm fungi and other fungi pathogenic for man, but, apart from one or two common moulds which are potential pathogens, there were very few records of these fungi being found as saprophytes in nature. This position has quite suddenly changed. By intensive search and by the use of selective techniques there have been isolated from the soil the fungi responsible for coccidioidomycosis (*Coccidioides immitis*), histoplasmosis (*Histoplasma capsulatum*), sporotrichosis (*Sporotrichum schencki*), a form of Madura foot (*Allescheria boydii*), and nocardiosis (*Nocardia asteroides*) (see Emmons, 1951). More recently still, dermatophytes and dermatophyte-like fungi have also been isolated from the soil (see Vanbreuseghem, 1952). The soil is thus very clearly an important reservoir of potentially pathogenic fungi. It is probably responsible for the higher incidence of a number of mycoses in agricultural than in urban populations.

Mycologists are traditionally trained as botanists. Many have been plant pathologists. This has given emphasis to studies of fungi pathogenic for plants, and for many such fungi the basic mechanism underlying their pathogenicity is well established. Much less is known about fungi pathogenic for animals, and this essay is an attempt to review the little that is known and to draw attention to certain host-parasite relationships, a study of which may contribute to the understanding of why certain fungi parasitize man and animals and the mechanisms underlying their pathogenic activity.

The pathogenicity of fungal parasites of plants is often determined by the production of enzymes able to affect critical components of the host tissue and of substances toxic to the host. An example of the first is the pectinase enzyme produced by the hyphal tips of *Botrytis cinerea* and of many other fungi which by its action on the middle lamella of the cell wall leads to the disintegration of the host tissue (see Wood, p. 263). Toxic substances may exert a local action, as does oxalic acid which by causing death of cells in the neighbourhood of the fungus may enable a normally saprophytic mould such as *Aspergillus niger* to function as a pathogen; or they may (when they are usually very complex compounds) cause pathological signs in host tissue remote from the site of the infection (see Brian, p. 294). Both of these general mechanisms are also exhibited by fungal pathogens of animals, and the dermatophytes, or ringworm fungi, provide examples of pathogenic effects both at, and at a distance from, the site of infection.

RINGWORM FUNGI

The pathogenic activity of ringworm fungi is restricted to keratinized tissue. This is clearly evident from the relationship shown by a dermatophyte to an infected hair. Hairs seem never to be directly infected by a germinating spore. The ringworm spore is believed always to germinate on the skin of the scalp and to invade the surrounding tissue. It is from the resulting epidermal focus of infection, which possibly provides the necessary 'food base' or 'inoculum potential' (Garrett, 1954), that special hyphae grow down into the hair follicle and invade the hair. Inside the hair, growth of the hyphae is always downwards, but their penetration stops just above the bulb where the growing hyphal tips form what is known as 'Adamson's fringe'. This is the region of the hair in which keratinization is taking place. Only rarely is the non-keratinized bulb invaded. Downward growth of the hyphae keeps pace with the elongation and keratinization of the hair; as a result the distal portions of the hair-shaft become invaded by the pathogen, which frequently sporulates in those regions. Additional evidence of the specificity of dermatophytes for keratinized tissue is shown by the fact that if the spores of a dermatophyte are introduced into the blood stream of an experimental animal they may remain viable for several days but no infection results unless the skin is scarified, when a ring-worm lesion develops at the point of injury (see Gregory (1935) for references).

There are many distinct species of ringworm fungi, but critical and diagnostic taxonomic features are rarely shown during the parasitic phase when the hyphae of one dermatophyte look very like those of another and the only spores (arthrospores) result from the fragmentation of hyphae. In spite of their predilection for keratin, the nutritional requirements of the ringworm fungi are not exacting, and dermatophytes make good growth on a number of common laboratory media and other substrates provided a source of organic (amino) nitrogen is available. Under such conditions growth is more luxuriant and there is a diversity of spores and other structures which enable specific distinctions to be readily made. It would thus appear that the pathogenic action of these fungi is determined rather by their ability to attack keratin than by a preference for this material of low nutritive value. Because of the inability of most other micro-organisms to utilize keratin, dermatophytes probably owe their success as pathogens, at least in part, to the lack of competitors for this particular substrate.

That dermatophytes must produce a keratolytic enzyme has for long been recognized. Microscopic examination of a naturally infected hair often shows clearly a system of longitudinal, air-filled, tunnels which once contained fungal hyphae, and a transverse section of the hair gives the appearance of a perforated plate; effects particularly well seen in human hair attacked by *Trichophyton schoenleini*, the cause of classical favus. On living hairs, attack on the keratinized parts of the hair is usually limited to this longitudinal tunnelling. On detached infected hairs main-tained in a moisture-saturated atmosphere and on detached healthy hairs laid on a living culture of a dermatophyte, there is invasion of the hair-shaft by special hyphae which penetrate the hair transversely and cause the development of rounded pits. This effect was first described and illustrated by Davidson & Gregory (1934, Plate II, figs. 3, 5) for *Microsporum canis* and *Trichophyton mentagrophytes*. Subsequently Vanbreuseghem (1949) described in detail the same effect, which was also independently noted by Page (1950). Vanbreuseghem, who developed a special technique for studying the attack of hairs *in vitro* by dermatophytes, gave the name of 'organes perforateurs' to the specialized penetrating hyphae and showed that most dermatophytes are able, in differing degrees, to attack hair *in vitro*. As regards keratin digestion, it is of interest to recall that Davidson & Gregory observed that the hyphae which penetrate the hair radially lie in wide pits which they do not fill and that the pits have rounded ends, effects which suggest that the keratin is eroded by enzyme action. This suggestion receives support from the work of Page (1950) who observed that although a fragment of horn was digested by *Microsporum gypseum* only when the hyphae and the particle of horn were in close proximity actual contact between them was not essential. Daniels (1953) studied the digestion of human hair by *M. canis* in distilled water and in a simple non-nitrogenous inorganic salt solution containing glucose. He examined the degradation of the hair by direct microscopic examination and confirmed the findings of the earlier workers. He also made chromatographic analyses of filtrates from the experimental cultures and, in the filtrate from hair in glucose-mineral salt solution, he was able to detect all the amino-acids obtained by the hydrolysis of hair by 6N-hydrochloric acid (HCl); in the distilled-water series, tyrosine, methionine and phenylalanine could not be detected.

Such observations as these clearly demonstrate the digestion of keratin by dermatophytes, and the circumstantial evidence that the process is enzymatic or that enzymes are involved is strong. However, neither Tate (1929), using acetone powder preparations from several dermatophytes, nor any other investigator has been able to demonstrate *in vitro* the presence of an enzyme able to attack keratin. Possible explanations for this failure are briefly discussed by Nickerson & Williams (1947), who suggest that dermatophytes are able to attack only a reduction product of keratin, as is the clothes moth (*Tineola biselliella*), in the intestine of which sulphydryl compounds render keratin susceptible to enzyme action.

There is another phenomenon which may have a bearing on this problem. As already mentioned, the morphology of a dermatophyte when parasitizing a living hair *in situ* is very limited and arthrospores are the only spores exhibited. Merely to remove infected hair from the host and to keep it in a moist chamber results, within a few days, in the development of macroconidia and other structures characteristic of the saprophytic phase on culture media. As also noted above, all dermatophytes under experimental conditions *in vitro* seem capable of attacking hair in some degree, even a species such as *Epidermophyton floccosum* which in natural infections is restricted to glabrous skin (Vanbreuseghem, 1949). Similarly, Page (1950) showed that *Microsporum gypseum* attacked human finger nails vigorously *in vitro*, although it appears never to have been recorded as responsible for onychomycosis. The reasons for these *in vivo* and *in vitro* differences are unknown.

Skin lesions produced by dermatophytes may be either inflammatory or non-inflammatory. Certain dermatophytes (e.g. *Microsporum audouini* and *Trichophyton tonsurans*) are normally restricted to man. Others, the so-called 'animal dermatophytes' (e.g. *Microsporum canis* from cats and dogs and *Trichophyton verrucosum* from cattle), though commonly found in man, particularly in rural areas, are considered to be normally pathogens of animals, and very frequently a human infection by one of these species can be traced to contact with an infected animal. It is possible to generalize by saying that the 'animal' species cause more inflammatory lesions in man than do the 'human' species. In other words, the human species are better adapted as parasites of man than are the animal types, because one result of an inflammatory reaction is the shedding of the infected hairs and thus the spontaneous elimination of infection. (This effect was at one time used as a basis for therapeutic measures, an inflammatory reaction and the subsequent loss of the hair was induced by the injection of croton oil into the hair follicle. It is modern practice to do nothing that would discourage the inflammatory reaction induced in man by the cattle ringworm fungi.)

A number of dermatophytes produce a penicillin-like antibiotic active against Gram-positive bacteria (Wolf, 1945). Not infrequently secondary infection by staphylococci or other bacteria complicates a ringworm infection. There is, however, apparently no correlation between the production of an antibiotic by a dermatophyte and the type of lesion induced, for although *Epidermophyton floccosum*, which is rarely associated with an inflammatory lesion, produces small amounts of antibiotic *in vitro*, *Microsporum audouini* does not, and the highest titres of antibiotic in the culture filtrates are produced by such animal species as *Trichophyton mentagrophytes* and *Microsporum gypseum*. The inflammation appears to be basically a host response to the infection in which sensitization of the host by the pathogen may play a part.

Mycotic infections in man and animals very frequently give rise to hypersensitivity of the skin of the affected subject, a sensitivity that is sometimes as reliable and specific an indication of present or past infection by a particular fungus as is the tuberculin test for tuberculosis. Dermatomycoses differ from such systemic mycoses as histoplasmosis (*Histoplasma capsulatum*) in that the immunological phenomena seem to be confined to the skin. In histoplasmosis it is possible to obtain immune serum; in dermatophyte infections it is not. Why this is so has yet to be explained. It may be due to deficiencies in serological techniques. It may be that the superficial infection by a dermatophyte does not induce the production of detectable amounts of antibodies in the blood. Whatever the explanation the general facts are not in dispute. Although it is not possible to produce immune serum by the injection of dermatophytes or their products into the blood, 1–2 weeks after infection by a dermatophyte, man or an experimental animal develops a skin sensitivity that can be demonstrated by the local erythematous reaction to the intradermal injection of an extract of the dermatophyte or of 'trichophytin' which is usually an extract of several dermatophytes. This sensitivity may persist for a varying period after the infection has been eliminated but in time it fades, and the subject, at first immune to reinfection, again becomes susceptible. This is not an occasion to consider in detail the serology of mycotic infections or to speculate on the mechanisms involved, but attention must be drawn to one serological aspect of ringworm infections that has been recognized since 1911 when the Swiss dermatologist Jadssohn described follicular eruptions in patients with the inflammatory type of ringworm lesion known as a kerion. These eruptions or 'dermatophytids' (which are sometimes distinguished as trichophytids and microsporids, according to the genus of ringworm fungi involved) appear, often symmetrically, on the body, feet and legs, and most frequently the hands. No fungus can be isolated from these lesions which disappear spontaneously on the elimination of the primary fungus infection which though characteristically one of the inflammatory type may be very slight or even subclinical. The usually accepted explanation of dermatophytids is that they are an allergic response of the hypersensitized skin either to some metabolic product of the fungus or, though this is perhaps less likely, to fungus spores or other structures carried in the blood stream from the site of the infection, for there are a number of records of the isolation of spores of dermatophytes from blood (see Gregory, 1935, p. 213).

It should now be clear that the mechanisms which determine the pathogenicity of the dermatophytes are not well understood. The dermatophytes were the first fungus pathogens of man to be recognized. They have received more attention than any other group of pathogenic fungi and there is, therefore, even less precise knowledge of the pathogenicity mechanisms of other fungi able to infect animals. During recent years, however, many observations have been made on the response of the host to infection, on the influence of the host in determining infection, and on the behaviour of the pathogen in the host, observations which, though often more relevant to such topics as susceptibility or immunity of the host or the virulence of the pathogen, have a bearing on the mechanism of pathogenicity or may provide clues to its investigation.

ASPERGILLOSIS AND MONILIASIS

Aspergillosis and moniliasis are two mycoses in which toxin production is possibly a major factor in determining pathogenicity. The classical and most usual cause of aspergillosis is *Aspergillus fumigatus*. This common and ubiquitous mould of soil and compost is usually and unequivocably a saprophyte. At other times it is equally clearly a primary and lethal pathogen which, as the cause of 'brooder pneumonia', takes a not inconsiderable annual toll of young poultry. Avian aspergillosis is also of frequent occurrence in zoological gardens where wild birds, especially water birds, appear to be particularly susceptible during the early weeks of captivity (Ainsworth & Rewell, 1949). Although overcrowding, unhygienic conditions, and exposure to mouldy litter undoubtedly play a part in initiating outbreaks of avian aspergillosis there are many gaps in the knowledge of the epidemiology of the condition. All investigators agree, however, that both 'saprophytic' and 'parasitic' isolates of *A. fumigatus* are equally pathogenic for experimental animals. Henrici (1939, 1940) made an extensive series of inoculations in rabbits, guinea-pigs, mice and chickens. He showed that while inoculated rabbits may survive for as long as a month there were two modal times for death, on the second day (if the inoculum was large) and on the tenth day (if the inoculum was small). Henrici attributed the early deaths to the action of a thermolabile endotoxin which he was able to demonstrate in the cell-sap of *A. fumigatus* but not in the culture-filtrate. The cell sap was haemolytic *in vitro* but non-toxic by oral administration. *In vivo* the symptoms induced by injection of the toxin resembled those of the well-known poisonous agaric, *Amanita phalloides*, in man. Pathogenic strains of *Aspergillus flavus* and *A. oryzae* were shown to possess a similar but milder toxicity. Earlier, Blakeslee & Gortner (1913) had recorded the occurrence in the saprophytic mould *Rhizopus stolonifer* of a toxin fatal for rabbits which differed from that from *Aspergillus* in being heat-stable and in the symptoms induced in susceptible animals.

After inoculation with a small dose of spores the course of experimental aspergillosis is rather different. Four to six days after inoculation well-defined abscesses develop, especially in the kidney. Histopathological examination shows that such abscesses contain abundant mycelium which is deeply basophilic. Caseation of the lesions follows and the mycelium becomes pale and acidophilic. Much mycelium is digested but some grows again in a radiating manner (the 'actino-mycetoid form' of Henrici) and the lesion becomes a tubercle. In animals living 10 days or longer there are obvious new lesions, especially in the lungs, which are all of the mycetoma type, as the tubercle-like lesions containing a radiating growth of a fungus are usually designated. It is interesting to note that about the tenth day, at the time the lesions change from abscesses to mycetomas, skin hypersensitivity to the fungus first develops, and Henrici draws attention to the similarity of this course of events to that shown by coccidioidomycosis (*Coccidioides immitis*), in which the primary phase, an acute pulmonary infection, may be followed by nodular eruptions (erythrema nodosum) over the shins. This eruption, which does not occur until skin tests are positive, may be considered to be similar to the dermatophytids associated with ring-worm infections.

Moniliasis (which has been reviewed by Skinner, 1947) shows interesting epidemiological contrasts to aspergillosis. *Candida albicans*, the yeast-like fungus usually responsible for moniliasis, is, like *Aspergillus fumigatus*, of widespread occurrence and more often saprophytic than parasitic. Unlike *A. fumigatus*, however, *C. albicans* is usually found not in soil or on some other external substrate but as a component of the microflora of the mouth, alimentary tract, or vagina of apparently normal individuals. It resembles *A. fumigatus* in that all isolates are pathogenic for the rabbit, death of the experimental animal resulting 4–5 days after inoculation, and it is believed that a toxin plays an important part in determining its pathogenicity. The common expressions of moniliasis in man, such as thrush (oral moniliasis) and intertriginous infections, are usually less severe and rarely fatal. In such conditions, although the pathogen may exhibit a mycelial habit and cause extensive tissue invasion, it rarely takes the form of a mycetoma. There may, however, be an allergic reaction on the skin far removed from the site of the infection resulting in eruptions which are characteristically sterile. It has not been established whether the eruptions are provoked by the yeast cells or by some metabolic product transported by the blood stream to the site of the allergic reaction.

FACTORS AFFECTING PATHOGENICITY

So far the approach has been mainly mycological, that is to say via the pathogen, and evidence has been presented that a fungus may be patho-genic on one occasion and saprophytic on another, and that a pathogen may be limited to certain tissues of the host or may on one occasion cause a local infection and on another a generalized infection. The mechanisms underlying this behaviour are usually obscure, and in an attempt to clarify the problems involved some of the factors affecting the incidence and severity of mycoses will now be considered; these factors were the subject of a brief but stimulating review by Rothman (1949).

The host

The age of the host sometimes plays an important part. As already mentioned, tinea capitis caused by *Microsporum audouini* is typically a disease of infancy. With the onset of puberty this frequently intractable infection spontaneously disappears. This is believed to be due to pubertal changes in the sebaceous glands which in the adult secrete either more, or a higher relative concentration, of straight-chain fatty acids with from eight (caprylic acid, $C_8H_{16}O_2$) to eleven (undecylenic acid, $C_{11}H_{22}O_2$) carbon atoms. *In vitro* experiments have shown these organic acids to be fungicidal or fungistatic, and Rothman suggested that because at puberty the follicular canal and the horny layer of the skin are impregnated with this fungicidal material infection can no longer spread from hair to hair. The fungicidal effects associated with the sebaceous glands possibly also explain the localization of the species of *Trichophyton* and of *Epidermophyton floccosum* in cases of tinea pedis in which the fungi are confined to the interspaces between the toes, the plantar surfaces of the toes, the soles and the sides of the feet. The fungus never invades the dorsa of the toes and feet nor the ankles or legs. That is, the infection is limited to skin surfaces which contain no hair follicles and no sebaceous glands. Rothman suggested that the regions where there are no sebaceous glands are more easily attacked by dermatophytes than other regions of the skin, and also that it is possible that fungi which invade other regions have acquired some degree of resistance to the fatty acids of the skin. Although Rothman was unable to demonstrate that fungi isolated from the feet are more sensitive to fatty acids than fungi isolated from other parts of the body, Murphy & Rothman (1949) were able to increase the resistance of *Trichophyton mentagrophytes* to pelargonic acid ($C_9H_{18}O_2$) sevenfold by subjecting it to gradually increasing concentrations of pelargonic acid in the culture medium, and there have been indications that the fungicidal activity of ether-soluble material from the palms and soles is significantly lower than that from other regions. In contrast to tinea capitis caused by *Microsporum audouini*, erythrasma (*Nocardia minutissima*) and tinea cruris (*Epidermophyton floccosum*) are characteristically post-pubertal infections. Further,

Nocardia minutissima infection is limited to the axilla or the inguinal fold, sites on which the fungus may persist for years, and *Epidermophyton floccosum* has a preference for the inguinal region from which, however, it may occasionally grow out from a well-established lesion on to the surrounding skin. The axillary and inguinal regions in males are regions of apocrine-gland secretion, and there is support for the suggestion that it is this secretion which determines the infection in that these two diseases are characteristically diseases of men; thus in one study of erythrasma cited by Rothman (1949) the male to female ratio was 39:2.

Candida albicans, also, shows intertriginous localization. Interdigital moniliasis is characteristically a disease of housewives and others whose occupations involve having the hands constantly moist. The lesions are commonly situated between the third and fourth digits, and Raubitschek (1946) found that this site could be more easily infected experimentally than other sites. But moisture and increased temperature are apparently not the critical factors in determining intertriginous moniliasis because the most severe lesions are found in women who are both diabetic and obese. The explanation commonly offered is that in a diabetic the glucose content of the epidermis and horny layer of the skin is higher than that in a normal person, and Rothman (1949) cites two cases of generalized moniliasis in which the patients had a disturbed carbohydrate metabolism. In addition, Rothman made the interesting claim that intractable infection with *Trichophyton rubrum* infection is associated with increased glucose tolerance of the infected individual, whereas *Candida albicans* infection is associated with decreased glucose tolerance.

Nutrition

Early nineteenth-century dermatologists frequently attributed ringworm infection to malnutrition, and though it is probable that for man at least the unhygienic conditions usually associated with malnutrition were of greater importance than undernourishment, there is some evidence that the level of nutrition may influence the pathogenicity as expressed by the severity of the symptoms produced in animals. Almeida, da Silva, Brandão, Monteiro & Moura (1950) recently claimed that when cats infected with *Microsporum canis* were given a vitamin-deficient diet the ringworm signs increased in severity and that they were further aggravated by the administration of sulphaguanidine, which, it was suggested, suppressed the production of folic acid by the intestinal bacteria. On change to a full diet the lesions resolved and the animals returned to 'normal' health, but the ringworm infection was not eliminated and lesions recurred after reversion to a deficient diet. The authors

point out that while on the deficient diet the cats lost their sexual activity
which suggests a possible parallel between *M. canis* infection in cats and
M. audouini head ringworm in man (see p. 250 above).

Avian moniliasis (*Candida albicans*) is possibly another mycosis in
which nutrition of the host plays a part. Occasional epizootics of this
infection are seen among poultry, especially in young turkeys in which
the death-rate may be high. The epidemiology is obscure, however.
Great difficulty is experienced in inducing experimental epizootics, even
with isolates of the pathogen obtained from natural epizootics (Blaxland
& Fincham, 1950; Blaxland, 1951; Blaxland & Markam, 1954).
C. albicans is present in the crops of many apparently normal birds, and
what determines the pathogenicity is unknown, as it is for the parallel
condition in man. Overcrowding and unhygienic conditions are not
thought to play a critical role. Scherr (1953a) has recently drawn
attention to the higher death-rate caused by experimental *C. albicans*
infection in mice maintained at 5–12° or at 35–37° than in those kept
at 15–20° and 28–32°, but it has yet to be determined whether this
observation has any relevance to avian moniliasis. Perhaps a more
likely suggestion is that vitamin B deficiency may be a critical factor.
This would not, however, explain why during a natural epizootic a 24 hr
exposure of healthy birds to an infected flock is sufficient for the contraction of infection; from this it would appear that exalted virulence
of the pathogen must also play a part.

Mucin and hormones

Efforts to obtain satisfactory experimental infections for testing new
chemotherapeutic products and for other purposes have revealed various
factors which enhance the pathogenic effects of a number of fungus
pathogens. Campbell & Saslaw (1950) were the first to show that
suspending the cells of the yeast phase of *Histoplasma capsulatum* in
5 % (w/v) hog mucin instead of in saline solution (a method introduced
by Miller (1933) for inducing experimental meningococcal infections in
mice) was a more satisfactory method of establishing infection and that
by varying the dose both the mortality rate and the interval between
inoculation and death could be altered to meet the particular experimental requirements. This effect was confirmed by Strauss & Kligman
(1951), who also found the method of use with a number of other fungi
responsible for systemic infections and for *Candida albicans*, to which
the method was also successfully applied by Salvin, Cory & Berg (1952)
using 2·5 % (w/v) mucin. More recently, studies by Scherr (1953b) have
shown that the pathogenicity of *C. albicans* for mice is enhanced when

either living or formalized washed cells of baker's yeast, *Saccharomyces cerevisiae*, are injected at intervals into the inoculated animals. Scherr was led to experiment with *S. cerevisiae* because of the isolation of 3-indole acetic acid from this yeast and because of his interest in the effects of auxins (hormones) on the systemic infection of *C. albicans* in mice. He was unable to determine the nature of the effect, but he showed that the presence of the whole yeast cell was required. The most probable explanation is that the effect of the yeast cells, like that of mucin and other substances such as starch, gelatin and agar, is due to some action on the defence mechanism of the body of the host. Further studies by Scherr (1953c, 1954) suggest this explanation to be an over-simplified generalization. His results on the effects of cortisone, somatotrophic hormone and sex hormones on the course of systemic moniliasis in mice showed that the environmental temperature, the sex of the animals, the type of aqueous vehicle, the amounts of the different hormones, the dosage schedules employed, and whether the pathogen and the various supplements were administered singly or in various combinations appeared to play interrelated roles.

Antibiotics

Much attention has recently been paid to the effect of antibiotics on the pathogenicity of fungi, and there is now quite an extensive literature on mycotic infections complicating antibiotic therapy. Moniliasis (*Candida albicans*), especially of the mouth, alimentary canal and lungs (e.g. Woods, Manning & Patterson, 1951), has been most frequently recorded in this connexion. Sometimes these infections are fatal (e.g. Brown, Propp, Guest, Beebe & Early, 1953). The two main, and not mutually exclusive, explanations for this association are that the anti-biotic has eliminated competing micro-organisms or that it has enhanced the growth or virulence of the fungus which might utilize either the antibiotic itself or products resulting from the lysis of antibiotic-sensitive organisms. There is also the possibility of lowered resistance of the host due either to a direct effect of the antibiotic or to an avitaminosis resulting from the destruction of intestinal bacteria. Little evidence has been obtained that antibiotics stimulate the growth of *C. albicans* or other potentially pathogenic fungi *in vitro*. Foley & Winter (1949) obtained evidence suggesting a slight stimulation of *C. stellatoidea in vitro*. They also observed increased mortality of 10-day chick embryos inoculated with *C. albicans* or *C. stellatoidea* and treated with one dose of 500 Oxford units of crystalline penicillin; a similar effect was observed in rabbits. The stimulation of *C. albicans* by preparations of aureomycin for oral administration was shown by Lipnik, Kligman & Strauss (1952) to be due to the phosphate content of the inert diluent employed, but, using a refined technique, Huppert, MacPherson & Cazin (1953) claimed that although penicillin, chloramphenicol, streptomycin and terramycin have no appreciable effect, the growth of *C. albicans* is stimulated by crystalline aureomycin. Evidence that aureomycin enhances the pathogenicity of *C. albicans* in mice is probably conclusive. Seligmann (1952) showed that a non-lethal dose of *C. albicans* could be rendered lethal for mice by the simultaneous injection of a non-toxic dose of aureomycin. Further studies (Seligman, 1953) on oral, intravenous and intraperitoneal routes of infection showed that the enhancing effect of the aureomycin was shown only when the antibiotic and the fungus were injected together intraperitoneally, and he concluded that the effect of the aureomycin appeared to be due, like that induced by cortisone or oxytetracycline, to a lowering of host resistance rather than to any stimulation of the pathogen. In oral and intestinal moniliasis after the use of antibiotics it would seem reasonable to assume that the elimination of competitors must contribute to the development of the disease, possibly by allowing a facultative parasite to build up an 'inoculum potential' sufficient to permit invasion of the host tissue.

DIMORPHISM

In this concluding section a return is made to the mycological approach for a consideration of certain aspects of the morphology of the pathogen in relation to pathogenicity. Most fungi are mycelial in habit. Some are unicellular, and of these an ill-defined assemblage, typically characterized by multiplication by budding, is collectively known as 'yeasts'. It is generally believed that the filamentous type was evolved from the unicellular, although it is equally probable that a number of the unicellular forms of to-day, although showing primitive characters, are not essentially primitive but are derived from mycelial forms. Whatever the phylogenetic interpretation, the fact remains that many mycelial fungi can produce a yeast or yeast-like phase, and that under suitable conditions many unicellular fungi are able to exhibit rudimentary or even well-developed mycelium.

Apart from a few groups such as the Chytridiales, an order of typically aquatic fungi of relatively simple morphology and of complex life history, most of the fungal pathogens of plants have a mycelial parasitic phase and show a similar morphology when grown as saprophytes. Many of the fungus pathogens of man and animals, and especially those responsible for systemic infections, have a yeast-like parasitic phase. A fungus pathogenic for animals if mycelial in the host is almost invariably also mycelial in culture. One that is yeast-like during the parasitic phase may also be yeast-like in culture. Alternatively, its saprophytic habit may be mycelial, and the condition in which there is a yeast-like parasitic phase and a mycelial saprophytic phase is known to medical mycologists as 'dimorphism', a phenomenon recently reviewed by Scherr & Weaver (1953).

Before considering dimorphism in greater detail certain aspects of the parasitic phase of non-dimorphic pathogens merit attention. First, it may be recalled that one very obvious aspect of the pathogenicity of a mycelial parasite such as a dermatophyte is the mechanical destruction of hairs, nails and other tissues by their being riddled by the hyphae of the pathogen. An analogous phenomenon in deeper tissues is perhaps exhibited by the *Cryptococcus neoformans*. This yeast, the cause of cryptococcosis, a serious and often fatal mycosis in man, has a pre-dilection for tissue of the central nervous system which may show extensive invasion. The globose cells of *C. neoformans* are 4–6μ in diameter and in the parasitic phase (and also, but less prominently, in old cultures) each cell is surrounded by a wide mucilaginous capsule, the thickness of which may equal or exceed that of the diameter of the cell. The large size of the encapsulated cells and their large numbers lead to a complete disorganization of the infected tissue while multiplication of the pathogen in the cerebro-spinal fluid, a very favourable medium, results in a marked increase in intracranial pressure. This gives rise to violent headaches in man (a symptom relieved by lumbar puncture), and in small laboratory animals such as mice the whole cranium may expand considerably (Lodder & de Minjer, 1947). Another characteristic of *C. neoformans* infection is the absence of tissue reaction, and this is correlated with the very low level or even absence of antibodies in the blood; possibly it is the thickness of the capsule which renders sensitization of the host difficult. These considerations suggest that the main pathogenic action of *C. neoformans* must be attributed to the mechanical breakdown of infected tissue and to pressure exerted on other tissues.

Certain mycelial fungi pathogenic for man and animals exhibit during the pathogenic phase a type of growth unknown elsewhere. This is the development in the infected tissue of small more or less globose masses of mycelium. The best-known examples of these structures are the so-called 'sulphur granules' which are a diagnostic character of the exudate from actinomycotic lesions; similar structures characterize Madura foot. Examination of a crushed granule either in 10 % (w/v) caustic potash or in tissue sections shows that it consists of non-septate hyphae 0·5–1·0 μ

in diameter. Analogous but less compact mycelial growths are commonly seen in lungs attacked by *Aspergillus fumigatus*; the mycelial growths consist of septate hyphae 2–4 μ in diameter, and the radiating peripheral hyphae may be seen to have their tips swollen or modified so that they stain differentially as do the 'clubs' of an actinomycete granule. In relation to pathogenicity, the interest of these structures lies in their being an expression of a host-pathogen interaction by which the host is able to limit the development of a not very invasive pathogen. Evidence in favour of the view that granule (or mycetoma) formation reflects some basic host-pathogen interaction is provided by the observations assembled by Moore (1946) and Almeida (1946) that the cells of a number of fungi (including *Coccidioides immitis*, *Paracoccidioides brasiliensis* and *Sporotrichum schencki*) which have a non-mycelial pathogenic phase occasionally show a peripheral microscopic fringe of radiating processes which may be interpreted as a defence reaction of the fungus to the host (see also p. 249 above).

The dimorphism shown by a number of the pathogens responsible for systemic mycoses is a very characteristic and striking phenomenon. *Histoplasma capsulatum* (histoplasmosis), *H. farciminosum* (epizootic lymphangitis of Equidae), *Blastomyces dermatitidis* (North American blastomycosis), and *Sporotrichum schencki* (sporotrichosis) all have a non-mycelial and yeast-like parasitic phase and a mycelial saprophytic phase. *Coccidioides immitis* (coccidioidomycosis) and the species of *Phialophora* which cause human chromoblastomycosis, a superficial infection of the cutaneous and subcutaneous tissues, also exhibit dimorphism. The differences in the appearance between the parasitic and the saprophytic phases of these fungi are so great that the two phases might be supposed to have no connexion if empirical studies had not revealed the necessary conditions for the mycelial-yeast transformation *in vitro*.

For *Blastomyces dermatitidis* temperature alone is the critical factor. At 25° the growth is mycelial and bears asexual spores. At 37° no spores are produced, and instead of mycelium the fungus takes the form of budding cells very similar to those present in the tissues of an infected animal. The conversion from one phase to the other can be made at will. For *Histoplasma capsulatum* the composition of the medium is also critical and to obtain the yeast phase *in vitro* incubation at 37° on blood agar or other cystein-containing agar (Salvin, 1949) is necessary. Salvin (1947) found that for *Sporotrichum schencki* the maximum quantity of budding cells and the minimum of mycelium required a temperature of 37°, 0·15–0·2 % (w/v) agar, pH 8·2, and an increase in the carbon dioxide tension to between 60 and 80 % (v/v), a result that was in general con-firmed by Drouhet & Mariat (1952), who, however, obtained a satis-factory growth of the yeast in 5 % (v/v) carbon dioxide on a synthetic medium containing growth factors. Subsequently, Bullen (1949) showed that an increase in carbon dioxide tension to 15–30 % (v/v) is essential for inducing the yeast phase of *Histoplasma farciminosum in vitro*. The dimorphism shown by *Coccidioides immitis* and *Phialophora* is not quite so clear-cut. In tissue *C. immitis* occurs as globose sporangia (the 'spherules') from which endogenously produced spores are liberated to give rise to further spherules. In culture *C. immitis* is mycelial and the cottony growth bears vast numbers of thick-walled chlamydospores, which readily become airborne, and to which the fungus owes its reputa-tion as the most dangerous pathogenic fungus to maintain in culture—probably most of those who work with this fungus eventually become infected. Sporangia or sporangium-like bodies, however, occasionally occur in cultures (Emmons, 1947), but there is no technique available for their production in quantity *in vitro*. The same is true for *Phialophora*, in which the parasitic phase is characteristically non-mycelial and the thick-walled, pigmented unicells exhibit multiplication by fission (not budding), while the mycelial saprophytic phase exhibits a diversity of spore forms and a sparse production of thick-walled cells similar to those developed in tissue.

A general explanation of dimorphism is probably that the unicellular phase is basically a response of the fungus to growth under favourable conditions. As already noted (p. 244 above), the parasitic growth of dermatophytes is less exuberant than is the saprophytic. Additional support for the view that the yeast phase is induced by unfavourable conditions is afforded by the Ustilaginales (Smuts), plant-pathogenic fungi in which the growth in the host (which may be considered to be that normal for these fungi) is mycelial, whereas the saprophytic ap-pearance of those which can be maintained in culture is often yeast-like and the production of spores, the usual climax of the parasitic phase, is rare *in vitro*. Similarly, such a typical mould as *Mucor mucedo* may become transformed into chains of budding cells when the fungus is grown submerged in a sugar solution. It is possible, however, that there is another aspect to dimorphism. As Baker, Mrak & Smith (1943) suggested, if the parasitic phase is the abnormal, it is possible that the parasitic form is that which gives the greatest number of reproductive structures with the minimum synthesis of new protoplasm. It was further suggested that the dermatophytes, which *in vitro* will grow over a wide temperature range, owe their inability to invade deeper tissues to the lack of a mechanism able to effect a mycelium-yeast transformation. It must be remembered that not all fungi able to invade deeper tissues are unicellular. The mycelial *Aspergillus fumigatus* may freely ramify the lungs or other tissues, and the predominantly yeast-like *Candida albicans* may produce abundant mycelium (pseudomycelium) in the tonsils, intestinal wall or kidneys; but as Duncan (1947) has emphasized, these infections are localized, as are the infections of the mycelial pathogens which form mycetomas in host tissues. The views of Baker *et al.*, which probably reflect part of the truth, led Scherr to postulate that any agent which would tend to transform the established parasitic yeast phase to the mycelial phase *in vivo* might serve to arrest the multiplication of the pathogen and he made a study of factors which influence the yeast-mycelial transformation in the non-pathogenic yeast *Saccharomyces cerevisiae* (Scherr, 1952) in the light of the earlier investigations by Nickerson and his collaborators on the mechanisms underlying such transformations.

The detailed results obtained by Nickerson cannot be concisely summarized, and the original papers should be consulted. Here it is possible only to indicate some of the more general conclusions relevant to the mechanism of pathogenicity. The investigations began from an observation of the mutual antagonism shown *in vitro* between the dermatophyte *Trichophyton rubrum* and *Candida albicans* when it was observed that in two-membered cultures there was complete inhibition of mycelial production by *C. albicans*. Further study showed that two metabolic products of *T. rubrum* inhibited the yeast to mycelium conversion. One of these was soluble in water and acetone, heat-stable, and adsorbed by Norite from which it could be eluted by dilute aqueous acid alcohol while the other was water soluble but insoluble in acetone, heat labile, and not adsorbed by Norite (Nickerson & Jillson, 1948; Jillson & Nickerson 1948). From a consideration of their results in the light of studies on the experimental induction of filamentous forms in bacteria a hypothesis was put forward that growth (defined as an irreversible increase in volume) involves two independent mechanisms, one of which controls cell division, the other cell elongation. If the first mechanism was inhibited the resulting growth would be filamentous, if the second a mycelial organism would tend to become unicellular. Dimorphism would thus be determined by the differential effect of the environment on these two processes. They showed that while the reversible mycelium (M)-to-yeast (Y) transformation in *Blastomyces dermatitidis* and in *Paracoccidioides brasiliensis* was dependent on temperature alone (Nickerson & Edwards, 1949), for *Candida albicans* the $M \rightleftharpoons Y$ conversion was independent of temperature. Nickerson & Mankowski (1953*a*, *b*) showed that *C. albicans* will develop exclusively as budding cells on a synthetic minimum growth medium with glucose as the carbon source. Replacement of the glucose by soluble starch, glycogen or dextrin resulted in somewhat diminished growth but in extensive filamentation. Nickerson & Van Rij (1949) had previously shown that compounds such as penicillin, cysteine, and glutathione which contain the sulphydryl (—SH) group promote cell division and hence inhibit $Y \to M$, and they contrasted such water-soluble materials having a direct effect on the cell-division enzyme mechanism with water-insoluble, non-specific narcotics, such as camphor, which may induce somewhat similar morphological changes in yeast cells, not by an effect on the cell division but on the formation of new discontinuous cellular-phase boundaries. Nickerson & Mankowski (1953*a*) found that cells showing multiple bipolar budding were abundantly produced in cultures on a polysaccharide medium to which M/100 cysteine had been added. Furthermore, formation of chlamydospores (thick-walled resting spores) was shown to occur under conditions such that there was inhibition of cell division and minimum support for cell growth. A folic acid analogue, aminopterin, was also shown to induce the formation of these structures. Nickerson & Van Rij (1949) showed that the $Y \to M$ transformation was stimulated without appreciable inhibition of growth by exposure of *C. albicans* to cobaltous ions; the inhibition of the yeast phase being most pronounced on magnesium-deficient media with soluble starch as the carbon source at high C/N ratios (Nickerson, 1949; see Nickerson & Zerahn (1949) for further observations on cobalt metabolism).

Of particular relevance to pathogenicity is the observation by Nickerson & Edwards (1949) that the endogenous respiratory rate of the yeast form of *Blastomyces dermatitidis* was several times that of the mycelial form (on a dry-weight basis) on which their comment was: 'If we assume that the velocity of the respiratory processes determines in some measure the energy supply available to an aerobic organism, then it follows that energy-consuming synthetic processes can be more evident in a rapidly respiring organism than in one utilizing oxygen slowly. While the M stages of the organisms considered are known to be infectious, it is highly probable that their virulence is, in some way, associated with the fact that, at the temperature of an animal host, $M \to Y$ will occur, resulting in a greatly increased energy potential available to the invading organism.'

Scherr (1952), from his study of factors which affect the development of the filamentous habit in the normally non-filamentous *Saccharomyces cerevisiae*, concluded that auxins may be responsible for cell elongation in that yeast, and in an attempt to apply the auxin concept to the $Y \rightarrow M$ transformation *in vivo* he treated mice systematically infected with *Candida albicans* with compounds having plant-growth-stimulating properties (auxins). The results were negative (Scherr & Weaver, 1953). And there the matter rests.

As forecast, this review has proved to be somewhat discursive. Not all the data presented have a strict relevance to the mechanisms of pathogenicity, and not all the facts recorded are well established. What should, however, have become evident is that the pathogenicity mechanisms exhibited by fungi parasitic on man and higher animals are both diverse and complicated. Their elucidation provides ample scope for future investigation.

REFERENCES

AINSWORTH, G. C. & REWELL, R. W. (1949). The incidence of aspergillosis in captive wild birds. *J. comp. Path.* **59**, 213–24.

ALMEIDA, F. P. DE (1946). Considerações sôbre as formações actinomycetoides, radiadas ou maças dos congumelos nos tecidos. *An. Fac. Med. Univ. S. Paulo,* **22**, 249–63.

ALMEIDA, F. DE, DA SILVA, A. C., BRANDÃO, C. H., MONTEIRO, E. L. & MOURA, R. A. (1950). Saprofitismo do *Microsporum canis* em gatos. *Rev. Inst. Adolfo Lutz,* **10**, 49–52.

BAKER, E. E., MRAK, E. M. & SMITH, C. E. (1943). The morphology, taxonomy, and distribution of *Coccidioides immitis*, Rixford & Gilchrist, 1896. *Farlowia,* **1**, 199–244.

BLAKESLEE, A. F. & GORTNER, R. A. (1913). On the occurrence of a toxin in juice expressed from the bread mould, *Rhizopus nigricans* (*Mucor stolonifer*). *Biochem. Bull.* **2**, 542. (See also GORTNER & BLAKESLEE, *Amer. J. Physiol.* **34**, 252, 1914.)

BLAXLAND, J. D. (1951). The causes of epidemic outbreaks of moniliasis in turkeys. *Off. Rep. World's Poult. Congr., Paris,* pp. 21–7.

BLAXLAND, J. D. & FINCHAM, I. H. (1950). Mycosis of the crop (moniliasis) in poultry with particular reference to serious mortality occurring in young turkeys. *Brit. vet. J.* **106**, 221–31.

BLAXLAND, J. D. & MARKHAM, L. M. (1954). Observations in the transmissibility and pathogenesis of moniliasis in turkey poults. *Brit. vet. J.* **110**, 139–45.

BROWN, C., PROPP, S., GUEST, C. M., BEEBE, R. T. & EARLY, L. (1953). Fatal fungus infections complicating antibiotic therapy. *J. Amer. med. Ass.* **152**, 206–7.

BULLEN, J. J. (1949). The yeast-like form of *Cryptococcus farciminosum* (Rivolta). (*Histoplasma farciminosum*). *J. Path. Bact.* **61**, 117–20.

CAMPBELL, C. C. & SASLAW, S. (1950). Use of mucin in experimental infections of mice with *Histoplasma capsulatum*. *Proc. Soc. exp. Biol., N.Y.,* **73**, 469–72.

DANIELS, G. (1953). The digestion of human hair keratin by *Microsporum canis* Bodin. *J. gen. Microbiol.* **8**, 289–94.

DAVIDSON, A. M. & GREGORY, P. H. (1934). *In situ* cultures of dermatophytes. *Canad. J. Res.* **10**, 373–93.

DROUHET, E. & MARIAT, F. (1952). Étude des facteurs déterminant le développement de la phase levure de *Sporotrichum schencki*. *Ann. Inst. Pasteur*, **83**, 506–14.

DUNCAN, J. T. (1947). Virulence of fungi in animals. *J. gen. Microbiol.* **1**, iv–v.

EMMONS, C. W. (1947). Biology of *Coccidioides*. In Nickerson, W. J. (ed.), *Biology of pathogenic fungi*, pp. 71–82.

EMMONS, C. W. (1951). The isolation from soil of fungi which cause disease in man. *Trans. N.Y. Acad. Sci.* Ser. II, **14**, 51–4.

FOLEY, G. E. & WINTER, W. D. (1949). Increased mortality following penicillin therapy of chick embryos infected with *Candida albicans* var. *stellatoidea*. *J. infect. Dis.* **85**, 268–74.

GARRETT, S. D. (1954). Function of the mycelial strands in substrate colonization by the cultivated mushroom, *Psalliota hortensis*. *Trans. Brit. mycol. Soc.* **37**, 51–7 (cf. *New Phytol.* **50**, 149, 1951).

GREGORY, P. H. (1935). The dermatophytes. *Biol. Rev.* **10**, 208–33 [95 refs.].

HENRICI, T. (1939). An endotoxin from *Aspergillus fumigatus*. *J. Immunol.* **36**, 319–38. (Abstr. *J. Bact.* **36**, 278, 1938.)

HENRICI, T. (1940). Characteristics of fungus diseases. *J. Bact.* **39**, 113–38.

HUPPERT, M., MACPHERSON, D. A. & CAZIN, J. (1953). Pathogenesis of *Candida albicans* infection following antibiotic therapy. I. The effects of antibiotics on the growth of *Candida albicans*. *J. Bact.* **65**, 171–6.

JILLSON, O. F. & NICKERSON, W. J. (1948). Mutual antagonism between pathogenic fungi. Inhibition of dimorphism in *Candida albicans*. *Mycologia*, **40**, 369–85.

LIPNIK, M. J., KLIGMAN, A. M. & STRAUSS, R. (1952). Antibiotics and fungous infections. *J. invest. Derm.* **18**, 247–60.

LODDER, J. & DE MINJER, A. (1947). On the biology of the pathogenic Torulopsidoideae. In W. J. Nickerson (ed.), *Biology of pathogenic fungi*, pp. 7–19.

MILLER, C. P. (1933). Experimental meningococcal infection in mice. *Science*, **78**, 340–1.

MOORE, MORRIS (1946). Radiate formation on pathogenic fungi in human tissue. *Arch. Path.* **42**, 113–53.

MURPHY, J. C. & ROTHMAN, S. (1949). Artificially induced resistance of *Trichophyton gypseum* to pelargonic acid. *J. invest. Dermat.* **12**, 5–6.

NICKERSON, W. J. (1949). Mechanism of cell division in pathogenic fungi. *Amer. J. Bot.* **36**, 812 (Abstract).

NICKERSON, W. J. & EDWARDS, G. A. (1949). Studies on the physiological bases of morphogenesis in fungi. I. The respiratory metabolism of dimorphic pathogenic fungi. *J. gen. Physiol.* **33**, 41–55.

NICKERSON, W. J. & JILLSON, O. F. (1948). Interaction between pathogenic fungi in culture. Considerations on the mechanism of cell division in the dimorphism of pathogenic fungi. *Mycopathologia*, **4**, 279–83.

NICKERSON, W. J. & MANKOWSKI, Z. (1953a). Role of nutrition in maintenance of the yeast-shape in *Candida*. *Amer. J. Bot.* **40**, 584–92.

NICKERSON, W. J. & MANKOWSKI, Z. (1953b). A polysaccharide medium of known composition favouring chlamydospore formation in *Candida albicans*. *J. infect. Dis.* **92**, 20–5.

NICKERSON, W. J. & VAN RIJ, N. J. W. (1949). The effects of sulfhydryl compounds, penicillin, and cobalt in the cell division mechanism of yeasts. *Biochim. biophys. Acta*, **3**, 461–75.

NICKERSON, W. J. & WILLIAMS, J. W. (1947). Nutrition and metabolism of pathogenic fungi. In Nickerson, W. J. (ed.), *Biology of pathogenic fungi*, pp. 130–56.

NICKERSON, W. J. & ZERAHN, K. (1949). Accumulation of radioactive cobalt by dividing yeast cells. *Biochim. biophys. Acta*, **3**, 476–83.

PAGE, R. M. (1950). Observations on keratin digestion by *Microsporum gypseum. Mycologia*, **42**, 591–602.

RAUBITSCHEK, F. (1946). Role of *Candida albicans* in the production of erosio inter-digitalis and paronychia, *Dermatologica*, **93**, 295.

ROTHMAN, S. (1949). Susceptibility factors in fungus infections in man. *Trans. N.Y. Acad. Sci.* ser. II, **12**, 27–33.

SALVIN, S. B. (1947). Multiple budding in *Sporotrichum Schenckii* Matruchot. *J. invest. Dermat.* **69**, 315–20.

SALVIN, S. B. (1949). Cysteine and related compounds in the growth of the yeast-like phase of *Histoplasma capsulatum. J. infect. Dis.* **84**, 275–83.

SALVIN, S. B., CORY, J. C. & BERG, M. K. (1952). The enhancement of the virulence of *Candida albicans* in mice. *J. infect. Dis.* **90**, 177–82.

SCHERR, G. H. (1952). Studies of the dimorphism mechanism in *Saccharomyces cerevisiae. Mycopathologia*, **6**, 182–230.

SCHERR, G. H. (1953a). The effect of environmental temperature on the course of systemic moniliasis in mice. *Mycologia*, **45**, 359–63.

SCHERR, G. H. (1953b). Enhanced dissemination of moniliasis in mice by the injection of yeast cells. *J. Creighton Univ. Sch. Med.* **8**, 20–4.

SCHERR, G. H. (1953c). The effect of cortisone and somatotrophic hormone on the course of systemic moniliasis in mice. *Raissunti delle Communicazioni vi Internat. Microbiol. Congr.* **3**, 44.

SCHERR, G. H. (1954). The influence of sex hormones, cortisone, and somatotrophic hormone on systemic moniliasis in mice. *Bact. Proc.* p. 86.

SCHERR, G. H. & WEAVER, R. H. (1953). The dimorphism phenomenon in yeasts. *Bact. Rev.* **17**, 51–92 [187 refs.].

SELIGMANN, E. (1952). Virulence enhancing activities of aureomycin on *Candida albicans. Proc. Soc. Exp. Biol., N.Y.*, **79**, 481–4.

SELIGMANN, E. (1953). Virulence enhancement of *Candida albicans* by antibiotics and cortisone. *Proc. Soc. exp. Biol., N.Y.*, **83**, 778–81.

SKINNER, C. E. (1947). The yeast-like fungi: *Candida* and *Brettanomyces. Bact. Rev.* **11**, 227–74 [303 refs.].

STRAUSS, R. E. & KLIGMAN, A. M. (1951). The use of gastric mucin to lower the resistance of laboratory animals to systemic fungus infections. *J. infect. Dis.* **88**, 151–5.

TATE, P. (1929). On the enzymes of certain dermatophytes or ringworm fungi. *Parasitology*, **21**, 31–54.

VANBREUSEGHEM, R. (1949). La culture des dermatophytes *in vitro* sur des cheveux isolés. *Ann. Parasit. hum. comp.* **24**, 559–73 (see also *Mycologia*, **44**, 176–82, 1952).

VANBREUSEGHEM, R. (1952). Intérêt théorique et pratique d'un nouveau dermato-phyte isolé du sol: *Keratinomyces ajelloi* gen.nov., sp. nov. *Bull. Acad. roy. Belg.* (Cl. Science), sér. 5, **38**, 1068–77.

WOLF, F. (1945). The production of a penicillin-like factor by dermatophytes. *Mycologia*, **37**, 796–7.

WOODS, J. W., MANNING, I. H. & PATTERSON, C. N. (1951). Monilial infections complicating the therapeutic use of antibiotics. *J. Amer. med. Ass.* **145**, 207–11.

PECTIC ENZYMES SECRETED BY PATHOGENS AND THEIR ROLE IN PLANT INFECTION

R. K. S. WOOD

Plant Pathology Laboratory, Imperial College of Science and Technology, London

INTRODUCTION

The invasion of higher plant tissue by certain micro-organisms is associated with breakdown of the cell wall and the separation of the individual cells from each other. This activity is commonly called maceration and is generally followed by death of the protoplasts. These effects, which occur before extensive degradation of the cell wall can be observed microscopically, are produced at an early stage of infection and are often observed in areas not yet invaded by the pathogen itself. After maceration, the individual cells are destroyed by autolysis and by the further action of the primary pathogen or other organisms which follow later. The pathogens responsible for diseases of this type are facultative parasites; they are readily cultured on artificial media and their mode of parasitism has been intensively studied for many years. Some of the earliest investigations showed that maceration was caused by the secretion of one or more substances by the pathogen because effects similar to those occurring naturally were produced by cell-free extracts of substrates on which the pathogen had grown. Early workers were divided in their opinions about the nature of these substances: some thought that they were enzymes of one sort or another, others considered that they were simpler materials, particularly soluble oxalates. There were also divergent views on whether the principles responsible for cell separation and for death of the protoplasts were separate and distinct or were one substance. These and related problems were largely resolved, at least for the fungus *Botrytis cinerea*, in a series of papers which have now become classical and which have been summarized together with other material in two reviews (Brown, 1934, 1936). This work showed that *B. cinerea* macerates plant tissue by secreting one or more pectic enzymes, that inorganic substances play no direct part in the process, and that death of the protoplasts is either the direct consequence of enzyme action or is caused by a toxin which does not act until the tissue has been macerated.

There is now a substantial body of evidence that the secretion of pectic enzymes plays an important and perhaps vital part in the invasion and breakdown of plant tissue by pathogens of the facultative type. This is not at all surprising because such organisms frequently produce these enzymes and because pectic materials are important components of cell walls, particularly of parenchymatous tissue, which is the type of tissue most readily attacked. The part played by enzymes attacking other cell-wall substances, especially the cellulose and hemicellulose fractions, is less well known; they must be significant, however, where the deposition of other materials has conferred special properties on the cell wall itself.

In recent years there has been a growing interest in the structure of pectic substances, particularly those of the cell wall, and in the production and mode of action of the enzymes acting upon these materials. In spite of its importance, little of this work has been done by plant pathologists; most of our more recent knowledge of the subject has come from the work of those interested in the industrial uses of pectic substances and enzymes, especially in food technology. The results of this work, although not immediately connected with plant pathology, are obviously of great significance in the more detailed study of the way in which micro-organisms invade and become established in the tissues of higher plants. This paper will therefore deal primarily with the secretion of pectic enzymes by plant pathogens and with their significance in the parasitic process in the light of recent knowledge of these enzymes and their substrates. Attention will largely be confined to the attack of parenchymatous tissue—that is, relatively undifferentiated tissue, because it is for such material that we have most information. However, diseases of the wilt type caused by pathogens confined to the vascular system of the host plant will be considered briefly because recent work has provided evidence that the secretion of one or more pectic enzymes by these organisms is at least partly responsible for the development of typical wilt symptoms.

Consideration of the action of pectic enzymes on plant tissue must involve discussion of the nature of pectic substances and of their relation to other components of the cell wall and to the protoplast itself. Since the recent work on these subjects may not be familiar to some plant pathologists, and since, in any case, the terminology of the pectic substances and enzymes is still not settled, the consideration of the part played by pectic enzymes in plant infection will be prefaced by an account of these enzymes, the pectic substances, and the composition of the cell wall.

NOMENCLATURE AND INTERRELATIONS OF PECTIC SUBSTANCES

The terminology commonly accepted at present is as follows.

Pectic substances are complex colloidal carbohydrate derivatives from plants; they contain a large proportion of anhydrogalacturonic acid units which are thought to exist in chain-like combination; the carboxyl groups of polygalacturonic acids may be partly esterified by methyl groups and partly or completely neutralized by one or more bases.

Protopectin is the water-insoluble parent pectic substance found in plants; it yields pectinic acids on restricted hydrolysis.

Pectinic acids are colloidal polygalacturonic acids containing more than a negligible proportion of methyl ester groups.

Pectins are water-soluble pectinic acids of varying (but generally high) methyl ester content which are able to form gels with sugar and acid under suitable conditions.

Pectic acids are pectic substances *essentially* free from methyl ester groups.

It should be noted that with the possible exception of pectic acid, these definitions refer to groups of substances; some pectic materials may therefore be regarded either as the lowest members of one group or as the highest member of the next group. In addition, it is difficult to assess the purity of crude pectic substances obtained from plants because the procedures used in further purification usually cause some degradation. Such crude preparations almost invariably contain a proportion of arabans and galactans, these being linear polymers of arabinose and galactose respectively. In the past, some workers have postulated that these substances are an integral part of the polyuronide chain, and quite recently it has been suggested that they may be linked to these chains by bonds other than those of primary valence. There is now, however, good evidence that in carefully purified preparations from some sources, arabans and galactans do not form part of the polyuronide chain.

The pectic substance of greatest interest to pathologists is undoubtedly protopectin; unfortunately, it is also the one about which least is known. The possible composition and structure of this substance will be described after a brief account has been given of the structure of plant cell walls and the distribution in them of various pectic substances.

The first readily recognizable membrane between cells, known as the middle lamella, is composed of isotropic material and is believed to consist largely, if not entirely, of pectic substances. The next layer, the primary cell wall, has cellulose as its major component; it also contains a proportion of insoluble pectic substances which may be quite high in some tissues. This layer is further characterized by being capable of growth and in this way is distinguished from the third layer, the secondary cell wall, which is generally laid down after active growth of the cell has stopped. The secondary cell wall may again contain appreciable amounts of pectic substances but is mainly composed of cellulose and a variety of other materials deposited during its formation.

In the parenchymatous cells with which this paper will be primarily concerned, the secondary wall remains relatively simple, containing only small quantities of substances such as lignin which so profoundly alter the physical and chemical characteristics of other, more highly differentiated cells. In parenchyma, therefore, materials elaborated from cellulose and pectic substances form the great bulk of the cell wall, and it seems probable that it is the structure and interrelation of these substances which determines the course of cell-wall degradation by micro-organisms.

A great deal is now known of the fine structure of cellulose and the way in which it is built up into the structure of the cell wall; our present knowledge of this subject has been well summarized in a recent monograph (Preston, 1952). The cellulose 'molecule' is, in the first place, a linear polymer of anhydroglucose units held together by C—O—C linkages between C atoms 1 and 4 of the pyranose ring. Adjacent chains are held together by hydrogen bonds between neighbouring —OH groups. In the cell wall, cellulose occurs in two states of aggregation; in the first the chains are arranged in a regular crystal lattice into which water and other substances penetrate only with difficulty; in the second, the arrangement of the chains is not crystalline, the chains being more loosely aggregated, so permitting easier penetration by various substances. Cellulose is therefore considered to have a micellar structure in which regions having a highly ordered structure, the micelles, alternate with less highly ordered regions, the inter-micellar spaces. Cellulose in the cell wall is further organized into fibrils of diameter in the range 100–450 Å.; these occur in the primary cell wall as a meshwork which is not very highly orientated. In the secondary cell wall the fibrils are well orientated, the angle of orientation differing in the separate lamellae which are found in this layer.

A fairly clear picture of the organization of cellulose within the cell wall is therefore available. In contrast, relatively little is known of the distribution and structure of the insoluble pectic substances. The solubility of the polygalacturonic acid chain depends upon its length and upon the degree of substitution of COOH by $COOCH_3$ in the side-chains. The completely de-esterified molecule of pectic acid is highly insoluble, as are its salts of divalent and higher valency cations. Proto-pectin may therefore be insoluble because it occurs in this form; many years ago it was in fact suggested that the protopectins of the middle lamella consisted mainly of calcium or magnesium pectates. Although this has not been fully corroborated, the solubility of middle-lamella protopectin certainly differs from that of the protopectin of the primary and secondary cell walls. On hydrolysis these yield soluble pectinic acids, normally of high methoxyl content. The insolubility of this second type of protopectin may be merely a function of polymer size, since it is well known that pectinic acids become more soluble on degradation. It is also possible that this protopectin is a combination of pectinic acids and cellulose; various degrees of union between these two substances have been suggested from chemical linkage to loose adsorption. The hypothesis of a chemical union between the two has been made more likely by the discovery of a small proportion of free COOH groups in cellulose. It has also been suggested recently (Bock, 1943) that in both types of protopectin linear chains of polygalacturonic acid are bound together by cross-linkages between adjacent COOH groups through calcium or other metals. The type of protopectin resulting from such association would depend on the extent to which adjacent chains were esterified. If there were relatively few free COOH groups, the chains would be connected by widely separated cross-linkages to give hydrophilic, loosely meshed complexes with little rigidity but with good swelling properties in water. Intermolecular cleavage would yield long chains of high methoxyl pectinic acids. With an increase in the number of COOH groups in adjacent chains, the number of cross-linkages might also be increased to give closely meshed complexes of high mechanical strength but with poorer swelling proper-ties in water. It is to be noted therefore that these workers and others before them attach great importance to the COOH groups of the con-stituent pectinic acids in protopectin and, on the basis of the hypothesis outlined, consider that the protopectins of the middle lamella and other parts of the cell wall are essentially similar, differing only in their COOH content and therefore in the degree of meshing through —Ca— or other linkages. Some indirect support for these views is provided by the fact that an enzyme which de-esterifies pectinic acids to give COOH groups is widespread in higher plant tissue.

Although little direct evidence is available, 1, 4-glycosidic linkages may not be the only ones present in the polygalacturonic acid chain;

arabinose or galactose may also occur at infrequent intervals. The rupture of such linkages, particularly if these were more labile than those between anhydrogalacturonic acid units, might well produce fragments of the chain sufficiently short to be soluble.

Finally, it may be mentioned that some primary cell walls contain appreciable quantities of protein, although it is not clear whether this is present in the wall proper or is a contaminant from the protoplast persisting during the process of isolation and purification. If protein forms an integral part of the cell wall, it is quite possible that it plays a part in the insolubility of protopectin.

The relation between pectic substances and other components of the primary and secondary cell wall is not known. It has been suggested that molecules of cellulose and pectinic acids may be linked between their COOH groups. At a higher level of organization pectic materials and cellulose may form a loose association in the intermicellar spaces or in the spaces between the microfibrils. In this connexion, recent work has provided evidence that the pectic material in collenchyma cell walls occurs as fibrils forming a poorly orientated meshwork (Roelofsen & Kreger, 1951). It is certainly true that removal of pectinic acids and other substances from primary cell walls greatly increases the sharpness of the X-ray diagram of cellulose, indicating a rather close association between the cellulose and the other materials of the cell wall. It is apparent that much further work will be necessary before a clear picture of the distribution of pectic substances in the outer layers of the cell wall will emerge. Similar considerations do not, however, apply to the middle lamella; as already stated, this is considered to consist almost entirely of polyuronide material.

PECTIC ENZYMES

In view of the gaps in our knowledge of the pectic substances, it is not surprising that our information on the enzymes degrading them is even less definite. Recently, however, these enzymes have attracted a great deal of attention, and the study of their mode of action may provide valuable clues about the structure of their substrates. In spite of this work, the nomenclature of these enzymes is still confused; for only two of them are the properties and mode of action at all well known, and much remains to be learned even about these. Perhaps the best known pectic enzyme is pectin-esterase which catalyses the hydrolysis of the methyl-ester groups in pectinic acids and pectin to give methyl alcohol and pectic acid or pectinic acids of lower methoxyl content. This enzyme has no effect on the main structure of the chain, but the production of

free COOH groups confers new properties on the molecular chains—
for example, this decreases solubility and increases the ability to form
insoluble complexes with polyvalent cations. This enzyme commonly
occurs in higher plants and is produced by a wide variety of micro-
organisms. The enzymes from these two sources differ a little in their
properties, particularly in their optimum pH values and in their reactions
to the presence or absence of certain salts.

The second well-known enzyme, polygalacturonase, hydrolyses the
1,4-glycosidic linkages between adjacent anhydrogalacturonic acid
residues with profound effects on the properties of the chain. Polygalacturonic acids of lower molecular weight are produced and, finally,
the monomer galacturonic acid. Polygalacturonase has been reported
from higher plant tissue only in isolated cases; it is produced, however,
by many of a wide variety of micro-organisms. The properties of polygalacturonase in certain commercial preparations, presumably of fungal
origin, are now well known. It has a relatively low pH optimum, in the
range of 3·0–5·0, and is activated by a number of cations. A striking
feature is that this enzyme is more active on pectinic acids of low
methoxyl content, and it has therefore been suggested that only 1,4-
glycosidic linkages bound on each side by free COOH groups are labile
so that, essentially, the substrate of this enzyme is pectic acid (Jansen &
MacDonnell, 1945). In view of this finding polygalacturonase can be
assayed accurately only in the absence of pectin-esterase and at pH
values at which de-esterification is relatively slow. Activity of this
enzyme is generally measured by determining the increase in reducing
groups formed on rupture of the glycosidic linkages.

In recent years, a number of other enzymes have been described which
resemble polygalacturonase in some ways but differ in that highly
esterified pectinic acids are readily attacked, indeed, in some cases, more
readily than low methoxyl pectins (Roboz, Barratt & Tatum, 1952;
Seegmiller & Jansen, 1952). The hydrolysis produced by these enzymes
is not as complete as that produced by polygalacturonase, and the reaction
stops before galacturonic acid is produced. Certain of these enzymes
also differ in having higher pH optima. These enzymes will be referred
to collectively as *depolymerases*, on the understanding that this term in
no way attempts to specify the way in which the enzymes act; enzymes
within this group are frequently assayed by measuring the rate at which
they reduce the viscosity of solutions of soluble pectic substrates.

The pectic enzyme of greatest interest to pathologists is *protopectinase*;
it is also the enzyme about which least is known. Its substrate is the
ill-defined protopectin, and its presence is generally recognized by its

action on living plant tissue—that is, on protopectin in its natural state. Methods for assaying this enzyme are necessarily rather crude; generally, slices of parenchymatous tissue of standard thickness are immersed in test solutions, the coherence of the tissue is tested periodically and the activity taken as the inverse of the time taken for the tissue to lose coherence. When this happens, the cells come away from each other along the line of the middle lamella, i.e. there is no rupture of the primary or secondary cell wall at this stage. It is therefore assumed that the first action of protopectinase is on the protopectin of the middle lamella; since other materials are not thought to occur in any quantity in the middle lamella, it is likely that at this early stage of attack it is the pectic enzymes which are most important. Later, enzymes degrading other cell-wall components may be involved; but even here the breakdown of pectic materials may be important, particularly if they occur in intimate association with the cellulose fibrils or micelles. A major study in plant pathology therefore is the characterization of the pectic enzymes secreted by plant pathogens and analyses of their effects on host tissue. Unfortunately, this is still a neglected field of investigation. The rest of the paper will deal with this subject and will refer chiefly to still unpublished work done in recent years at Imperial College; only passing reference will be made to other work in this field.

TYPES OF PROTOPECTINASE AND OTHER PECTIC ENZYMES SECRETED BY PLANT PATHOGENS

It must first be emphasized that, although for convenience protopectinase will be referred to as if it were a single enzyme, protopectinase *activity* may well involve the action of more than one enzyme. This must also be borne in mind in interpreting data based on the somewhat crude assay methods used for this enzyme.

The protopectinases secreted by the following pathogens have been studied in some detail at Imperial College: *Pythium debaryanum* (Gupta, 1953), *Fusarium moniliforme* (Singh, 1953), *Botrytis cinerea* (Jarvis, 1953), *Verticillium dahliae* (Kamal, personal communication), *Sclerotium rolfsii* (Abeygunawardena, personal communication) and *Bacterium aroideae* (Jarvis, 1953; Wood, 1951, 1954). *Verticillium dahliae* causes a typical wilt disease; the others produce a typical soft-rot of susceptible tissue.

A striking fact which has emerged from these investigations is that the properties of the protopectinase from each organism differ in one or more ways from those of the other organisms in the group. The ways in which these enzymes differ will be briefly summarized.

With the exception of *Pythium debaryanum* the organisms produce protopectinase on relatively simple media. They differ, however, in their reaction to pectic substances in the culture solutions. *Bacterium aroideae* and *Pythium debaryanum* produce active solutions in the absence of pectic substrates, *Botrytis cinerea* and *Verticillium dahliae* produce quite active preparations without pectic substances but produce much more active solutions when they are present, *Sclerotium rolfsii* and *Fusarium moniliforme* produce protopectinase only in the presence of pectic substances. Where a response is obtained from the addition of pectic materials, a wide range of these substances is effective from protopectin to pectic acid; the response would therefore seem to be to the 1,4-glycosidic linkage.

The enzymes differ widely in their pH optima. *Sclerotium rolfsii* has an optimum in the range 3–5·5; *Botrytis cinerea* has an optimum at 6·2 with a secondary high value at 2·6, whereas the other four organisms have surprisingly high optima which are not easy to determine accurately but are in the range 8·5–9·5. Optima at such high values are difficult to interpret owing to the de-esterification of pectinic acids in alkaline media; this matter will be referred to later.

The protopectinases from these six organisms react quite differently to heat treatment. The most sensitive seems to be the enzyme from *Pythium debaryanum* which loses activity rapidly on exposure to temperatures in the range of 40–45° and is almost completely inactivated after one minute at 55°. The enzymes from *Fusarium moniliforme* and *Botrytis cinerea* are gradually inactivated as the temperature of exposure increases, little activity remaining after 5 min. at 100 and 60° respectively. *Bacterium aroideae* shows anomalous behaviour; although activity is largely lost after short exposures at 70°, there is a slight but definite increase in activity after exposure at 80°. This effect is particularly pronounced for *Sclerotium rolfsii*; protopectinase from this fungus is rapidly inactivated at 60 and 70°; heating at 80, 90 and 100° produces much less loss of activity. For example, certain preparations which macerate tissue slices in 20 min. at 25°, after exposure to 100° for 10 min., macerate similar slices in 60 min. at 25°. The enzyme from *Verticillium dahliae* also shows remarkable resistance to high temperatures; considerable activity remained after exposure for 5 min. at a series of temperatures up to and including 100°.

These enzymes also react differently to dialysis and the presence of salts. The enzyme from *Fusarium moniliforme* has a slightly greater activity after dialysis; the activity of the others is reduced by dialysis, although not seriously so except for *Bacterium aroideae*, where the activity which is lost is almost completely restored by the addition of Ca^{++}.

The gross effect of each of these protopectinases on plant tissue is the same: separation of the cells along the line of the middle lamella followed by death of the protoplasts. There are, however, some differences in detail. Thus, slices of potato tuber macerated by *B. aroideae* enzyme are limp, are picked up only with difficulty by a forceps, and are slimy to the touch; in contrast, slices placed in solutions of *Botrytis cinerea* enzyme retain their turgidity even when macerated, quite small fragments are easily picked up and the tissue is not slimy to the touch. The basis of these differences is quite unknown. It is apparent, however, from what has been said above that there are real differences in the properties of the protopectinases from the different organisms; these differences may well be reflected in the ways in which the enzymes degrade the proto-pectin of the cell wall.

Solutions containing protopectinases almost always contain enzymes which degrade soluble pectic substances so that any soluble substances of very high molecular weight produced by the action of protopectinase on protopectin are immediately broken down to compounds of lower molecular weight. It is therefore important to determine whether any of these enzymes are identical with protopectinases. So far, this has been done only indirectly by comparing the protopectinase, poly-galacturonase and depolymerase activities of solutions under different conditions. Such comparisons have now been made in some detail for a number of pathogens and will be referred to briefly here. In con-sidering the results which have been obtained, it should be noted that, rather surprisingly, filtrates from liquid cultures of the pathogens tested had little or no pectin-esterase activity except in the case of *B. cinerea*; even here, however, activity was relatively low. Complications were not, therefore, caused by this factor.

Enzyme solutions from *Bacterium aroideae* assayed viscometrically (depolymerase) and on tissue slices (protopectinase) had generally similar properties in the following respects: pH optimum, thermal inactivation, loss of activity on dialysis, activation by Ca^{++}, inactivation at pH 2·7, and optimum pH for precipitation from solution with acetone or ethanol (Wood, 1954). There is in fact a good deal of circumstantial evidence that the enzyme which reduces the viscosity of solutions of pectin, sodium pectate or sodium ammonium pectate is the same as that which degrades protopectin. Solutions containing these enzymes also contain polygalacturonase, but this enzyme has not been as well characterized as the other two. It has a similar pH optimum but behaves differently after exposure to high temperatures. On present evidence therefore depolymerase and protopectinase may be regarded as closely similar enzymes which are distinct from polygalacturonase. The combined effect of the enzymes on solutions of pectin or sodium pectate is quite distinct from that of fungal polygalacturonase (Lineweaver, Jang & Jansen, 1949; Jansen & MacDonell, 1945). Pectin is attacked as readily as sodium pectate, and activity on both substrates is highest at high pH values, 8·5–9·5. In solutions of pectin the reaction stops when 20 % of the reducing groups have been liberated; and in solutions of sodium pectate the reaction stops when 40 % of the reducing groups have been liberated. Moreover, galacturonic acid is not detectable among the breakdown products even after prolonged incubation.

The relations between the three enzymes contained in filtrates from cultures of *Botrytis cinerea* are more complex and have recently been studied (Jarvis, 1953). This work will not be considered in detail; in summary, it may be stated that evidence was obtained that the polygalacturonase produced by this pathogen was distinct from the depolymerase and protopectinase; these two enzymes behaved similarly in relation to pH and thermal inactivation. Analysis of the activities of the three enzymes in cultures of different ages and with different proportions of glucose and pectin as carbohydrate sources revealed further differences. Thus while maximum production of polygalacturonase and depolymerase was attained in 3-day cultures, protopectinase reached a maximum only after 7 days' incubation. It seems probable therefore that these three enzymes are distinct.

Comparisons have also been made between the protopectinase and depolymerase activities of solutions from cultures of *Fusarium moniliforme* and *Pythium debaryanum*. Dealing first with *Fusarium moniliforme*, both enzymes have pH optima in the range of 8·5–9·5 and react similarly after exposure to high temperatures; phosphate, at relatively high concentrations, reduces the activity of both. Differences between the two enzymes were evident, however, when filtrates from cultures of different ages were assayed; depolymerase activity reached a maximum after 4 days' growth of the fungus at 25° and thereafter decreased gradually over a further period of 11 days; in contrast, protopectinase activity, which also reached a maximum in 4 days, remained constant. Fifteen-day cultures therefore gave solutions of high protopectinase but relatively low depolymerase activity. Little more can be said at present about the relation between these two enzymes, but certain interesting features relating to the action of culture fluids on soluble pectic substances may be noted. In the first place the depolymerase reduces the viscosity of pectin and sodium pectate solutions only relatively slowly compared with preparations from *Bacterium aroideae* having similar protopectinase activity. Furthermore, chromatographic analysis shows that pectin and sodium pectate are degraded in different ways by enzymes from this pathogen. Breakdown of pectin gives galacturonic acid only, whereas the action of the enzyme on sodium pectate (derived from the pectin by de-esterification with tobacco-leaf pectin-esterase) gives, in addition to galacturonic acid, a series of intermediate products which finally disappear. It would therefore seem either that two enzymes are involved or that the mode of action of a single enzyme on the different substrates is quite different (Singh, 1953).

No important differences in the depolymerase and protopectinase activities of solutions from cultures of *Pythium debaryanum* have been observed; the solutions have properties quite different, however, from those from the other pathogens. The most striking differences are that they rapidly reduce the viscosity of pectin but not of sodium pectate solutions, that prolonged incubation with solutions of pectin yields only some 5 % of the theoretical reducing groups and that no breakdown products appear on chromatograms. Only compounds of relatively high molecular weight, therefore, would seem to be produced by the action of depolymerase from this pathogen (Gupta, 1953).

The pectic enzymes secreted by the two remaining pathogens are still being studied; a number of interesting features have already been found. Filtrates from cultures of *Verticillium dahliae* have little or no pectin-esterase activity but contain a protopectinase which is remarkably heat-resistant. These filtrates also contain an enzyme with optimal activity at pH 8·5–9·0 which rapidly reduces the viscosity of pectin solutions. Rather surprisingly, at this value, there is little effect on the viscosity of a sodium pectate solution. With this substrate, activity is highest at pH 7·0, reaches a minimum at pH 8·0, and has a secondary peak at pH 9·5. Even at optimum pH values, the filtrates are relatively more active on solutions of pectin than on solutions of sodium pectate. Similar results are obtained for polygalacturonase activity (Kamal, personal communication).

No detailed comparison has been made of the protopectinase and depolymerase activities of the culture filtrates. It may be noted, however, that after treatment at 100° there is a relatively greater loss of depolymerase than of protopectinase activity.

A striking feature about the protopectinase produced by *Sclerotium rolfsii* is the low pH optimum of 2·5–3·0 and the relative inactivity above pH 4·5. Below pH 3·0, the viscosity of sodium pectate solutions is so high that viscometric assays are difficult to make; pectin solutions may, however, still be used and the pH-activity curves for depolymerase and protopectinase are then similar. Once again, solutions which rapidly reduce the viscosity of pectin solutions have little pectin-esterase activity. A further point of interest is that the protopectinase behaves anomalously at high temperatures. Preparations kept at 60° for 5–10 min. lost most of their activity. At higher temperatures there is much less loss of activity, so that after 5 min. at 100° some 20–30 % of the original activity is retained. Again, dilute solutions lose little if any of their activity after storage at 30° for 4 weeks (Abeygunawardena, personal communication).

Enough has now been said to show that the pectic enzymes produced by these six pathogens have widely different properties. The most important points which emerge are as follows:

(i) Some pathogens produce more than one pectic enzyme (other than pectin-esterase).

(ii) Breakdown of protopectin and high methoxyl pectin may take place in solutions having little or no pectin-esterase activity.

(iii) Each of the pathogens studied produces an enzyme which rapidly reduces the viscosity of high methoxyl pectin solutions.

(iv) The pectic enzymes secreted by some organisms attack esterified pectic substances more readily than de-esterified compounds.

(v) There is no uniformity in the end-products of pectic substances degraded by the different organisms.

Dealing first with the degradation of soluble pectic substances and assuming, for the moment, that these are composed only of poly-galacturonic acid chains esterified to a greater or less extent, some of the enzymes secreted by the pathogens which have been studied differ from fungal polygalacturonase (Jansen & MacDonnell, 1945; Lineweaver *et al.* 1949) in that high methoxyl pectins are rapidly degraded, in some cases more rapidly than the corresponding pectates. This is best illustrated by the enzymes from *Pythium debaryanum* which are virtually inactive on solutions of sodium pectate. It may well be, therefore, that complex relations exist between the ability of the enzymes from different organisms to attack the 1,4-glycosidic linkages between adjacent units and the extent to which these linkages are bound on one or both sides by methoxyl or carboxyl groups. On this basis, enzymes from *P. debaryanum* might be envisaged as attacking only those linkages bound by methoxyl groups so that a sodium pectate having very few such linkages would be attacked only slowly. Similarly, enzymes from other organisms would be more active on de-esterified pectinic acids but could still degrade high methoxyl pectin quite rapidly since such substances are normally about 75 % esterified.

The mode of action of the enzymes described as depolymerases and their specific substrates are not known. If the soluble pectic substances are composed entirely of anhydrogalacturonic residues in 1,4-glycosidic linkage, the primary action of the depolymerases must resemble that of polygalacturonase; the depolymerases from different sources may differ from polygalacturonase as normally understood in being differently affected by the carboxyl or methoxyl content of the chain as described in the previous paragraph. If this were so, depolymerases would merely be special types of polygalacturonase. There is evidence, however, that some organisms secrete a number of enzymes which resemble polygalacturonase in their general action but differ in having as specific substrates molecular chains of different size (Ayres, Dingle, Phipps, Reid & Solomons, 1952). Somewhat similar results reported for cellulases produced by cellulolytic organisms (Reese, 1954) indicate that different enzymes are responsible for the breakdown of cellulose in different states of aggregation or solubility. If plant pathogens also produce a similar series of pectic enzymes, depolymerase would be regarded as a polygalacturonase having high-molecular-weight compounds as specific substrates. Other hypotheses which explain how the action of depolymerase might differ from that of polygalacturonase depend upon further assumptions about the structure of pectic substances—for example, the existence of branched chains or rings, the presence of units other than those of anhydrogalacturonic acid in the main chain, and the association between chains through carboxyl or other groups. At present the evidence for such structures is only circumstantial.

Turning now to the breakdown of middle-lamella protopectin: if this is composed primarily of insoluble pectates or low methoxyl pectinates, there seems no reason why organisms producing enzymes able to degrade soluble pectates should not bring into solution, perhaps very slowly, the substance of the middle lamella. Although the types of substrate are not strictly comparable, it is rather surprising that preparations which rapidly macerate thin slices of plant tissue, only very slowly degrade calcium-pectate gels produced in the laboratory; this may be primarily a matter of the relative surface areas exposed to the action of the enzyme. It remains to be explained, however, why *P. debaryanum* enzymes which degrade soluble pectates only slowly should cause such rapid maceration. It is possible that occasional linkages labile to this type of enzyme are present and that their rupture might give fragments which were soluble although of very high molecular weight. If the insolubility of middle-lamella protopectin depends mainly on cross-linkages through carboxyl groups of adjacent chains (linkage through calcium being a special instance), the breakdown of protopectin might depend, in part at least, on the rupture of such linkages. The effect of breaking 1,4-glycosidic linkages but not the cross-linkages does not seem to have been considered. There is as yet no evidence for the existence of enzymes having this activity, nor are there any substantial reasons for believing that the degradation of protopectin depends upon the rupture of linkages of the type mentioned in the last paragraph.

The consideration of the breakdown of the protopectins of the primary and secondary cell wall presents the same problems and also others which are related to the esterification of the pectic substances present and to the admixture of these substances with cellulose and other components. Acid hydrolysis of this type of protopectin gives pectinic acids of relatively high methoxyl content; de-esterification by pectin-esterase or other agents would therefore be necessary before it could be rapidly degraded by enzymes of the polygalacturonase type. It has been shown, however, that each of the pathogens studied, although producing little pectin-esterase, secretes enzymes able to degrade soluble high-methoxyl pectins. With these, therefore, de-esterification, at least in the preliminary stages of degradation, would not be important, although it is possibly significant that some of the pathogens studied caused media suitable for enzyme production to become alkaline; this itself would bring about slow de-esterification of pectinic acids.

The reasons for the insolubility of this type of protopectin may be those already mentioned; it is also possible that the insolubility is partly caused by intimate admixture with the cellulose microfibrils or even with the micelles. If this were so, one of the main factors affecting the production of soluble pectic substances of lower molecular weight would be the rate of diffusion inwards of enzymes attacking the main chain structure and the diffusion outwards of the breakdown products. In this connexion, the action of enzymes degrading other insoluble components of the cell wall would also assume importance; but even less is known about these than about pectic enzymes. The hemicellulases have been comparatively little studied, and most of our knowledge of the cellulases has come from studies of their action on cotton or its derivatives. The attack upon native cellulose in the cell wall has received little attention. These later stages of cell-wall breakdown are likely to be of greatest importance in providing low-molecular-weight compounds suitable as energy sources for the pathogen.

EFFECT OF NUTRIENT CONDITIONS ON ENZYME
PRODUCTION

Little difficulty has been experienced in obtaining media which, after supporting growth of various pathogens, give solutions producing typical pathological effects on host tissue. These media were generally relatively simple; *Pythium debaryanum*, however, required a complex medium for maximum production of protopectinase. Two special features may first be noted: (i) some organisms produced proto-pectinase only if grown in the presence of pectic substances, others produced this enzyme more abundantly under these conditions, and some did not require these substances; (ii) protopectinase production was often not related to growth of the organism, so that with some media enzyme production was high and growth poor and vice versa. Another rather surprising result was that some of the pathogens, e.g. *Sclerotium rolfsii*, although requiring pectic substrates for the secretion of protopectinase, produced little or no pectin-esterase; in the past pectin-esterase has generally been regarded as an adaptive enzyme which is readily produced in the presence of the specific substrate.

Certain substances inhibit the secretion of protopectinase, or in-activate the enzyme after secretion, but have little effect on the growth of the organism. This is well illustrated with *S. fructigena*, which causes a brown rot of apple and other fruit. The fungus grows well on an undiluted apple juice clarified by centrifuging at 10,000 r.p.m. for 10 min. No protopectinase is produced on this medium even when various nitrogen sources are added (Cole, 1953). Similarly, *Fusarium moniliforme* produces protopectinase abundantly on a variety of plant tissue extracts but not on apple extract; the yield of protopectinase on apple extract was not affected by the presence or absence of different sources of carbon and nitrogen by buffering at different pH values, or by dialysis. Furthermore, the addition of one part of an apple extract to three parts of a medium suitable for enzyme production consider-ably reduced the activity of the culture filtrate. The nature of the in-hibitory factor is not known; recent work has provided evidence of the existence of similar inhibitors in pear fruit (Weurman, 1953).

The effect of carbon:nitrogen ratio in media has also been studied to some extent; the general result is that (within certain limits) high ratios increase mycelial growth, whereas lower ratios give poorer growth and result in a great increase in enzyme secretion. The possible significance of this factor under natural conditions is indicated by the work of Vasudeva (1930), who showed that *Botrytis allii*, not normally parasitic on apple fruit, invaded this tissue when a source of nitrogen was added to the inoculum.

Another important factor is the pH of the medium into which protopectinase is being secreted. This depends partly upon the effect of pH on the growth of the organism itself. In general, with the organisms so far studied, the pH optima of the protopectinases produced are close to the final pH of the culture fluids in which they are contained: for example, *Sclerotium rolfsii* protopectinase has a pH optimum in the neighbourhood of 3·0, and culture fluids on a wide variety of media have final pH values in the range 2·5–3·5. In the other direction, *Verticillium dahliae* produces an alkaline drift in media which support good growth and the protopectinase produced has an optimum in the pH range 8·0–9·0. An intermediate case is that of *Bacterium aroideae*, which on some media produces an acid drift which limits growth and protopectinase production. More active preparations are therefore obtained by buffering the media so that the pH does not fall below 7·0 during growth. These culture fluids, having pH values 7·5–8·0, contain a protopectinase having a pH optimum in the range 8·5–9·5.

It is apparent that, to exert full parasitic activity the metabolism of the pathogen needs to be such that the pH of the rotted tissue is close to the optimum pH for protopectinase activity. There is, however, the possibility that the pH optimum of the enzyme depends, in part at least, on the pH of the medium into which it is being secreted (Fernando, 1937). This point needs further investigation; if it were generally true, pH optima as usually determined might have less significance in the parasitic process. It might also explain certain anomalous results obtained with *B. aroideae* protopectinase prepared in alkaline media which has a pH optimum in the range 8·5–9·5. The cut surface of a potato tuber which is actively invaded by this pathogen, however, has a pH in the range 6·0–6·5; furthermore, the pathogen produces an acid drift in the early stages of growth on potato juice.

In studies of protopectinase secretion, attention has largely been confined to the exocellular enzyme; few studies have been made with the endocellular enzyme and on the relative proportions of both. Because the production of exocellular protopectinase by some pathogens is adaptive and because the enzyme must originate in the cytoplasm of cells of the pathogens, it is hard to understand how an adaptive enzyme may be produced in response to an insoluble substrate. It is possible that small quantities of the enzyme are produced constitutively and that their action produces a sufficient amount of pectic compounds of molecular weight low enough to permit penetration of the cell membranes of the pathogen; further production of enzyme would then be stimulated and released to produce more of the soluble substrate, and so on. If, however, the endocellular enzyme is produced in response to specific linkages this hypothesis assumes that the linkages, which on rupture lead to the breakdown of protopectin, are also present in the lower-molecular-weight compounds which pass into the cell. The way in which exocellular enzymes are released from cells must also be considered. In bacterial cultures containing a proportion of dead cells some of the exocellular enzyme may come from autolysing cells, but with some fungi the secretion of protopectinase is associated with young, actively growing mycelium in which there is little or no autolysis; in this case it appears that enzyme protein is liberated through the membranes of living cells.

Finally, some of the organisms studied grow well with pectic substrates as the only carbon source apart from that contained in organic nitrogen compounds when these are required. The secretion of pectic enzymes therefore has two purposes: (i) the breakdown of plant tissue, and (ii) the further degradation of the primary breakdown products to give substances which will pass into the cell and be used in growth. This process might obviously become cumulative, but it is likely that the supply of nitrogen required for the synthesis of enzyme protein soon becomes limiting; factors such as these probably explain the increased pathogenicity sometimes observed when nitrogen is added to an inoculum. Very little is known of the metabolism of the breakdown products of polyuronides. This is undoubtedly of great importance, particularly in the parasitism of tissue composed of poorly differentiated cells, where the proportion of pectic substances is high.

ACTION OF PECTIC ENZYMES ON LIVING CELLS

In his early work on this aspect of the action of pectic enzymes, Brown (1915) concluded either that the death of the cells after maceration was caused by the substance or group of substances responsible for cell separation or that the killing substance, although different, was unable to act upon the protoplast until this had been modified in some way by the action of the macerating enzymes. Moreover, if no toxins other than the enzymes were present it must be postulated either that these enzymes act directly on the protoplasmic membranes or that their action upon the cell wall modifies the relationship between it and the outer surface of the protoplast.

In recent years there has been a renewed interest in the toxins secreted by plant pathogens; those produced by organisms causing wilt diseases have attracted most attention, but the killing of cells by solutions containing protopectinases has also been reinvestigated by Tribe (1951), who used a simple but effective method of studying the relation between maceration and killing. Mesocarp tissue of cucumber fruit was found to be a particularly suitable material for these investigations; slices of potato tuber or turnip root were also used. Slices of standard size (10 mm. diameter ×0·3–5·0 mm. thick) were injected with water by removing air from the container; they were then well washed and placed in the test solution. Maceration was recorded when the disks fall apart upon being lifted; and toxicity was estimated by placing the disks in a plasmolysing solution (potassium nitrate or sucrose) suitably buffered and containing 0·01 % (w/v) neutral red chloride, a vital stain which accumulates in living but not in dead cells. Cells were considered to be living when they became plasmolysed under these conditions. Toxicity was recorded according to the following scale: 0=all cells killed; 2·5=50 % of the cells killed; 5=all cells alive. This was called the Neutral Red (N.R.) Index. Using these methods, Tribe confirmed Brown's results with *Botrytis cinerea* and also showed that filtrates from *Bacterium aroideae* behaved similarly. Typical results are shown in Table 1.

Table 1. *Toxic action of protopectinase solutions on plant cells*
(Tribe, 1951)

B. cinerea protopectinase (pH 5·5)			B. aroideae protopectinase (pH 8·6)		
Time (min.)	Condition of slice	N.R. Index	Time (min.)	Condition of slice	N.R. Index
15	Not macerated	5	10	Not macerated	5
20	Barely macerated	2–4	15	Not macerated	2
25	Just macerated	1–2	20	Just macerated	0–1
30	Definitely macerated	1–2			
45	Definitely macerated	0–1			

The cells of slices placed in autoclaved preparations remained alive for long periods under these conditions.

It is noteworthy that preparations similar to the above had little or no toxic action on the thallus of *Fegatella*, on the filaments of the alga, *Cladophora*, or on free-swimming cells of *Chlamydomonas*.

Comparable results were obtained with solutions from both organisms at other pH values; at values far removed from the optima, tissues were macerated only slowly and the cells remained alive for long periods. Furthermore, *Botrytis cinerea* preparations lost activity on dialysis and toxicity decreased proportionately. Dialysed solutions from cultures of *Bacterium aroideae* also lost their macerating activity and toxicity on dialysis but behaved in the same manner as untreated solutions on the addition of Ca^{++}, which is required for full protopectinase activity.

An unexpected result was obtained when plasmolysed slices of tissue were placed in protopectinase preparations. At slightly hypertonic concentrations, maceration was very little retarded but the cells remained alive for long periods. Various plasmolysing agents were effective, the retardation of killing becoming pronounced in each case at concentrations just sufficient to cause plasmolysis. The following is an example of the effects obtained in a *B. aroideae* preparation which macerated slices in 20 min.; with 0.05M-KNO_3, very few cells were alive after 20 min., but with 0.1M-KNO_3, the majority of the cells were alive after 20 hr.

Much of the above work has been repeated and extended more recently by Fushtey (1953), who used essentially the same techniques. It was shown that tissue slices, plasmolysed and then carefully de-plasmolysed, behaved like untreated slices; the cells were resistant to killing during and after maceration only as long as they were plasmolysed. These effects were obtained with sucrose, urea, magnesium sulphate, calcium chloride, and potassium nitrate. It was also observed that plasmolysis retarded the killing of cells by toxins such as oxalic acid or mercuric chloride. The macerating and killing activity were not separated by fractional precipitation of the enzyme preparation with different concentrations of acetone at different pH values, by dilution, by dialysis, or by heating. If tissue slices were partially macerated (i.e. placed in solutions for half the time required for complete maceration), washed and transferred to enzyme-free solutions at a pH value unfavourable for maceration, cell separation still occurred but was considerably delayed; killing of the cells under these conditions was also delayed until maceration had occurred. Here it is interesting to note that some evidence was obtained that partial maceration also increased the rate at which cells were killed by oxalic acid or mercuric chloride. No evidence was obtained that degradation products of maceration were toxic. For example, 160 disks of turnip root measuring 10×0.5 mm. were immersed in 10 ml. of a *B. aroideae* protopectinase solution until completely macerated; the fragments were then removed by centrifuging and the process repeated twice. Untreated enzyme solutions were then diluted with a clarified solution obtained from the above or with water; the macerating and killing activities of both sets of solutions were very similar.

The original findings of Brown (1915) have thus been amply con-

firmed and have also been shown to be true for *B. aroideae* protopectinase. Additional results have shown that a considerable number
of treatments affecting the rate of maceration have a similar effect on
the rate at which cells are killed; this might be taken as circumstantial
evidence that it is the action of the protopectinase itself which kills the
cell. There is some evidence that maceration increases the susceptibility
of cells to simple toxins; maceration may remove the pectic substances
between the cellulose microfibrils and therefore aid the movement of the
toxins through the cell wall. But even in the absence of maceration
mercuric chloride kills cells quite quickly, whereas the postulated toxin
in the protopectinase preparations does not. The difficulty of attributing
a toxic action to a protopectinase or any other pectic enzyme is that
these enzymes, by their very nature, must be considered specific in their
action, and at present their substrates are considered to be restricted to
the cell wall and the cell vacuole. If protopectinase acts only on inert
wall material, it is difficult to see why cells should be so rapidly killed,
for if the tissue under test is allowed to macerate undisturbed there
seems no reason why the plasmodesmata should not remain intact, the
cytoplasm merely being now limited by a more permeable cell wall. On
the other hand, if pectic compounds play some part in the relation
between the innermost layer of the cell wall and the outermost layer of
the cytoplasm, degradation of this layer might well affect the vital
properties of the protoplast. As far as the writer is aware, no one has
ascribed a special role to pectic materials in the structure of the outer
protoplasmic layer which is generally considered to be a lipoid-protein
complex. The assumption of a boundary layer containing pectic substances does little to explain why plasmolysis increases the resistance of
cells to killing. This remains one of the most puzzling features of the
work described. Even if protopectinase acts upon a special pectic layer
at the protoplast surface, it is difficult to imagine why the retraction of
the cytoplasm from the cell wall should make this layer immune to attack.
If toxicity is caused by a specific toxin, it is possible that the change
from the unplasmolysed to the plasmolysed state may greatly affect the
rate at which toxins pass into the cytoplasm.

At present, therefore, there can be no complete understanding of the
way in which protopectinase acts upon living cells, and it is obvious that
the above work needs to be repeated with much purer enzyme preparations to reduce the possibility of misinterpretation, which is always
present when crude preparations are used. It is apparent, however, that
the results so far obtained indicate that the relation between the outer
layers of the cytoplasm and the innermost layer of the cell wall may be

quite complex and that the study of it may be important for a fuller understanding of the way in which toxins enter and kill cells.

In general terms, results similar to the above have been obtained recently with protopectinase preparations from *Sclerotium rolfsii* (Abeygunawardena, personal communication) and *Verticillium dahliae* (Kamal, personal communication). With the latter, however, certain differences have been noted. Untreated enzyme preparations behave in the same way as those from *Botrytis cinerea* and *Bacterium aroideae*; heat-treated solutions behave quite differently as is shown by the results in Table 2.

Table 2. *Effect of high temperatures on toxicity of* Verticillium dahliae *protopectinase*

Treatment of enzyme at 100° (time in min.)	Maceration time (min.)	Time (min.) to reach a N.R. Index of 2·5
0	10	25
5	35	> 240
15	60	> 240

After 35 min. in the heat-treated enzyme solution, the disks of tissue are fully macerated but there is little sign of killing after 120 min. immersion; even after 240 min. only about 20 % of the cells are dead if the disks are left undisturbed. Attempts to obtain suspensions of living cells from these macerated slices by disintegrating them with shaking have so far been unsuccessful. This suggests that separation of the cells, involving rupture of the plasmodesmata, immediately leads to death. Maceration by the heat-treated enzyme is of the 'brittle' type—that is, the slices remain turgid; in contrast, maceration by untreated enzyme is of the 'flaccid' type.

Slices which have been macerated in heat-treated solutions are still susceptible to the toxins contained in untreated preparations showing that, in this case, a thermolabile toxin is involved. This may, of course, be an enzyme; indeed, the different types of maceration produced by heat-treated and untreated solutions suggests that more than one enzyme is involved in maceration by protopectinase preparations from *Verticillium dahliae*.

In concluding this section, the work of Chayen (1949) will be referred to briefly. Root-tips of *Vicia faba* were macerated with an aqueous extract of a culture of *Penicillium digitatum* for 2 days; mitosis continued for 7 days in individual cells suspended in Ringer's solution. In further work (Chayen, 1952), a commercial 'pectinase' preparation was used in the presence of peptone and for much shorter periods; cell separation occurred after treatment for 1 hr. and the cells were stated to be apparently alive. Peptone presumably retarded the killing of the cells which otherwise would have occurred; it was suggested that peptone acted as an alternative substrate for proteolytic enzymes, present as impurities, so delaying attack of the cell proteins. The results obtained with meristematic and parenchymatous tissue do not agree therefore. No explanation for this can be given at present, since the tissues and the protopectinases used were quite different; it should be stated, however, that the preparations used by Tribe had little or no proteolytic activity, and that root-tip tissue is considerably more resistant to maceration than the parenchymatous tissue which was used in the experiments described above.

LACK OF CORRELATION BETWEEN PATHOGENICITY AND ENZYME SECRETION

From the above it will be apparent that the secretion of pectic enzymes able to cause disintegration of tissue and death of the cells is likely to be an important factor in the pathogenicity of some organisms. But the ability of an organism to secrete these enzymes in pure culture may be quite unrelated to its ability to invade and parasitize plant tissues. In certain cases this is readily understandable; the organism may not grow well on the natural substrate or, if it does, nutrient conditions may not be favourable for enzyme secretion. Furthermore, any enzymes which are secreted may be absorbed or inactivated by the plant tissue or tissue sap. But other explanations must be found for examples of the following kind. A number of bacteria may be isolated which, grown on media obtained from potato tubers in a variety of ways, produce solutions having high protopectinase activity when tested on slices of potato tuber. Such bacteria may differ widely in their pathogenicity for potato tubers, e.g. *Bacterium aroideae* introduced into a superficial wound causes a rapidly spreading soft-rot; others, such as *Pseudomonas syringae*, cause little if any rot. The reason for this has recently been investigated (Lapwood, 1953) and is still being studied. A possible explanation is provided by results of a study of the growth of the organisms on dilute potato extract, particularly during the first 24 hr. after inoculation. Pathogenic forms such as *Bacterium aroideae* have a relatively short lag phase, active growth occurring after 4 hr. With non-pathogenic forms this is delayed for 12 hr. The differences between the growth of pathogenic and non-pathogenic forms is much less pronounced after 24 hr. growth. On a medium consisting of juice expressed from thawed tubers and sterilized by passing it through porcelain filter-candles, the differences between the growth of pathogenic and non-pathogenic forms is still more pronounced; on synthetic media, however, the differences are not marked. Protopectinase may be detected in a culture of *B. aroideae* on dilute potato extract after 4 hr. growth, in *Pseudomonas syringae* cultures after 10 hr. After 24 hr. growth cultures of these organisms have similar protopectinase activity.

These results agree with observations on the initial stages of attack of normal tubers so that as a working hypothesis it has been suggested that one of the main factors affecting the pathogenicity of these organisms is the rate at which they grow and secrete protopectinase relative to the rate at which the host tissue reacts to form surface layers resistant or immune to attack. Thus, even the superficial attack of wounded surfaces by non-pathogenic organisms is eliminated if inoculation is delayed for 24 hr., with a pathogen such as *Bacterium aroideae* a delay of 72 hr. is necessary to prevent attack.

Other effects are suggested by the work of Fernando & Stevenson (1952), in which a comparison was made between the behaviour of the soft-rot organisms *Botrytis cinerea* and *B. carotovorum* on potato tubers. *B. carotovorum* attacks tubers readily, *B. cinerea* attacks them not at all under normal conditions. Both organisms produce active protopectinase preparations on potato extracts, and these preparations readily macerate tissue slices at their respective pH optima. Cell-free solutions also produce quite different amounts of rot when added to cavities in whole tubers, the enzymes behaving in the same way as the organisms. This is unlikely to be a pH effect as the pH of tubers is closer to the optimum of *Botrytis cinerea* protopectinase. The differences in the rotting produced by the organisms or their enzymes are very much reduced when the water content of the host tissue is increased by soaking or injecting with water under reduced pressure. This result is also obtained with the pathogenic and non-pathogenic bacteria described earlier. A striking feature is that *injected* tissue becomes much more susceptible than soaked tissue, although the further increase in water content may be quite low. A typical example of this is given in Table 3.

Table 3. *Effect of water content on pathogenicity*
(Lapwood, 1953)

	Rot (weight in g.) after 24 hr.	
% water content of tissue	*B. aroideae*	*P. syringae*
Untreated 79·10	0·24	0
Soaked 83·07	0·40	0·54
Injected 83·24	0·76	0·92

The reasons for this are not known. More rapid movement of bacteria or readier diffusion of the enzymes produced immediately suggests itself, but this would hardly explain the great increase in rotting in soaked compared with injected tubers, or why non-pathogens are able to penetrate normal tissue only superficially. Moreover, some evidence has been obtained that the movement of dyes through untreated tissue is almost as fast as through soaked tissue.

There is the further possibility that there are substances in potato sap which inhibit the activity of pectolytic enzymes generally but which have more effect on some than on others; this is not unlikely in view of the evidence that the protopectinases secreted by different organisms have very different properties. Brown (1915) pointed out that slices of potato tuber soaked overnight in an extract of broad-bean (*Vicia faba*) leaves became remarkably resistant to the action of *Botrytis cinerea* proto-pectinase, and Chona (1932) showed that potato juice had an effect similar to that of bean-leaf extract. Cole (1953) has shown recently that oxidized extracts from a number of plant tissues strongly inhibited the protopectinase and depolymerase obtained from *B. cinerea*, but had far less effect on these enzymes produced by *Monilia fructigena*. Weurman (1953) has also demonstrated recently a thermolabile inhibitor of the 'pectinase' normally present in pear fruit.

Inhibitors of pectic enzymes or, indeed, of other enzymes produced by plant pathogens have been little studied; it seems quite likely that the resistance of some plant tissues is due to their presence.

PECTIC ENZYMES AND WILT DISEASES

In recent years the mechanisms by which certain pathogens cause their host plants to wilt have been much studied. This work is dealt with more fully in other papers of this Symposium; only the recent work which has ascribed some importance to pectic enzymes in the wilting process will be dealt with here.

As a result of earlier studies with the tomato-wilt organism, *Fusarium oxysporum* var. *lycopersici*, it was suggested that the peptide, lyco-marasmin, which is produced by the pathogen in old cultures was in part at least responsible for the symptoms of wilt (Gäumann, 1951). The work of Scheffer & Walker (1953), Gothoskar, Scheffer, Walker & Stahmann (1953) and Winstead & Walker (1954), has now provided evidence that lycomarasmin is not important as a cause of wilt in the living plant, but that many of the symptoms of disease are produced by pectin-esterase which is secreted quite freely by the pathogen on sterile, moist wheat-bran. Solutions containing this enzyme caused typical vascular browning and wilt of the test plants but, rather surprisingly, had little or no polygalacturonase activity. Pectin-esterase preparations from other micro-organisms were also effective in producing typical wilt symptoms; the solutions used contained variable amounts of polygalacturonase, but there was no correlation between activity of this enzyme and severity of wilt symptoms. As a result of these observations it was postulated that the production of pectin-esterase by the pathogen was an important cause of wilt symptoms in infected plants. The mechanism involved was not suggested, but, presumably, it is envisaged that the pectin-esterase acts upon high-methoxyl pectins of the xylem walls to give low-methoxyl pectinic acids or pectic acid, which then react with polyvalent cations in the vascular stream to give gels which would interfere with the upward flow of water. Gäumann, Stoll & Kern (1953) have also described a substance termed vasinfuscarin which causes browning of the vascular elements of tomato plants and have stated that it may be an enzyme.

The results of similar work with cotton wilt caused by *Verticillium dahliae* suggest that different mechanisms are involved (Kamal, personal communication). Cell-free filtrates on synthetic media have little or no pectin-esterase activity and only slight protopectinase activity. When the cut ends of young seedlings are placed in these solutions for 8 hr. the plants wilt irreversibly, no recovery taking place when they are washed and transferred to water. Similar results are obtained after these solutions have been autoclaved or dialysed; this suggests that wilting is caused by a high-molecular-weight, thermostable, compound; but the treatment does not produce some of the other disease symptoms, in particular, vascular browning. These are obtained, however, when cell-free filtrates from media containing pectin are used; such solutions have high protopectinase and depolymerase activity but contain little or no pectin-esterase. Typical symptoms are produced by these solutions before and after dialysis and partial purification by precipitation in 67 % (v/v) acetone at pH 8·0. When these solutions are autoclaved, plants still wilt, but there is no vascular browning and the leaf symptoms are atypical. Wilting by such solutions may be caused by high-molecular-weight degradation products of the pectin contained in the original medium, since uninoculated solutions containing as little as 0·02 % (w/v) of a high-methoxyl pectin cause young plants to wilt irreversibly in 8–10 hr.

The wilt caused by filtrates from pectin media or pectin-free media is irreversible in the sense that there is no recovery if the plants are transferred to water after washing. If a portion of the lower part of the stem is removed, recovery takes place; the amount of stem which must be removed depends on the period of immersion in the test solution. Wilting is greatly delayed if plants are kept in the dark or in a moisture-saturated atmosphere; measurements made during the period up to the appearance of definite wilt symptoms in the leaves show that while the treated plants lose water as readily as control plants, the water uptake by them is greatly reduced, being intermediate between that taken up by normal plants and plants in which the cut ends have been sealed by wax. There is in fact very good circumstantial evidence that wilting is caused either by high-molecular-weight compounds already in the culture filtrate or by similar compounds produced by the action of the filtrates on the plant itself.

Pectin-esterase does not seem to be an important direct cause of wilt in this case because culture filtrates which produce typical wilt symptoms have little or no pectin-esterase activity. In contrast, preparations of orange-peel pectin-esterase of high activity cause less vascular browning. Again, filtrates from *Sclerotium rolfsii* with high protopectinase but no pectin-esterase activity readily produce vascular browning of young cotton plants. It is not easy to see why the action of pectin-esterase produced in the vascular stream by a pathogen should *directly* lead to wilting and vascular browning even in the case of *Fusarium oxysporum* var. *lycopersici*. Normally, the production of pectin-esterase by a pathogen is accompanied by the production of one or other of the pectic enzymes attacking the main structure of the chain molecule. Even if only small quantities of this type of enzyme were produced it would seem likely that its action over a long period would degrade the low-methoxyl pectinate or pectate gels which might be formed by the action of pectin-esterase. There is, of course, the possibility that the effective enzyme is of the polygalacturonase type which, having pectic acid as its substrate, would only be fully active in the presence of pectin-esterase or some other agent able to de-esterify pectinic acids. If this were so, the development of typical wilt symptoms might well be correlated with the pectin-esterase content of the test solution. This assumes, however, that the pathogens do not produce enzymes able to degrade esterified pectic substances and also that such substances are important substrates in the vascular elements. Although in these matters it is dangerous to argue from one organism to another, the first of these assumptions seems unlikely in view of the results which have been obtained with each of the pathogens so far studied, in which enzymes degrading high-methoxyl pectins in the absence of pectin-esterase were readily produced.

It seems apparent that much further work needs to be done before any precise role can be ascribed to specific pectic enzymes in the development of symptoms of wilt diseases.

CONCLUSIONS

The most striking feature of soft-rot diseases is that the cells of the affected tissue become separated from each other and sooner or later die. Since similar effects are produced by cell-free extracts from cultures of the organisms causing these diseases or from rotted tissue, but not by such extracts after these have been boiled or autoclaved, it is assumed that the disintegration of the tissue is brought about by the action of one or more exocellular enzymes produced by the pathogen. It has long been supposed that the enzymes which act upon pectic substances in the cell wall are of greatest importance in this process. Even now, however, only indirect evidence for this assumption is available. The precise importance of pectic enzymes must remain conjectural until more is known of the structure of the cell wall and of the activities of other enzymes in macerating solutions. It will also be necessary to obtain much purer preparations of pectic enzymes from plant pathogens and to compare the effects of their action on specified pectic substrates and on plant tissue in the natural state. Such studies will, in all likelihood, give valuable information on the nature and distribution of pectic substances in the cell wall. But, as has already been stated, standardized and well-characterized preparations of pectic materials are not easily obtained, and progress in the study of the mode of action of pectic enzymes will be slow and uncertain until they are generally available.

It seems reasonably certain, however, that the earliest stages of maceration involve degradation of the middle lamella and that this layer is composed largely, if not wholly, of pectic substances. Although the presence of quite small amounts of other substances such as proteins may have profound effects on the susceptibility of this layer to enzymic degradation, it is probably safe to assume, at least for parenchymatous tissue, that it is the pectic enzymes which are most important at this stage.

It is also significant that the breakdown of the middle lamella is associated with death of the cells which become separated. It remains to be decided whether this is a direct consequence of maceration or whether it can occur only after cell separation. Further investigation of the effects of pure enzyme preparations on the protoplast itself is obviously required. Post-mortem changes in the cell will lead to the release of nutrients for growth of the pathogen; it is probable too that further breakdown of the cell wall by the action of pectic and other enzymes together with autolytic changes in the cytoplasm releases materials previously protected from attack by the exocellular enzymes secreted by the pathogen. In these later stages the activity of pectic enzymes may be secondary; their primary importance is probably in initiating a series of degradations having dead and separated cells as a starting point. If this is the primary role of pectic enzymes in the invasion of plant tissue by pathogens, it is not difficult to suggest why many organisms which secrete these enzymes are not pathogenic, because the breakdown of the middle lamella, although an essential preliminary, would be only the first of a complex series of reactions necessary for the process to become cumulative and for the infection to become progressive. It is apparent, however, that even for such relatively simple systems as the invasion of parenchyma by bacteria our knowledge is still fragmentary and that a great deal of work will be necessary before the process is known even in outline. The part played by pectic enzymes in wilt diseases may prove more amenable to detailed analysis because the host-parasite relationship is, in some respects at least, relatively simpler; the pathogen is more or less confined to the vascular system, and the pathological effects are the result of the action of the organism or its products on a non-living system. Moreover, with modern methods, it should be possible to obtain a reasonably accurate picture of the medium in which the pathogen is growing, i.e. the solutions contained in the vascular elements. If pectic enzymes are really of major importance in this type of disease, the methods by which pathological effects are produced are likely to be quite different from those found in soft-rot diseases.

Little or nothing is known of the importance of pectic enzymes in other types of disease. But from what is known already of the differences in properties of these enzymes secreted by some plant pathogens it may be predicted with some assurance that their relative importance and mode of action in parasitism are likely to differ greatly from one host-parasite relationship to another.

REFERENCES

AYRES, A., DINGLE, J., PHIPPS, A., REID, W. W. & SOLOMONS, G. L. (1952). Enzymic degradation of pectic acid and the complex nature of polygalacturonase. *Nature, Lond.*, **170**, 834.

BOCK, H. (1943). *Theorie und praxis der pektingewinnung.* Karlsruhe: Technische Hochschule.

BROWN, W. (1915). Studies in the physiology of parasitism. 1. The action of *Botrytis cinerea. Ann. Bot., Lond.*, **29**, 313.

292   R. K. S. WOOD

BROWN, W. (1934). Mechanism of disease resistance in plants. *Trans. Brit. mycol. Soc.* **19**, 11.

BROWN, W. (1936). The physiology of host-parasite relations. *Bot. Rev.* **2**, 236.

CHAYEN, J. (1949). Squash preparations of living root-tip cells. *Nature, Lond.*, **164**, 930.

CHAYEN, J. (1952). Pectinase technique for isolating plant cells. *Nature, Lond.*, **170**, 1070.

CHONA, B. L. (1932). Studies in the physiology of parasitism. XIII. An analysis of the factors underlying specialization of parasitism, with special reference to certain fungi parasitic on apple and potato. *Ann. Bot., Lond.*, **46**, 1033.

COLE, J. S. (1953). A comparative study of the pathogenicity of *Botrytis cinerea, Sclerotinia fructigena* and *Sclerotinia laxa*, with special reference to the part played by pectic enzymes. Ph.D. Thesis, University of London.

FERNANDO, M. (1937). Studies in the physiology of parasitism. XV. Effect of the nutrient medium upon the secretion and properties of pectinase. *Ann. Bot., Lond.*, N.S. **1**, 727.

FERNANDO, M. & STEVENSON, G. (1952). Studies in the physiology of parasitism. XVI. Effect of the condition of potato tissue, as modified by temperature and water-content, upon attack by certain organisms and their pectinase enzymes. *Ann. Bot., Lond.*, N.S. **16**, 103.

FUSHTEY, S. G. (1953). Studies on the cell-killing action of extracts derived from various fungi and bacteria. Ph.D. Thesis, University of London.

GÄUMANN, E. (1951). Some problems of pathological wilting in plants. *Adv. Enzymol.* **11**, 401.

GÄUMANN, E., STOLL, C. & KERN, H. (1953). Über vasinfuscarin, ein drittes Welketoxin des *Fusarium lycopersici* Sacc. *Phytopath. Z.* **20**, 345.

GOTHOSKAR, S. S., SCHEFFER, R. P., WALKER, J. C. & STAHMANN, M. A. (1953). The role of pectic enzymes in *Fusarium* wilt of tomato. *Phytopathology*, **43**, 535.

GUPTA, S. C. (1953). The production and properties of pectolytic enzymes secreted by *Pythium debaryanum* Hesse. Ph.D. Thesis, University of London.

JANSEN, E. F. & MACDONNELL, L. R. (1945). Influence of methoxyl content of pectic substances on the action of polygalacturonase. *Arch. Biochem.* **8**, 97.

JARVIS, W. R. (1953). A comparative study of the pectic enzymes of *Botrytis cinerea* Pers., and *Bacterium aroideae* (Townsend) Stapp., plant pathogens of the soft-rotting type. Ph.D. Thesis, University of London.

LAPWOOD, D. H. (1953). An investigation of the parasitic vigour of various bacteria in relation to their capacity to secrete pectic enzymes. Ph.D. Thesis, University of London.

LINEWEAVER, H., JANG, R. & JANSEN, E. F. (1949). Specificity and purification of polygalacturonase. *Arch. Biochem.* **20**, 137.

PRESTON, R. D. (1952). *The Molecular Architecture of Plant Cell Walls.* London: Chapman and Hall.

REESE, E. T. (1954). Multiple factors in cellulose hydrolysis. *Proc. Eighth Int. Bot. Congr.*

ROBOZ, E., BARRATT, R. W. & TATUM, E. L. (1952). Breakdown of pectic substances by a new enzyme from *Neurospora*. *J. biol. Chem.* **195**, 459.

ROELOFSEN, P. A. & KREGER, D. R. (1951). The submicroscopic structure of pectin in collenchyma cell-walls. *J. exp. Bot.* **2**, 332.

SCHEFFER, R. P. & WALKER, J. C. (1953). The physiology of *Fusarium* wilt of tomato. *Phytopathology*, **43**, 116.

SEEGMILLER, C. G. & JANSEN, E. F. (1952). Polymethylgalacturonase, an enzyme causing the glycosidic hydrolysis of esterified pectic substances. *J. biol. Chem.* **195**, 327.

SINGH, R. K. (1953). The production and properties of pectolytic and macerating enzymes secreted by *Fusarium moniliforme* Sheldon. Ph.D. Thesis, University of London.

TRIBE, H. T. (1951). Studies on the killing of the plant cell by pathogens of the soft rot type. Ph.D. Thesis, University of London.

VASUDEVA, R. S. (1930). Studies in the physiology of parasitism. XI. An analysis of the factors underlying specialisation of parasitism, with special reference to the fungi *Botrytis allii* Munn., and *Monilia fructigena* Pers. *Ann. Bot., Lond.*, **44**, 469.

WEURMAN, C. (1953). Pectinase inhibitors in pears. *Acta bot. neerl.* **2**, 107.

WINSTEAD, N. N. & WALKER, J. C. (1954). Production of vascular browning by metabolites from several pathogens. *Phytopathology*, **44**, 153.

WOOD, R. K. S. (1951). Pectic enzymes produced by *Bacterium aroideae*. *Nature, Lond.*, **167**, 771.

WOOD, R. K. S. (1954). Studies in the physiology of parasitism. XVIII. Pectic enzymes secreted by *Bacterium aroideae*. *Ann. Bot., Lond.*, N.S. (in the Press).

THE ROLE OF TOXINS IN THE ETIOLOGY OF PLANT DISEASES CAUSED BY FUNGI AND BACTERIA

P. W. BRIAN

Imperial Chemical Industries Limited, Butterwick Research Laboratories, Welwyn

INTRODUCTION

When a plant is infected by a fungal or bacterial parasite characteristic disease symptoms usually appear, apart from any visible multiplication of the pathogen. These symptoms may take the form of general or local necrosis, or loss of turgor, of abnormal growth, or of any combination of these. One or more organs may be affected. How are these disease symptoms caused?

There seem to be three possible causes, not necessarily incompatible with one another:

(1) The mass of parasitic cells may have some purely mechanical effect on the host plant;

(2) By absorption of nutrients from surrounding host tissue, the parasite may deny essential nutrients to the host;

(3) Escape of metabolites from cells of the parasite, if they are substances not normally found in the host cell, or found in the normal host only at lower concentration levels, may interfere with host metabolism in such a way as to produced lesions characteristic of the infection.

Disorganization of host tissues invaded by the parasite by one of these three mechanisms may release host metabolites which will themselves lead to production of abnormal symptoms in tissues which they reach. Mechanical effects have been invoked as a cause of wilt in vascular diseases, but in many such cases the amount of occlusion of vascular tissue directly caused by cells of the parasite is less than would be expected to cause water-deficit in tissues distal to the occlusion. It is not easy to see how mere physical presence of a parasite can cause such symptoms as necrosis or hyperplasia. Indeed, in some diseases caused by specialized parasites, such as the rust or smut fungi, there may be considerable development of the parasite in the host tissues in early stages of the disease without obvious harm.

Withdrawal of nutrients, if severe, could conceivably lead to necrosis, but could scarcely be a cause of abnormal forms of growth as in various diseases characterized by hyperplasia. In the rust and smut diseases, considerable development of mycelium of the pathogen must be at the expense of host nutrients, yet the only visible effect may be some reduction in vigour of growth.

On general grounds, escape of metabolites from the parasite or from invaded host cells is more probably a potent factor in producing disease symptoms. A variety of metabolic products escape from the cells of plant-parasitic fungi and bacteria during growth on artificial media; it therefore seems unlikely that such substances should not also escape from cells of these organisms growing within the tissues of a host plant. Many extracellular metabolites produced *in vitro* are phytotoxic. It seems reasonable to suppose that production of such substances *in vivo* is partly responsible for the symptoms of plant disease. Let us consider the evidence for this.

(1) In many plant diseases, symptoms develop in tissues in advance of the parasite; the most simple explanation of such an occurrence is diffusion, or translocation by other means, of some phytotoxic metabolic substance released by the parasite, or released from host cells in response to the presence of the parasite.

(2) If cell-free filtrates from pure cultures of a parasite are introduced into a healthy plant, all or some symptoms of the disease characteristic of infection with the parasite may be produced. It is tempting to conclude that phytotoxic substances present in culture filtrates are also produced *in vivo*.

Observations of this kind may strongly indicate a toxigenic origin of disease symptoms, especially if there is agreement in detail between natural symptoms and symptoms produced by metabolites from culture filtrates. However, such evidence is indirect. Dimond & Waggoner (1953a) have suggested that before any toxic substance produced *in vitro* can be considered to cause symptoms *in vivo*, it should be isolated *from an infected host plant* in identifiable form and shown to be capable of reproducing at least a portion of the disease syndrome when reintroduced into a healthy plant. This rigorous attitude is a valuable corrective to a great deal of uncritical work.

Dimond & Waggoner's criteria have been satisfied in very few cases, possibly, in fact, only in their own (Dimond & Waggoner, 1953b) demonstration of the role of ethylene in production of tomato-wilt symptoms. In some cases the volume and nature of the indirect evidence is so great that conclusions can be drawn with some confidence; in many others it can be claimed only as a possibility that symptoms are caused by toxins. The situation is thus very different from that prevailing in animal pathology where the antigenic property of some important toxins has made it possible to identify them or to infer their presence *in vivo* by serological methods. Consequently in animal disease the pathological significance of some toxins has been established, but in plant disease their role is much less firmly established and many authorities (e.g. Brown, 1936) doubt whether toxin production *in vivo* has any significance.

The main purpose of the present communication, therefore, is to review the evidence that toxins may produce symptoms in plant diseases, noting at the same time the evidence for implication of specific substances. Four different kinds of plant disease are considered: (i) vascular diseases; (ii) soft-rots; (iii) leaf spots; and (iv) diseases involving hypertrophy or hyperplasia of host tissues. Vascular diseases are considered at greater length than the other types of disease, because it is in this type that toxin production has been most frequently postulated. After this general review, the role of toxins in pathogenicity will be briefly discussed.

Plant pathologists have tended to distinguish between enzymes and toxins secreted by phytopathogens; the term 'toxin' usually being reserved for thermostable and dialysable substances. This is a matter of convenience only because both may be phytotoxic, and in succeeding pages this implicit distinction is not made; there is growing evidence that both types of substance may be involved.

VASCULAR DISEASES

In these diseases the infective agent first establishes itself in peripheral tissues of root or stem and thence invades the vascular system. It is characteristic that symptoms appear at a distance from the pathogen—that is, in parts of the plant higher up the shoot than the pathogen has yet reached. The phrase 'at a distance' has often been loosely used; in different instances it may mean very different things. In *Verticillium* wilt of the hop, the pathogen pervades the whole vascular system and is usually found to have penetrated into most tissues which show disease symptoms; some leaves, however, may show symptoms although not infected. In *Fusarium cubense* wilt of bananas, on the other hand, the pathogen is usually restricted to the root and base of the stem, yet symptoms can be detected in the youngest leaves. In the wilt of tomatoes caused by *F. oxysporum* var. *lycopersici* an intermediate condition is usually found.

The most easily observed and most frequent symptom of vascular disease is loss of turgor and wilting of foliage. Wilting may be caused by: (i) occlusion of the xylem vessels by the pathogen or by host material produced in response to the presence of the parasite, the occlusion denying water to the distal parts of the plant; or (ii) upward diffusion of toxins produced by the pathogen, or liberated from infected tissues as a result of parasitic attack. Both these explanations, or combinations of the two, have at various times been suggested; the evolution of opinion is described below. Two somewhat different kinds of vascular disease are dealt with separately: (i) wilt diseases arising from infection of roots or stem-bases, diseases of many annual crop plants falling into this group; and (ii) vascular diseases of shrubs or trees, in which infection is usually inititated through wounds in the shoots. To a great extent this distinction is arbitrary, but it is of convenience in the presentation of results.

Wilt diseases

Wilt symptoms were first attributed to plugging of the xylem vessels with cells of the pathogen—for example, in the bacterial wilt of maize caused by *Xanthomonas stewarti* (Stewart, 1897) and in wilts of various plants caused by *Fusarium vasinfectum* (Smith, 1899). Subsequently, production of a diffusible toxin by the pathogen was more commonly suggested as the cause of wilt—for example, in the tobacco wilt caused by *Pseudomonas solanacearum* (Hutchinson, 1913), in 'sleepy disease' of tomato caused by *Verticillium albo-atrum* (Bewley, 1922), and in a wilt of Michaelmas daisies caused by *V. vilmorinii* (Dowson, 1922, 1923). The reasons for this change of view were: (i) that the observed occlusion of vessels by cells of the pathogen did not appear to be sufficient to account for the wilt, because experimental blocking of vessels did not cause wilt unless nearly all vessels were blocked; (ii) that if cut shoots of host plants were placed in cell-free filtrates of liquid cultures of the pathogen, symptoms similar to those of the disease were produced; and (iii) that symptoms other than wilting, e.g. production of brown gummy material in the vessels, or necrosis and disintegration of tissues, were seen in advance of the pathogen, and that such symptoms could not easily be explained by any simple physical effect of the pathogen.

The nature of the toxin produced in cultures of *V. albo-atrum* was investigated by Bewley (1922). He found that if cut tomato shoots were placed in culture filtrate, several symptoms typical of 'sleepy disease' developed, viz. browning of cell walls of the xylem, production of occlusive gums in the vessels, some dissolution of cambial cells and wilt. Heated filtrates failed to produce the first three symptoms, though wilt was occasionally produced. Alcohol precipitates of the filtrates were active in producing all symptoms. Bewley concluded that the fungus liberated an enzyme which might act directly as a toxin or indirectly by stimulating gum production by the host. Very similar results were obtained with culture filtrates of *Pseudomonas solanacearum* by Hutchinson (1913). The toxin in culture filtrates of *Verticillium vilmorinii* was dialysable (Dowson, 1922) and therefore unlikely to be an enzyme; its thermostability was not studied.

Linford (1931 *a, b*), in his work on the pea wilt caused by *Fusarium orthoceras* var. *pisi*, pointed out that in trying to analyse the causes of symptoms in this disease it was inadequate to concentrate on the single symptom of wilting, because this might be caused in several quite distinct ways and because, in the natural disease, it was preceded by a long series of other symptoms, such as hypertrophy of xylem parenchyma, increased rigidity and vascular browning. He found that though wilting could be caused by culture filtrates, not all the other symptoms listed above were produced, and concluded that in the state of knowledge at that time (1931), the symptoms of pea wilt could not be accounted for either by blocking of vessels or by production of such toxins as could be detected in culture filtrates.

Reviewing work on wilt diseases in 1936, Brown concluded that the evidence so far presented was not convincingly in favour of the view that wilt was caused by toxic substances liberated by the parasite. Since then a good many more investigations have been reported, above all on the *Fusarium* wilt of tomatoes. This more recent work is summarized below.

The symptoms of tomato wilt caused by *F. oxysporum* var. *lycopersici* are: (i) clearing of the veins in upper leaflets; (ii) epinasty of the lower leaves; (iii) production of adventitious roots on the stem; (iv) yellowing of the lower leaves; (v) vascular browning and production of gum in the vessels; and (vi) wilting of leaves, followed by death of the whole plant in acute disease. The first four and the last of these symptoms may be produced in tissues or organs not containing mycelium of the pathogen; it is less certain that the fifth symptom, vascular browning, takes place in advance of the invading fungus. Nearly all these symptoms were also observed in the *Verticillium* wilt of tomatoes by Bewley (1922).

The toxin theory of wilting was placed on a firm foundation by the demonstration that centrifugates from the vessels of wilted plants would cause wilting and vascular browning if introduced into healthy plants (Gottlieb, 1943, 1944). This result encouraged further work on the nature of the toxins; unfortunately most of this work has been concerned with cultures *in vitro*. A group of workers in Zurich have isolated three toxins from such culture filtrates—lycomarasmin, fusaric acid, and vasinfuscarin. It is convenient to consider this Swiss work first.

Lycomarasmin was isolated from cultures of *Fusarium oxysporum* var. *lycopersici* in Richard's solution incubated for about 36 days at 25° (Plattner & Clauson-Kaas, 1944; Clauson-Kaas, Plattner & Gäumann, 1944). It is a simple peptide of the structure N-(α(α-hydroxypropionic acid))-glycylasparagine (Woolley, 1948). Its wilt-producing properties have been studied in great detail (Gäumann & Jaag, 1947 a, b, c; Gäumann, Naef-Roth & Miescher, 1950). If cut shoots of tomato are placed in dilute solutions of lycomarasmin (10^{-4}–10^{-5} M) some of the symptoms of tomato wilt are produced—namely, wilt and some yellowing of the leaves. The other typical symptoms are not produced. Some necrosis of the leaves is also produced—but this is not a typical symptom of the natural disease. The phytotoxic activity of lycomarasmin is increased in the presence of iron salts, owing to the formation of an iron-lycomarasmin complex (Plattner & Clauson-Kaas, 1944; Waggoner & Dimond, 1953). In addition to their obvious phytotoxic effects both lycomarasmin and its iron complex affect the transpiration of tomato shoots in a characteristic way. Shortly after the beginning of treatment the rate of water uptake and loss falls sharply (shock phase), then both increase rapidly, the plant entering into a phase of excessive transpiration. Finally, both uptake and loss decline, uptake declining more rapidly than loss, so that overall loss of water finally results in wilting and desiccation (Gäumann & Jaag, 1947 a). The water deficit at which wilting occurs (c. 20 %) is greater than that at which wilting occurs under conditions of physiological drought (c. 10 %); this observation led Gäumann & Jaag (1947 c) to suggest that lycomarasmin has a 'coagulating effect' on the leaf cytoplasm, thus conferring abnormal rigidity. Drought-induced wilting is reversible, whereas wilting caused by lycomarasmin is irreversible.

The phytotoxic properties of lycomarasmin are of great interest, but evidence for its production *in vivo* is not strong. On balance, however, Gäumann *et al.* (1950) concluded that lycomarasmin was at least partly responsible for the symptoms of tomato wilt. They admitted that no direct chemical evidence was available but claimed that three indirect lines of evidence were suggestive: (i) culture filtrates produced most of the symptoms of the disease and lycomarasmin was the main phytotoxic substance present; (ii) expressed sap of diseased plants had similar wilt-inducing properties to those of lycomarasmin (but they gave no detailed experimental evidence for this); and (iii) the pathogen produced lycomarasmin when grown on expressed sap. They considered that in the plant, lycomarasmin acted in the form of the iron complex, since more iron than that required for complex formation in a 1:1 ratio is normally present in tomato tissues. The mode of action was believed to be an effect on the permeability of leaf mesophyll cells (Gäumann, Naef-Roth, Reusser & Ammann, 1952).

On the other hand, there are many reasons to suppose that lycomarasmin cannot be responsible for all symptoms of tomato wilt. Indeed, four reasons have been given for the view that it plays no part at all: (i) lycomarasmin is a product of senescence of the fungus, appearing in culture filtrates in quantity only after autolysis has set in, and therefore unlikely to be produced in sufficient quantity *in vivo* in the period (*c.* 15 days) usually intervening between inoculation of a plant and the development of wilt (Luz, 1934; Dimond & Waggoner, 1953*c,d*); (ii) no differences in disease intensity can be seen between normal and iron-deficient plants, as would be expected if the iron-lycomarasmin complex was of importance (Scheffer & Walker, 1953); (iii) there are no signs of excessive water loss in early stages of the disease, as would be expected from the effects of lycomarasmin on cut shoots (Scheffer & Walker, 1953); (iv) the iron-lycomarasmin complex is unstable in the presence of cupric ions, which chelate preferentially with lycomarasmin, producing a complex much less phytotoxic than iron-lycomarasmin; it is unstable also in the presence of 8-quinolinol, which produces a more stable iron complex than iron-lycomarasmin. Nevertheless, treatment of diseased plants with copper salts or 8-quinolinol does not reduce the intensity of wilt symptoms in artificially infected plants (Waggoner & Dimond, 1953).

The two other toxins described by Gäumann and his colleagues, fusaric acid (Gäumann, Naef-Roth & Kobel, 1952) and vasinfuscarin (Gäumann, Stoll & Kern, 1953), have received less attention. There is no reason to suppose from published work that fusaric acid is of any greater significance than lycomarasmin, although it is a metabolic product of an earlier stage of growth of the fungus. Like lycomarasmin it causes wilting and some leaf necrosis without any of the symptoms that normally precede wilting. Vasinfuscarin may be of greater importance but little information is yet available. It produces the vascular browning so typical of wilt diseases, and the few published details of its properties suggest that it is a protein.

It now appears that the work of Gäumann and his colleagues has not adequately explained symptom production in tomato wilt, but some recent American work appears likely to be more fruitful. This is best summarized if we consider the specific symptoms of tomato wilt in turn.

(1) *Clearing of veins.* This symptom was first noticed by Foster (1946), who showed that it could sometimes be produced by crude culture

filtrates of *F. oxysporum* var. *lycopersici*. This observation was confirmed by Gäumann & Jaag (1947*b*), who also showed that lycomarasmin was not responsible. Blocking of vessels will not cause vein-clearing in tomato plants; the symptom is probably due to a toxin, but its nature remains unknown (Scheffer & Walker, 1953). Strains of *F. oxysporum* pathogenic to cotton and cabbage produce in young cultures a thermo-stable and dialysable substance which will cause vein-clearing in these plants (Winstead & Walker, 1954*b*).

(2) *Epinasty, production of stem roots and yellowing of leaves*. When Wellman (1941) first observed epinasty as a characteristic symptom, he noted the similarity to the effects produced by ethylene and suggested that epinasty, stem rooting and yellowing of the leaves were all produced by ethylene. Ethylene is produced in small quantities by all plant tissue, in considerably larger amounts by various diseased or mechanically in-jured plant tissues (Williamson, 1950; Ross & Williamson, 1951), and by certain fungi in culture (Nickerson, 1948). *F. oxysporum* var. *lycopersici* produces ethylene in culture; it is also produced by infected tomato plants in a quantity sufficient to account for the symptoms of epinasty and production of roots on the stem (Dimond & Waggoner, 1953*b*).

(3) *Vascular browning and wilt*. These are the key symptoms of tomato wilt and of most other vascular diseases. Because they are invariably associated they probably have a common cause. Recent work supports this view. Ludwig (1952) re-investigated tomato wilt to deter-mine whether wilting was due to direct effects of a toxin, as postulated by Gäumann, or to some form of vascular plugging. A detailed study of wilt-infected plants failed to show any indication of excessive trans-piration or reduced absorption of water, but there was evidence of impaired conduction of water through the stem. This was confirmed by showing that sections of stems of wilt-infected plants offered greater resistance to water flow than comparable sections from healthy plants. Obstruction of vessels to account for this could not be seen in fixed tissue, but sections of fresh tissue showed vessels plugged with a hyaline viscous material. It is remarkable that this had not been observed before in tomato wilt, especially because similar observations were made by Bewley in 1922 for *Verticillium* wilt. Production of this material, which occurred in quantities likely to reduce water conduction, was associated with browning of the xylem. It appeared to be a pectic material. Ludwig thought that formation of the plugging material and vascular browning were reactions of the cell walls or living cells of the xylem to a toxin released by the fungal pathogen, and that this plugging resulted in restricted water supply and caused wilting. He showed that culture

filtrates could induce increased resistance to water-flow in healthy stems. The importance of this work lies in the consequent synthesis of the rival theories of vascular plugging and toxigenic induction of wilt.

Almost simultaneously, Scheffer (1952) and Scheffer & Walker (1953) concluded that wilt was due to vascular plugging and showed that young culture filtrates of *Fusarium oxysporum* var. *lycopersici* contained a thermolabile substance of high molecular weight which would induce this plugging. There is some evidence that the active material in young culture filtrates may be a pectin-methyl-esterase (PME) (Gothoskar, Scheffer, Walker & Stahmann, 1953). It is not clear how this produces all the symptoms, but Gothoskar *et al.* suggested that the PME disrupted cellular organization in the xylem, thus releasing viscous substances into the vessels; vascular discoloration might be due to interaction of phenols and phenoloxidases of the host plant released during the cellular disorganization. PME may have a similar role in other *Fusarium* wilts. The substance vasinfuscarin, recently isolated from culture filtrates by Gäumann *et al.* (1953), may be found to be PME or some similar enzyme.

A group working at Connecticut approached the problem rather differently, but arrived at essentially similar conclusions. Dimond & Waggoner (1953e) found that radioactive phosphate moved much more slowly in diseased stems than in healthy ones, that wilted leaves regained turgor if excised and placed in water, and that leaves from diseased plants which had not yet wilted showed symptoms of 'drought-hardening'. A somewhat similar phenomenon to drought-hardening was observed by Linford (1931b) in his study of pea wilt. The similarity to the coagulating effect of lycomarasmin described by Gäumann & Jaag (1947c) is worthy of note. They interpreted their results as meaning that wilt was not due to irreversible intoxication of leaf tissue, as postulated by Gäumann, but that reduced water supply was responsible for the wilt and that this was due to a resistance to flow in the xylem of the stem. The presence in diseased plants of a toxin causing wilt and vascular browning was elegantly demonstrated by Davis (1953b). He grafted plants immune to *F. oxysporum* var. *lycopersici* on to susceptible tomato plants and showed that symptoms of the disease developed without any fungal invasion. Vascular browning was attributed (Davis, Waggoner & Dimond, 1953) to production of melanin from host phenoloxidase and phenols possibly liberated from conjugated phenols in the host by hydrolytic enzymes produced by the fungus; production *in vitro* by the fungus of glucosidases capable of liberating phenols from β-glucosides and tannins was demonstrated experimentally. The vascular plugging could be attributed to liberation of carbohydrate fractions from conjugated phenols, and to accumulation of melanin particles (Davis, 1953a).

The tomato-wilt syndrome may now be tentatively explained as follows: (i) epinasty, leaf-yellowing, and production of stem roots are caused by excessive ethylene production; (ii) vascular browning and plugging of the vessels are due directly or indirectly to release of enzymes by the infecting fungus, PME and glucosidases possibly being involved; (iii) the wilt is consequent upon vascular plugging. This view more easily explains the marked similarity in symptoms in various wilt diseases than any explanation based on direct intoxication of leaves by thermostable toxins, though the possibility that these may also be involved, especially in vein clearing, cannot be finally ruled out. An essentially similar explanation of the symptoms of bacterial wilts caused by *Bacterium tracheiphilum* and *Xanthomonas stewarti* has been advanced by Harris (1940), and of brown stem rot of soya bean, caused by *Cephalosporium gregatum* by Chamberlain & McAlister (1954).

Vascular infections of trees and shrubs

These diseases have been less intensively investigated and a number of examples can be dealt with briefly.

Silver-leaf disease of fruit trees (Stereum purpureum). The fungus enters through wounds in twigs or branches and spreads rapidly into the vessels of the wood. Its progress in the wood is marked by browning of the cell walls and production of much gummy material. The most striking and characteristic symptom of the disease on plum trees is 'silvering' of the foliage. This is due to separation of the upper epidermis from the palisade cells of the mesophyll, the resulting air-space reflecting light. Earlier workers (Percival, 1902; Güssow, 1912; Bintner, 1919) attributed this effect to dissolution of the middle lamella of the cell walls of the palisade cells, where they abutted on the epidermis, presumably by pectic enzymes released by the parasite. Tetley (1932) disagreed with this view but considered that, in infected plants, cell division in the palisade cells was held up, while epidermal cells continued to stretch normally, the stresses set up by the unequal expansion of the two tissues resulting in rupture of the epidermis from the palisade cells. *Stereum purpureum* cannot be found in the leaves but occurs in the stem some distance below. Brooks & Brenchley (1929, 1931) found that browning and gum formation in the xylem and silvering of the foliage could be induced by injection of cell-free culture filtrates of *S. purpureum* into healthy branches. They therefore suggested that silvering was caused by upward transport of toxins released by the fungus. Their results were not always entirely consistent, but strongly suggested that browning of the xylem and gum formation, and necrosis of the leaves, were caused by a thermostable dialysable substance and that silvering was caused by a thermolabile constituent of the culture filtrate. They finally concluded that the thermolabile constituent was not an enzyme because it sometimes appeared to be dialysable, but this point needs further investigation. They produced no direct evidence that such diffusible toxins were produced *in vivo*, but the fact that the highly specific symptom of silvering could be induced by culture filtrates is highly suggestive.

Coral spot of fruit trees (Nectria cinnabarina). This parasite also gains entry by wounds in the stem. It causes local brown discolorations of the cortex and xylem; vessels are invaded by hyphae and to a great extent plugged with brown gummy material. No mycelium can be seen beyond the discoloured parts, but leaves above this level frequently show signs of necrosis and wilting. Line (1923) attributed these last symptoms to vessel plugging. Uri (1948) agreed with this view but also showed that a phytotoxic substance could be found in culture filtrates and that, in a considerable number of strains tested, the pathogenicity of a strain was closely correlated with its capacity to produce this substance *in vitro*. She found that phytotoxicity of culture filtrates of *Nectria cinnabarina* was parallel to their capacity to inhibit growth of the fungus *Pythium debaryanum*, which thus afforded a convenient method of bioassay. Her work was followed up by Kobel (1951), who considered that injection of cell-free culture filtrates could simulate all the symptoms of the natural disease. He further showed that culture filtrates greatly increased the resistance to water flow in the xylem, and that if the culture filtrate was forced through the stem under pressure wilting was not produced, although necrotic symptoms still resulted. He suggested that constituents of the culture filtrate caused blocking of the xylem and consequently wilting of leaves above the block, and that the necrosis of xylem and leaves were toxigenically induced. Using a bioassay based on antifungal activity of the culture filtrate, he isolated the acidic and basic fractions of benzene-soluble material. Though these produced necrosis they did not appear to cause vessel blocking or wilt. The general similarity of these findings to those reported for tomato wilt is striking.

Oak wilt (Endoconidiophora fagacearum). In this disease too, infection takes place through wounds in branches. The leaves wilt, become brown and fall, and the disease progresses rapidly upward and downward through the tree. The fungus penetrates to all parts of the tree, except the acorns, conidia moving freely in the vessels. At first sight it would appear that there is little need to postulate intervention of a toxin but there is some evidence for one. Culture filtrates contain a toxic material capable of reproducing many symptoms of the disease (Young, 1949). Beckman, Kuntz & Riker (1953) and Beckman, Kuntz, Riker & Berbee (1953) showed that, after infection, there was a sudden and marked drop in the rate of movement of solutes in the trunk, this reduced mobility preceding the development of wilt by 3–4 days. The resistance of twigs to water flow increased at the same time. In trees with incipient or severe wilt a majority of the vessels in the outer annual rings were blocked with tyloses,* absent from healthy plants. They considered it possible, but presented little experimental evidence to support their view, that production of tyloses was stimulated by pectic enzymes and auxins secreted by the invading fungi.

Dutch elm disease (Ceratostomella ulmi) is carried by bark beetles (*Scolytus* spp.) which introduce spores of the fungus into healthy elm twigs when feeding. The fungus spreads downwards to the trunk and then pervades the whole tree, spores being freely carried upward in the vessels. The most striking symptom of the disease is wilting and browning of leaves in the crown of the tree. Injection of cell-free culture filtrates produces symptoms similar to those of the disease, viz. vascular browning, production of tyloses in the vessels and wilt. There is no direct evidence of toxin production *in vivo* (Feldman, Caroselli & Howard, 1950; Frederick & Howard, 1951).

There are certain common features in this group of vascular diseases: (i) infection through wounds in branches and twigs; (ii) vigorous development of the parasite in the vascular system; (iii) production of vascular browning, gum formation and tyloses; and (iv) wilting or necrosis of leaves. There is evidence that some of these symptoms may develop in advance of the fungus and may be produced by injection of culture filtrates. The work of Brooks & Brenchley on silver-leaf suggests that enzymes secreted by the pathogenic fungus are of importance in producing symptoms. Further investigation may show that the processes underlying symptom production in this group of diseases are similar to those active in the wilts of non-woody plants, and that enzymes produced by the parasite play an important part.

SOFT ROTS

Soft rots are caused by invasion of fleshy plant tissues by parasites such as *Botrytis cinerea*, *Sclerotinia* spp., *Rhizopus stolonifer*, *Pythium* spp. and *Bacterium carotovorum*. The pathology of soft rots has been care-

---

* Tyloses: cellular proliferations of the medullary-ray parenchyma in the lumen of the vessels.

fully reviewed in recent years by Brown (1936, 1948), whose work has contributed so much to our knowledge of them. In diseases of this type, after the parasite enters the plant tissues, it advances rapidly and host cells become macerated and killed. This maceration and death of cells usually takes place slightly in advance of the parasite. The first important research on the pathology of soft rots was the investigation by de Bary (1886) of *Sclerotinia libertiana*. He concluded that an enzyme secreted by the fungus caused dissolution of the middle lamella of cells near the parasite. He was not able to identify with certainty the cause of death of the cells but suggested that it was due to oxalic acid, which he showed could be produced *in vitro* by the fungus. Brown (1936) showed that in rots caused by *Botrytis cinerea*, a pectinase type of enzyme was responsible both for the macerating effect and, apparently, for the toxic effects; he could find no evidence of a thermostable toxin. Reviewing all other work in this field, Brown (1936, 1948) concluded that, although it was not possible to dismiss entirely the possibility that thermostable toxins were involved, in most cases all the observed effects of invasion by soft-rot organisms could be attributed to secretion of pectic enzymes by the pathogen. Recent work has not appreciably altered the picture. Some indirect evidence has been presented (Brandenburg, 1950) that in some *Pythium* diseases a diffusible toxin is involved, but the described properties of the toxin are not inconsistent with its being a pectic enzyme. Gentile (1951), Sauthoff (1952) and Bazzigher (1953) claimed that *Botrytis cinerea* produces a toxin *in vitro* but have presented no evidence of its significance in natural infection. The toxin described by Gentile was thermostable, but those described by Sauthoff and by Bazzigher were thermolabile. Overell (1952) showed that a thermostable toxin was produced *in vitro* by *Sclerotinia sclerotiorum* after prolonged incubation; he identified the toxin as oxalic acid but gave no evidence that it is produced in plant tissues.

In only one case has clear evidence been presented for intervention of a thermostable toxin in pathogenesis. This is in the crown rot of groundnut seedlings caused by *Aspergillus niger*. Gibson (1953) showed that the pathogenicity of a series of isolates was correlated with their capacity to produce acid *in vitro*, but not with their capacity to produce citric acid. Moreover, aqueous solutions of oxalic acid (0·1 %) applied to the hypocotyl produced similar lesions to those seen in the natural disease, but citric acid (1·0 %) had no effect. Nevertheless, it is clear that in general nearly all the toxigenic effects seen in soft rots can be attributed to enzymes and that thermostable toxins are of little importance.

LEAF SPOTS

In this type of disease numerous small local lesions are produced on leaves, and in severe attacks they may coalesce to cause widespread necrosis. In three such diseases toxin production by the pathogen has been suspected.

Tobacco wildfire (Pseudomonas tabaci). In this disease, which may become seriously epidemic, the most characteristic symptoms is production of numerous small, angular, brown necrotic spots on the leaves; each necrotic spot being surrounded by a broader (1–2 cm. diam.) chlorotic halo. It was recognized very early in the study of the disease that the chlorotic haloes were probably produced by diffusion of a toxin from the site of infection, because whereas bacteria could be isolated from the nectrotic spots, they were absent from the haloes. Cell-free filtrates from cultures *in vitro* of *Pseudomonas tabaci* if pricked into tobacco leaves produced characteristic haloes. Many plants other than tobacco are susceptible to this toxin, though immune to infection by the pathogen (Johnson & Murwin, 1925; Clayton, 1934). Another disease known as blackfire is similar to wildfire in most respects save that no haloes surround the leaf spots. The causal organism, *P. angulatum*, appears to differ little if at all from *P. tabaci*, except that it produces no toxin *in vitro* (Braun, 1937*a*). *P. tabaci*, if kept in culture for a long period, frequently loses the power to produce the toxin *in vitro*; it remains able to infect tobacco plants but produces symptoms indistinguishable from those of *P. angulatum*. This suggests that such attenuated strains are also unable to produce the toxin in the host plant. The toxin is produced *in vitro* on a medium containing glucose, nitrate and mineral salts (Braun, 1937*b*) and is thermostable. Taken together, all this earlier work afforded strong evidence that in the natural wildfire disease, the chlorotic haloes were toxigenically induced.

More recently, evidence has been obtained about the mode of action and chemical nature of the toxin. Braun (1950) found that cell-free culture filtrates were highly inhibitory to the unicellular alga *Chlorella* and that this inhibition was competitively reversed by L-methionine; D-methionine was inactive. He was unable to show inactivation of the toxin by L-methionine in the tobacco leaf, but demonstrated that a known methionine antagonist, methionine sulphoxime, produced haloes indistinguishable from those produced by *Pseudomonas tabaci* toxin. The toxin has been isolated (Woolley, Pringle & Braun, 1952); it is water-soluble, ninhydrin-positive and highly unstable in aqueous solution. On hydrolysis in 6N-hydrochloric acid another ninhydrin-positive substance is produced, which is not phytotoxic and has been shown to be α-ϵ-diamino-β-hydroxypimelic acid (Woolley, Schaffner & Braun, 1952). Its structural similarity to methionine and methionine sulphoxime supports Braun's earlier conclusion that the toxin interferes with methionine metabolism of the leaf.

Canker, die-back and shot-hole of stone-fruits (Pseudomonas mors-prunorum). In summer, infection with *Pseudomonas mors-prunorum* usually results in a typical leaf spot, in which the necrotic infected areas become dry and may drop out; autumn infections give rise to serious cankers of the twigs, so that death of complete shoots may result. This disease is therefore to some extent intermediate between the leaf spots and the vascular diseases. Tissues frequently die well ahead of the actual bacterial invasion, and Erikson & Montgomery (1945) considered that this might be due in part to a toxin secreted by the pathogen. Moreover, they showed that a toxin is produced not only on conventional culture media but also on bark extracts, and if this cell-free culture filtrate is injected into cherry or plum shoots, symptoms very similar to the natural disease are produced. Varieties of cherry and plum resistant to the disease are little affected by such toxin preparations, whereas susceptible varieties are very sensitive. There is an impressive amount of indirect evidence, therefore, that the toxin produced *in vitro* is also active *in vivo*. There is some evidence that the toxin is a protein endotoxin, liberated into the medium on autolysis of the bacterial cells.

Early blight of tomatoes and potatoes (Alternaria solani). The fungus infects leaves, stems and fruits, usually producing numerous dark necrotic spots; the lesions on leaves eventually become papery and brittle. In severe cases these lesions may coalesce, whole leaves becoming necrotic and desiccated, and such plants may become completely defoliated. The fungus can usually be isolated from the lesions. On occasion, more particularly when the primary infection is at the base of the stem of young plants, stem and leaf lesions appear to be sterile. In mature plants, when primary infections develop on petioles, sterile lesions may appear on the leaf. These observations have been interpreted as indicating that the fungus produces a toxin at the site of infection and that this travels upward in the plant causing lesions in advance of the actual spread of the fungus (Whipple, 1938; Thomas, 1940; Pound & Stahmann, 1951).

A metabolic product of *Alternaria solani* has been isolated which possesses marked phytotoxic properties (Brian, Curtis, Hemming, Unwin & Wright, 1949; Brian, Curtis, Hemming, Jefferys, Unwin & Wright, 1951; Pound & Stahmann, 1951; Brian, Elson, Hemming & Wright,

1952). This substance, alternaric acid, is an optically inactive unsaturated dibasic acid of molecular formula $C_{21}H_{30}O_8$ (Grove, 1952). If it is introduced into healthy tomato or potato shoots, lesions very similar to those observed in the natural disease are produced in stems and leaves. The effect of alternaric acid on the water balance of these plants is similar to that of lycomarasmin (Gäumann, Kern & Sauthoff, 1952; Gäumann, Naef-Roth, Reusser & Ammann, 1952), but it is active in much lower doses, and of all known phytotoxic substances produced by plant pathogens it most closely approaches in activity the bacterial toxins produced by animal pathogens.

There seems to be little doubt that *A. solani* produces a toxin in naturally infected plants (Pound & Stahmann, 1951); production of a substance with properties like those of alternaric acid has been demonstrated in artificially infected tomato fruits (Brian *et al*. 1952); alternaric acid in very low concentrations produces lesions similar to those found in natural disease. There is thus considerable evidence that alternaric acid may be implicated in the etiology of diseases caused by *A. solani*. Moreover, alternaric acid has been isolated from strains of *A. solani* collected in England (Brian *et al*. 1949), the United States (Pound & Stahmann, 1951) and France (Darpoux, Faivre-Amiot & Roux, 1950). Most of this evidence is indirect, and final proof of the significance of alternaric acid will be obtained only by its isolation from diseased plants. It has not proved possible to isolate alternaric acid from cultures of some virulent strains of *A. solani* (Brian *et al*. 1952), and it is possible that other toxins are involved.

DISEASES INVOLVING HYPERTROPHY OR HYPERPLASIA

In many plant diseases caused by parasitic fungi or bacteria the characteristic symptom is the proliferation of host tissue with the formation of galls. These galls may be due to increased cell division, increased size of cells, or to a combination of these. Such effects are particularly characteristic of diseases caused by some highly specialized parasites—for example, Ustilaginales, Uredinales, and Plasmodiophorales. But these highly specialized parasites can cause diseases other than those characterized by hypertrophy and hyperplasia; and less specialized organisms can produce galls—for example, the well known crown-gall disease caused by *Bacterium tumefaciens*.

The nature of the stimulus for gall formation is not understood. The discovery that some auxins, notably indolylacetic acid and certain auxin analogues, would initiate gall formation if applied to healthy plant tissues in appropriate concentrations, and the knowledge that indolylacetic acid is a metabolic product of certain fungi and bacteria, suggested a possible mechanism.

The maize smut (*Ustilago maydis*) produces large swellings on leaves, stems, and inflorescences of infected plants. Application of indolyl-acetic acid to maize plants will cause somewhat similar swellings. The galls in natural disease contain more indolylacetic acid than normal tissue. When grown in appropriate media in pure culture *U. maydis* produces appreciable quantities of indolylacetic acid (Wolf, 1952); trypto-phane must be supplied as a precursor. It is thus possible that the parasite produces excessive quantities of indolylacetic acid in the host tissues and that this is responsible for the hyperplasia. *U. nigra*, a smut which infects barley without production of galls, produces little or no indolylacetic acid *in vitro*. Thus it is possible that the mechanism under-lying gall formation is that postulated by Wolf, but there is still no evidence that *U. maydis* produces indolylacetic acid *in vivo* or that it can produce enough to cause the very marked disturbances in tissue growth observed in the natural disease.

A similar situation exists in the crown-gall disease caused by *Bacterium tumefaciens*. In these galls also there is a higher concentration of indolyl-acetic acid than is usual in normal tissue, and crown-gall bacteria produce indolylacetic acid *in vitro*. Nevertheless, there are adequate reasons for supposing that indolylacetic acid production *in vivo* only partially accounts for the symptoms of the disease (de Ropp, 1951). Indolylacetic acid may well be involved, the most significant observation being that attenuated strains of *B. tumefaciens*, which will not cause tumour-formation alone, will do so if indolylacetic acid is applied to the infected plant. Braun & Laskaris (1942) have therefore concluded that there are two phases in gall formation: (i) transformation of host cells into tumour cells and (ii) stimulation of tumour cells to continuous multiplication by indolylacetic acid or related substances, leading to the formation of typical galls. All attempts to isolate the transforming system active in stage (i) have so far failed.

Baldacci (1952) pointed out that it is not necessary to assume in such diseases as this that the pathogen produces a growth-promoting sub-stance. In the growing plant auxin levels are determined by a balance of the processes of synthesis and degradation. It is quite conceivable that metabolic products of the parasite, although themselves inactive as growth-promoting substances, could affect auxin levels by influencing host systems involved in synthesis or degradation of auxin. This type of approach has been used by Sequeira & Steeves (1954) to explain the leaf-drop of coffee caused by the fungus *Omphalia flavida*. The fungus produces leaf spots on coffee and other plants, which usually result in premature defoliation. Defoliation occurs when there is a lesion on the leaf blade near the petiole. It was assumed that this caused mechanical weakening, but Sequeira & Steeves could find no evidence for this. Leaf abscission in a normal deciduous plant is due to reduction in the flow of auxin from the leaf-blade to the petiole. The premature abscission caused by *O. flavida* can be prevented by application of indolylacetic acid to the petiole below the lesion. Sequeira & Steeves therefore considered the possibility that the fungus might accelerate abscission by destruction of auxin. In support of this they found that the organism grown in pure culture produced an oxidative enzyme readily able to inactivate indolylacetic acid. This is the first record of the production of such an enzyme by fungi, though similar enzymes are known to occur in some plant tissues.

One further disease in which increased host growth is an important symptom needs to be mentioned. Rice crops in Japan and other far eastern countries, and also occasionally in Italy, may become infected with *Gibberella fujikuroi* (*Fusarium moniliforme*), a soil-borne foot-rot fungus. One of the first signs of infection is that the seedlings become paler and much taller than healthy plants. The increased length of leaves is mainly or entirely due to increased length of cells (Seto, 1928). From the fungus grown in pure culture a metabolic product was isolated, which produced the typical symptoms of chlorosis and overgrowth when applied to healthy plants in very low concentrations. Its effects can be observed not only in rice plants but also in other species. This metabolite, named gibberellin (Yabuta & Hayashi, 1939 *a*, *b*) has been studied in some detail; it does not appear to be chemically related to known auxins (Yabuta, Sumiki, Aso, Tamura, Igarashi & Tamari, 1941), and in many ways it is not at all physiologically similar to the auxins. The specificity of the response produced makes it almost certain that gibberellin is produced in infected host tissues. This disease is the only case where a hypertrophic or hyperplastic response is at all understood.

CONCLUSIONS

If it does nothing else, this survey shows the backward state of our knowledge of the chemical bases of the symptomatology of plant disease. It will clearly be impossible to come to any firm general conclusions. Nevertheless, it is possible to provide tentative answers to two questions: (i) To what extent are plant diseases toxigenically induced? (ii) What part does toxin production play in pathogenicity?

To what extent are plant disease symptoms toxigenically induced?

There are few instances in which there is unequivocal evidence that disease symptoms of plants are produced by toxins, and fewer instances in which phytotoxic metabolites have been characterized. Nevertheless, the evidence reviewed here leaves little doubt that the escape of phytotoxic metabolic products from pathogens into host-plant tissues is an important factor in the production of disease symptoms.

Three almost universal symptoms of vascular diseases of plants are: (i) brown discoloration of the internal cell walls of the xylem vessels; (ii) production of occlusive gums and tyloses in the xylem; and (iii) wilt of the foliage distal to the infection of the xylem. Recent research has sought to produce a unitary explanation of these symptoms; this has led to rejection of theories based on production of thermostable toxins by the parasite, since such thermostable toxins as have been isolated from cultures *in vitro* rarely produce wilt symptoms precisely like those found in the natural disease and still less frequently produce the vascular symptoms. There is evidence that the vascular symptoms are caused by thermolabile substances of high molecular weight produced by the parasite; enzymes of the pectin-methyl-esterase type appear to be implicated, but other enzymes may also be of importance. The vascular tissues of the host are considered to respond to the presence of these enzymes produced by the parasite in various ways which result in reduced flow of water and solutes through the vessels, so that wilt results. It may yet be found, of course, that thermostable, phytotoxic substances of lower molecular weight are also involved in symptom production. Ethylene produced by infected tissue seems to be responsible for epinasty and yellowing of the foliage in tomato wilt.

In soft rots, production of enzymes of the pectinase type by the pathogen is undoubtedly of great importance and is responsible both for macerating effects and the death of cells in infected tissue. Very little work has been done with purified enzyme preparations, and here also it is quite possible that other enzymes, such as cellulases, are involved. In a few cases, production of thermostable toxic substances, such as oxalic acid, may be of some secondary importance.

Only three leaf-spot diseases have been seriously investigated—early blight of tomatoes and potatoes (*Alternaria solani*), tobacco wildfire (*Pseudomonas tabaci*) and shot-hole of stone-fruits (*P. mors-prunorum*). In each of these diseases there is evidence of toxigenic induction of disease symptoms, thermostable substances of low molecular weight being involved in the first two, a protein in the last.

The hypertrophic and hyperplastic responses of the host characteristic of some diseases are still little understood. It seems likely on general grounds that the parasite somehow dislocates the auxin growth-regulating system in the host. The overgrowth of rice seedlings caused by infection with *Gibberella fujikuroi* is the only disease of this kind in which a characterized metabolite of the pathogen is definitely implicated.

On the whole, we may conclude that in plant diseases, as in animal diseases, production of toxic metabolic products by the invading pathogen is a potent cause of disease symptoms. As far as we know at present, such phytotoxic substances are of a lower order of activity than the bacterial toxins involved in animal disease.

What part does toxin production play in pathogenicity?

Plant pathologists have not given a great deal of thought to what they mean by pathogenicity. The best theoretical discussion is that of Gäumann (1951), who distinguishes between aggressiveness and pathogenicity. By aggressiveness he means the qualities of a pathogen that enable it to infect a host plant and then spread from the initial point of infection. The complex conception of aggressiveness emphasizes the following: size of inoculum, rapidity with which infection is established, and length of the interval between the establishment of infection and the first appearance of symptoms. He has two criteria of pathogenicity: (i) the ability of an organism to cause disease symptoms in the host and (ii) the severity of these symptoms.

Most of the experimental work reviewed in this paper fails to distinguish between these two aspects of the host-parasite relationship; in any case it is difficult to do so because they are closely interrelated. In general, it appears that production of toxins has little influence on aggressiveness in so far as it concerns the establishment of an infection, but there seems to be evidence that toxins can influence pathogenicity.

There are two main methods of experimental approach to this question. In the first place we may compare a number of strains of a pathogen differing in pathogenicity (that is, in the severity of the disease symptoms they produce), to see whether their capacity to produce phytotoxic metabolites *in vitro* and if possible *in vivo* is in any way correlated with their pathogenicity. The results of a number of experiments of this kind are summarized in Table 1. Secondly, a number of species of host plant, or of varieties within one species of host, often differ in their susceptibility (viz. in the severity of disease symptoms produced) to a pathogen. Some insight into the connexion between toxin production and pathogenicity may be obtained by finding out whether toxins produced *in vitro* have an effect on these groups of host plants in any way parallel to the effect of the pathogen. The results of some experiments of this kind are summarized in Table 2.

Table 1 shows an almost equal division between cases where a correlation was found between *in vitro* toxin production and pathogenicity and cases where no correlation was found. In tomato wilt, results obtained by different experimenters were completely different. Nevertheless, the number of cases where a correlation has been found is much greater than when Brown (1936) considered experimental evidence of this kind. A negative result in experiments of this kind is not proof of any lack of relation between toxin production and pathogenicity—it might be that the culture conditions *in vitro* were not suitable. For instance, the results (Tables 1 and 2) presented by Gäumann *et al.* (1950) were obtained with old culture filtrates in which lycomarasmin would be the main phytotoxic constituent. As we have seen, there is strong evidence for believing that lycomarasmin is not involved *in vivo*, so that a correlation between lycomarasmin production and pathogenicity should not be expected. The culture filtrates used by Haymaker (1928) were produced differently and may have contained some more significant toxic metabolite.

In Table 2 there is a similar distribution of positive and negative results. The results reported by Winstead & Walker (1954*a*, *b*) are particularly instructive. In one set of experiments they used culture filtrates containing pectinase (pectin-methyl-esterase and polygalacturonase mixtures) from a number of fungal and bacterial pathogens and showed that each of these caused vascular browning in all of a range of hosts, although the pathogens themselves could only affect one host. Thus the capacity to produce this generalized symptom, vascular browning, was not in any way correlated with pathogenicity. On the other hand, the thermostable phytotoxic substances in culture filtrates of a number of physiologic races of *Fusarium oxysporum* produced characteristic symptoms only in their appropriate hosts—an example of a strong correlation between toxin production and pathogenicity.

Evidence of a correlation between toxin production *in vitro* and pathogenicity is accumulating gradually. This affords additional evidence in favour of the view that escape of phytotoxic metabolites from the cells of pathogens is a cause of disease symptoms in infected plants.

Table 1. *Relation between phytotoxicity of filtrates from in vitro cultures and pathogenicity of fungal and bacterial parasites of plants*

Pathogen	Host	Toxin present in culture filtrate (where known)	Correlation between toxin production and pathogenicity	Reference
Alternaria solani	Tomato, potato	Alternaric acid and others	−	Brian et al. 1952
Aspergillus niger	Ground nut	Oxalic acid	+	Gibson, 1953
Ceratostomella ulmi	Elm	Unknown	−	Frederick & Howard, 1951
Fusarium oxysporum var. lycopersici	Tomato	Unknown	+	Haymaker, 1928
Fusarium oxysporum var. lycopersici	Tomato	Lycomarasmin and others	−	Gäumann, Naef-Roth & Miescher, 1950; Uri, 1948
Nectria cinnabarina	Redcurrant	Unknown	+	Braun, 1937a
Pseudomonas tabaci	Tobacco	Unknown	+	

Table 2. *Relation between susceptibility of hosts to attack by a pathogen and sensitivity to phytotoxic metabolites of the pathogen produced in vitro*

Pathogen	Host	Phytotoxic preparation used	Correlation between susceptibility of host to pathogen and sensitivity to toxic metabolites of pathogen	Reference
Alternaria solani	Various species	Alternaric acid	−	Brian et al. 1952
Fusarium oxysporum var. lycopersici	Tomato	Culture filtrates	+	Haymaker, 1928
Fusarium oxysporum var. lycopersici	Tomato	Lycomarasmin	−	Gäumann, Naef-Roth & Miescher, 1950
Fusarium oxysporum vars.	Cabbage, radish, cotton	Culture filtrates*	+	Winstead & Walker, 1954b
Pseudomonas mors-prunorum	Plum	Culture filtrates	+−	Erikson & Montgomery, 1945
Verticillium vilmorinii	Michaelmas daisies	Culture filtrates	−	Dowson, 1922
Various pectinase-producing pathogens	Tomato, cotton, cabbage, pea	Culture filtrates	−	Winstead & Walker, 1954a

* Heat-treated and dialysed to isolate as far as possible the thermostable dialysable constituents.

REFERENCES

BALDACCI, E. (1952). In merito alla relazione fra le sostanze di crescita e i fenomeni patologici dello svillupo, nei vegetali. *Nuovo G. bot. ital.* **59** (2–4), 500.

DE BARY, A. (1886). Über einige Sclerotinien und Sclerotienkrankheiten. *Bot. Zbl.* **44**, 377, 393, 409, 433, 449, 465.

BAZZIGHER, G. (1953). Über mutmasslich induzierte Abwehrreaktionen bei *Phaseolus vulgaris* L. *Phytopath. Z.* **20**, 383.

BECKMAN, C. H., KUNTZ, J. E. & RIKER, A. J. (1953). The growth of the oak wilt fungus with various vitamins and carbon and nitrogen sources. *Phytopathology*, **43**, 441.

BECKMAN, C. H., KUNTZ, J. E., RIKER, A. J. & BERBEE, J. G. (1953). Host responses associated with the development of oak wilt. *Phytopathology*, **43**, 448.

BEWLEY, W. F. (1922). 'Sleepy disease' of tomato. *Ann. appl. Biol.* **9**, 116.

BINTNER, J. (1919). Silver leaf disease. *Kew Bull.* no. 241.

BRANDENBURG, E. (1950). Über die Bildung von Toxinen in der Gattung Pythium und ihre Wirkung auf die Pflanzen. *NachrBl. dtsch. PflSchDienst, Stuttgart*, **2**, (5), 69.

BRAUN, A. C. (1937a). A comparative study of *Bacterium tabacum* Wolf & Foster and *Bacterium angulatum* Frohme & Murray. *Phytopathology*, **27**, 283.

BRAUN, A. C. (1937b). Beitrage zur Frage der Toxinbildung durch *Pseudomonas tabaci* (Wo. & Fo.) Stapp. *Z. Bakt.* Abt. II, **97**, 177.

BRAUN, A. C. (1950). The mechanism of action of a bacterial toxin on plant cells. *Proc. nat. Acad. Sci., Wash.*, **36**, 423.

BRAUN, A. C. & LASKARIS, T. (1942). Tumor formation by attenuated crown-gall bacteria in the presence of growth-promoting substances. *Proc. nat. Acad. Sci., Wash.*, **28**, 468.

BRIAN, P. W., CURTIS, P. J., HEMMING, H. G., JEFFERYS, E. G., UNWIN, C. H. & WRIGHT, J. M. (1951). Alternaric acid: a biologically active metabolic product of *Alternaria solani* (Ell. & Mart.) Jones & Grout. Production, isolation and antifungal properties. *J. gen. Microbiol.* **7**, 619.

BRIAN, P. W., CURTIS, P. J., HEMMING, H. G., UNWIN, C. H. & WRIGHT, J. M. (1949). Alternaric acid, a biologically active metabolic product of the fungus *Alternaria solani*. *Nature, Lond.*, **164**, 534.

BRIAN, P. W., ELSON, G. W., HEMMING, H. G. & WRIGHT, J. M. (1952). The phytotoxic properties of alternaric acid in relation to the etiology of plant diseases caused by *Alternaria solani* (Ell. & Mart.) Jones & Grout. *Ann. appl. Biol.* **39**, 308.

BROOKS, F. T. & BRENCHLEY, G. H. (1929). Injection experiments on plum trees in relation to *Stereum purpureum* and silver-leaf disease. *New Phytol.* **28**, 218.

BROOKS, F. T. & BRENCHLEY, G. H. (1931). Further injection experiments in relation to *Stereum purpureum*. *New Phytol.* **30**, 128.

BROWN, W. (1936). The physiology of host-parasite relations. *Bot. Rev.* **2**, 236.

BROWN, W. (1948). Physiology of the facultative type of parasite. *Proc. Roy. Soc.* B, **135**, 171.

CHAMBERLAIN, D. W. & MCALISTER, D. F. (1954). Factors affecting the development of brown stem rot of soybean. *Phytopathology*, **44**, 4.

CLAUSON-KAAS, N., PLATTNER, P. A. & GÄUMANN, E. (1944). Über ein welkeerzeugendes Stoffwechselprodukt von *Fusarium lycopersici* Sacc. *Ber. schweiz. bot. Ges.* **54**, 523.

CLAYTON, E. E. (1934). Toxin produced by *Bacterium tabacum* and its relation to host range. *J. agric. Res.* **48**, 411.

DARPOUX, H., FAIVRE-AMIOT, A. & ROUX, L. (1950). Sur un nouvel antibiotique, l'Alternarine, et sur quelques autres substances extraits des cultures d'une souche d'*Alternaria solani*. *C.R. Acad. Sci., Paris*, **230**, 993.

DAVIS, D. (1953a). The role of enzymes in the etiology of *Fusarium* wilt of tomato. *Phytopathology*, **43**, 470.

DAVIS, D. (1953b). The use of intergeneric grafts to demonstrate toxins in the *Fusarium* wilt disease of tomato. *Phytopathology*, **43**, 470.

DAVIS, D., WAGGONER, P. E. & DIMOND, A. E. (1953). Conjugated phenols in the *Fusarium* wilt syndrome. *Nature, Lond.*, **172**, 959.

DIMOND, A. E. & WAGGONER, P. E. (1953a). On the nature and role of vivotoxins in plant disease. *Phytopathology*, **43**, 229.

DIMOND, A. E. & WAGGONER, P. E. (1953b). The cause of epinastic symptoms in *Fusarium* wilt of tomatoes. *Phytopathology*, **43**, 663.

DIMOND, A. E. & WAGGONER, P. E. (1953c). The physiology of lycomarasmin production by *Fusarium oxysporum* f. *lycopersici*. *Phytopathology*, **43**, 195.

DIMOND, A. E. & WAGGONER, P. E. (1953d). Effect of lycomarasmin decomposition upon estimates of its production. *Phytopathology*, **43**, 319.

DIMOND, A. E. & WAGGONER, P. E. (1953e). The water economy of *Fusarium* wilted tomato plants. *Phytopathology*, **43**, 619.

DOWSON, W. J. (1922). On the symptoms of wilting of Michaelmas daisies produced by a toxin secreted by a *Cephalosporium*. *Trans. Brit. mycol. Soc.* **7**, 283.

DOWSON, W. J. (1923). The wilt disease of Michaelmas daisies. *J. R. hort. Soc.* **48**, 38.

ERIKSON, D. & MONTGOMERY, H. B. S. (1945). Certain aspects of resistance of plum trees to bacterial canker. Part III. The action of cell-free filtrates of *Pseudomonas mors-prunorum* Wormald and related phyto-pathogenic bacteria on plum trees. *Ann. appl. Biol.* **32**, 117.

FELDMAN, A. W., CAROSELLI, N. E. & HOWARD, F. L. (1950). Physiology of toxin production by *Ceratostomella ulmi*. *Phytopathology*, **40**, 341.

FOSTER, R. E. (1946). The first symptom of tomato *Fusarium* wilt: clearing of the ultimate veinlets in the leaf. *Phytopathology*, **36**, 691.

FREDERICK, L. & HOWARD, F. L. (1951). Comparative physiology of eight isolates of *Ceratostomella ulmi*. *Phytopathology*, **41**, 12.

GÄUMANN, E. (1951). *Pflanzliche Infektionslehre*. Basel: Verlag Birkhauser.

GÄUMANN, E. & JAAG, O. (1947a). Die physiologischen Grundlagen des parasitogenen Welkens. I. *Ber. schweiz. bot. Ges.* **57**, 3.

GÄUMANN, E. & JAAG, O. (1947b). Die physiologischen Grundlagen des parasitogenen Welkens. II. *Ber. schweiz. bot. Ges.* **57**, 132.

GÄUMANN, E. & JAAG, O. (1947c). Die physiologischen Grundlagen des parasitogenen Welkens. III. *Ber. schweiz. bot. Ges.* **57**, 227.

GÄUMANN, E., KERN, H. & SAUTHOFF, W. (1952). Untersuchungen über zwei Welketoxine. *Phytopath. Z.* **18**, 404.

GÄUMANN, E., NAEF-ROTH, S. & KOBEL, H. (1952). Über Fusarinsäure, ein zweites Welketoxin des *Fusarium lycopersici* Sacc. *Phytopath. Z.* **20**, 1.

GÄUMANN, E., NAEF-ROTH, S. & MIESCHER, G. (1950). Untersuchungen über des Lycomarasmin. *Phytopath. Z.* **16**, 257.

GÄUMANN, E., NAEF-ROTH, S., REUSSER, P. & AMMANN, A. (1952). Über den einfluss einiger Welketoxine und Antibiotica auf die osmotischen Eigenschaften pflanzlicher Zellen. *Phytopath. Z.* **19**, 160.

GÄUMANN, E., STOLL, C. & KERN, H. (1953). Über Vasinfuscarin, ein drittes Welketoxin des *Fusarium lycopersici* Sacc. *Phytopath. Z.* **20**, 345.

GENTILE, A. C. (1951). A study of the toxin produced by an isolate of *Botrytis cinerea* from *Exochorda*. *Physiol. Plant.* **4**, 370.

GIBSON, I. A. S. (1953). Crown rot, a seedling disease of groudnuts caused by *Aspergillus niger*. *Trans. Brit. mycol. Soc.* **36**, 198.

GOTHOSKAR, S. S., SCHEFFER, R. P., WALKER, J. C. & STAHMANN, M. A. (1953). The role of pectic enzymes in *Fusarium* wilt of tomato. *Phytopathology*, **43**, 535.

GOTTLIEB, D. (1943). The presence of a toxin in tomato wilt. *Phytopathology*, **33**, 126.

GOTTLIEB, D. (1944). The mechanism of wilting caused by *Fusarium bulbigenum* var. *lycopersici*. *Phytopathology*, **34**, 41.

GROVE, J. F. (1952). Alternaric acid. Part I. Purification and characterization. *J. chem. Soc.* p. 4056.

GÜSSOW, H. T. (1912). Der Milchglanz der Obstbäume. *Z. PfllKrankh.* **22**, 385.

HARRIS, H. A. (1940). Comparative wilt induction by *Erwinia tracheiphila* and *Phytomonas stewarti*. *Phytopathology*, **30**, 625.

HAYMAKER, H. H. (1928). Relation of toxic excretory products from two strains of *Fusarium lycopersici* to tomato wilt. *J. agric. Res.* **36**, 697.

HUTCHINSON, C. M. (1913). Rangpur tobacco wilt. *Mem. Dep. Agric. India, Bact.*, **1**, (2) 67.

JOHNSON, J. & MURWIN, H. F. (1925). Experiments on the control of wildfire of tobacco. *Bull. Wisc. agric. Exp. Sta.* **62**, 1.

KOBEL, F. (1951). Untersuchungen über toxische Stoffwechselprodukte von *Nectria cinnabarina* (Tode) Fr. *Phytopath. Z.* **18**, 157.

LINE, J. (1923). The parasitism of *Nectria cinnabarina* (Coral spot), with special reference to its action on red currant. *Trans. Brit. mycol. Soc.* **8**, 22.

LINFORD, M. B. (1931a). Transpirational history as a key to the nature of wilting in the *Fusarium* wilt of peas. *Phytopathology*, **21**, 791.

LINFORD, M. B. (1931b). Studies of pathogenesis and resistance in pea wilt caused by *Fusarium orthoceras* var. *pisi*. *Phytopathology*, **21**, 797.

LUDWIG, R. A. (1952). Studies on the physiology of hadromycotic wilting in the tomato plant. *Tech. Bull. Macdonald agric. Coll.* **20**, 3.

LUZ, G. (1934). Über den Stoffwechsel von *Fusarium lycopersici* und *Fusarium lini*. *Phytopath. Z.* **7**, 585.

NICKERSON, W. J. (1948). Ethylene as a metabolic product of the pathogenic fungus *Blastomyces dermatitidis*. *Arch. Biochem.* **17**, 225.

OVERELL, B. T. (1952). A toxin in culture filtrates of *Sclerotinia sclerotiorum*. *Aust. J. Sci.* **14**, 197.

PERCIVAL, J. (1902). 'Silver-leaf' disease. *J. Linn. Soc. (Bot.)*, **35**, 390.

PLATTNER, P. A. & CLAUSON-KAAS, N. (1944). Über Lycomarasmin, den Welkstoff aus *Fusarium lycopersici* Sacc. *Experientia*, **1**, 195.

POUND, G. S. & STAHMANN, M. A. (1951). The production of a toxic material by *Alternaria solani* and its relation to the early blight of the tomato. *Phytopathology*, **41**, 1104.

DE ROPP, R. S. (1951). The crown-gall problem. *Bot. Rev.* **17**, 629.

ROSS, A. F. & WILLIAMSON, C. E. (1951). Physiologically active emanations from virus-infected plants. *Phytopathology*, **41**, 431.

SAUTHOFF, W. (1952). Über Stoffwechselprodukte bei *Botrytis cinerea* Pers. *Phytopath. Z.* **19**, 483.

SCHEFFER, R. P. (1952). The wilting mechanism in *Fusarium* wilt of tomato. *Phytopathology*, **42**, 18.

SCHEFFER, R. P. & WALKER, J. C. (1953). The physiology of *Fusarium* wilt of tomato. *Phytopathology*, **43**, 116.

SEQUEIRA, L. & STEEVES, T. A. (1954). Auxin inactivation and its relation to leaf drop caused by the fungus *Omphalia flavida*. *Plant Physiol.* **29**, 11.

SETO, F. (1928). The reactions of rice seedlings to infection of the causal fungus of the Bakanae disease and to the filtrates of its cultures. *Mem. Coll. Agric. Kyoto*, **7**, 23.

SMITH, E. F. (1899). Wilt disease of cotton, watermelon and cowpea (*Neocosmospora* nov. gen.). *Bull. U.S. Dep. Agric.* **17**, 1.

STEWART, F. C. (1897). A bacterial disease of sweet corn. *Bull. N.Y. St. agric. Exp. Sta.* **130**, 423.

TETLEY, U. (1932). The development and cytology of the leaves of healthy and 'silvered' Victoria plum-trees. *Ann. Bot., Lond.*, **46**, 633.

THOMAS, H. R. (1940). Collar-rot infection of direct-seeded tomatoes. *Plant Dis. Reptr.* **24**, 8.

URI, J. (1948). Het parasitisme van *Nectria cinnabarina* (Tode) *Fr. Tijdschr. PlZiekt.* **54**, 29.

WAGGONER, P. E. & DIMOND, A. E. (1953). Role of chelation in causing and inhibiting the toxicity of lycomarasmin. *Phytopathology*, **43**, 281.

WELLMAN, F. L. (1941). Epinasty of tomato, one of the earliest symptoms of *Fusarium* wilt. *Phytopathology*, **31**, 281.

WHIPPLE, O. C. (1938). *Macrosporium* blight of tomatoes. *Summ. Doct. Diss. Univ. Wisconsin*, **3**, 65.

WILLIAMSON, C. E. (1950). Ethylene, a metabolic product of diseased or injured plants. *Phytopathology*, **40**, 205.

WINSTEAD, N. N. & WALKER, J. C. (1954a). Production of vascular browning by metabolites from several pathogens. *Phytopathology*, **44**, 153.

WINSTEAD, N. N. & WALKER, J. C. (1954b). Toxic metabolites of the pathogen in relation to *Fusarium* resistance. *Phytopathology*, **44**, 159.

WOLF, F. T. (1952). The production of indoleacetic acid by *Ustilago zeae*, and its possible significance in tumor formation. *Proc. nat. Acad. Sci., Wash.*, **38**, 106.

WOOLLEY, D. W. (1948). Studies on the structure of lycomarasmin. *J. biol. Chem.* **176**, 1291.

WOOLLEY, D. W., PRINGLE, R. B. & BRAUN, A. C. (1952). Isolation of the phytopathogenic toxin of *Pseudomonas tabaci*, an antagonist of methionine. *J. biol. Chem.* **197**, 409.

WOOLLEY, D. W., SCHAFFNER, G. & BRAUN, A. C. (1952). Isolation and determination of structure of a new amino-acid contained within toxin of *Pseudomonas tabaci*. *J. biol. Chem.* **198**, 807.

YABUTA, T. & HAYASHI, T. (1939a). Biochemistry of the 'Bakanae' fungus. 2. Isolation of gibberellin, a metabolic product of *Gibberella fujikuroi* Wr. which promotes the growth of rice seedlings (in Japanese). *J. agric. chem. Soc. Japan*, **15**, 257.

YABUTA, T. & HAYASHI, T. (1939b). Biochemistry of the 'Bakanae' fungus. 3. On the action of gibberellin, a growth-promoting substance, on the physiology of plants (in Japanese). *J. agric. chem. Soc. Japan*, **15**, 403.

YABUTA, T., SUMIKI, Y., ASO, K., TAMURA, T., IGARASHI, H. & TAMARI, K. (1941). Biochemistry of the 'Bakanae' fungus. 10–12. The chemical constitution of gibberellin (in Japanese). *J. agric. chem. Soc. Japan*, **17**, 721, 894, 975.

YOUNG, R. A. (1949). Studies on oak wilt caused by *Chalara quercina*. *Phytopathology*, **39**, 425.

STUDIES ON THE MECHANISM OF INVASION OF PLANTS BY VASCULAR PATHOGENS

W. G. KEYWORTH

National Vegetable Research Station, Wellesbourne, Warwicks

The object of this paper is to draw attention to an aspect of the parasitization of plants by vascular fungi on which more information would be desirable. This is the mechanism of growth of the fungus within different parts of the plant and the influence of the growth of the fungus in one part on its subsequent invasion of another part.

Information on the factors governing the growth of vascular parasites is scanty and theories on the mechanisms involved must thus be largely speculative. One reason for this is the difficulty of assessing the extent of growth of an internal organism, a difficulty which has perhaps hampered the collection of exact data. The studies to be described comprise experiments made at different times, often with objects other than that of assessing fungal invasion. Viewed as a whole, however, they indicate further ways in which the subject can be investigated and enable preliminary hypotheses to be formulated on which such investigations might be based.

THEORETICAL CONSIDERATION OF RESISTANCE

The work to be described deals with the resistance of the host plant. The study of host resistance is complementary to that of fungal pathogenicity, and each may give information about the other. The degree of resistance shown by a plant is normally measured by the effects produced when it is invaded by a pathogen. Because these effects depend on the invasive potentialities of the pathogen, they do not permit of any absolute assessment of resistance, but they can be used for comparative assessments by subjecting two plants or groups of plants of two varieties to invasion under identical conditions. Thus one plant can be said to have a higher resistance than another under a defined set of conditions.

The resistance of plants is presumably determined by their genetic constitution, and they thus possess an *inherent resistance* to particular pathogens. If means were found of assessing resistance without the use of a pathogen (e.g. by the chemical constitution of the plants), this assessment would be more indicative of inherent resistance, and it might be possible to determine why two plants show a different *effective resistance* when invaded. The concept of inherent resistance and effective resistance is particularly important in considering the invasion of parts of plants, as will be shown later. Thus while the normal uninvaded tissues of part of a plant may have a certain inherent resistance this may have been modified or overcome by the time that the tissues are entered by the pathogen, if this pathogen has made previous growth on another part of the plant. Under other circumstances, however, with the same pathogen, the inherent resistance may be less modified, so that the effective resistance may be higher than in the first case. For this reason comparisons of the resistance of parts of different plants must be conducted under the same identity of environmental and invasive conditions as is necessary in comparing the resistance of whole plants. In some comparative studies of the resistance of parts of plants to wilt pathogens, this point seems to have been overlooked. Attempts have thus been made to assess inherent resistance by the extent of invasion of the plant part under one set of conditions only, or to compare the resistance of plant parts invaded under widely differing conditions.

The plants or plant parts compared in the present study are referred to as having high or low resistance. This refers to the reaction of the plants or plant parts to invasion (i.e. to the disease). It is more usual to refer to plants as resistant or susceptible to a disease, but this may suggest that these terms are absolute and opposite in sense. Used in this connexion, however, both terms are matters of degree and should thus be qualified (i.e. high or low, etc.). One of the terms, therefore, becomes redundant. The terms susceptible has been rejected since it may also mean (in the writer's opinion more correctly) 'capable of being invaded by a pathogen'. In this sense it is the opposite of 'immune'.

Resistance to vascular pathogens seems likely to be particularly complex, since not only is the xylem of both root and stem invaded but also much of the parenchymatous tissue, e.g. in the root and in the vascular bundles. Studies of the mechanism of such resistance therefore necessitate some analysis of the factors operating in different parts of the plant. Theoretically there is no limit to the subdivision of the plant for this purpose, but in the present studies two regions only are considered: the above-ground and below-ground parts of the plant. These are here termed stem and root irrespective of their exact anatomical status.

The experiments to be described deal with two wilt diseases: *Fusarium* wilt of the tomato (caused by *F. lycopersici*) and *Verticillium* wilt of the hop (caused by *V. albo-atrum*). The effects of normal invasion through the roots of plants of different resistance will be considered first.

REACTION OF THE HOST PLANT TO NORMAL ROOT INVASION BY WILT PATHOGENS

(a) Fusarium *wilt of the tomato*

The tomato variety Bonny Best has low resistance and the variety Pan America has high resistance to wilt.

In the variety Bonny Best the fungus grows vigorously in the xylem elements of the root and invades many vessels. It does likewise in the stem, causing a dark discoloration of most or all of the vascular bundles and advancing rapidly up the xylem to the top of the plant. Wilt symptoms appear on successively higher leaves in close association with the growth of the pathogen up the stem. Eventually the plant may die, and this happens within 2–3 weeks under optimal conditions for disease development.

In the variety Pan America the fungus seems to grow less vigorously in the xylem elements of the root. It may invade the stem xylem, but if so its growth is slight and attenuated. It is confined to a few vessels and it does not advance more than a few centimetres up the stem. Leaf symptoms are usually very slight or absent.

(b) Verticillium *wilt of the hop*

The hop variety Fuggle has low resistance to wilt (caused by *V. albo-atrum*—progressive race) and the variety OR 55 has high resistance.

In Fuggle plants infected through their roots the growth of the fungus is similar to that of *Fusarium* in the Bonny Best tomato. It grows readily in both root and stem, and in the stem xylem it invades most or all of the xylem elements in the stele. Leaf symptoms are severe but affected leaves do not collapse. Instead, they develop yellow and then necrotic areas on the lamina and eventually become completely desiccated. The development of symptoms on successive leaves up the stem is, as in the tomato, closely associated with the rate of advance of the fungus up the stem.

In OR 55 plants the fungus grows less extensively in the roots. Its growth in the stem is attenuated but, in contrast to the growth of *Fusarium* in the stems of the tomato variety Pan America, *Verticillium* may grow for considerable distances (often many feet) up the OR 55 stem. It does not affect all of the xylem however; it is often restricted to an area in the centre of the stele or a sector of the wood. In addition, the invaded stem may grow new, uninvaded, xylem tissue, apparently in response to the invasion.

Another aspect of resistance has been studied in hops and will be described in more detail later. This is the comparison of the reaction of one variety (Fuggle) to two races of *V. albo-atrum*. The Fuggle variety has low resistance to the race of *V. albo-atrum* designated 'Progressive'. It has high resistance, however, to another race ('Fluctuating'). The terms 'progressive' and 'fluctuating' refer to the types of disease seen in the field when Fuggle plants are attacked by the races of pathogen. In their effects on the Fuggle plant the races will here be referred to as 'virulent' and 'mild'.

The effect of the mild race on Fuggle plants closely simulates that of the virulent race on OR55 plants. Although extensive longitudinally, growth in the stem is slight and attenuated, new xylem is formed by the invaded stem, and leaf symptoms are slight or absent.

(c) Conclusions from the above data

In assessing the resistance of a tomato or hop to wilt disease the criteria employed usually relate to the reactions of the stems. These are considered to reflect the resistance of the whole plant. Although the roots are rarely studied there is evidence, as noted above, that the vigour of growth of the pathogens in the roots of different varieties is of a similar degree to that in the stems. Thus each plant *appears* to offer a resistance to fungal invasion which is fairly evenly distributed throughout the xylem of the whole plant. If this is correct it must follow that in the same sense as the inherent (or varietal) resistance of one entire plant differs from that of another so the inherent resistance of the stems differs. This conclusion is based solely on the assumption that in resistance to invasion the whole plant behaves as a homogeneous unit. Is this assumption justified?

As already pointed out, comparative tests of the resistance of plant parts should be made only under identical conditions of environment and invasion. If these principles are applied to the present examples, it is apparent that the stems of different plants invaded through their own roots are not under identical conditions either of environment or invasion. They are growing on roots of different varieties and therefore possibly subject to rootstock influence irrespective of the presence of the fungus. But probably a more important factor is that these roots are invaded by the fungus and the fungus in the roots provides the inoculum for the stems. Since there is a difference in the growth of the fungus in the roots of the two varieties the stem of each variety may presumably be affected in a different way.

It thus appears that the resistance shown by the stems of two plants invaded through their own roots may not necessarily be indicative of their inherent resistance.

Two methods of assessing the resistance of stems grown and invaded under similar conditions have been used in the present studies. These are as follows:

(a) Grafting some of the stems of one variety on the rootstocks of the other and inoculating the composite plants through their rootstocks. In this way the reaction of each type of stem on each type of rootstock can be determined.

(b) Inoculating the stems directly. This obviates differences in the number of organisms in the inoculum, but with different varieties the rootstock effects are still present. It would be possible to eliminate these by grafting but experiments on this have not been made. Instead, the differences in reaction of one variety of hop to two races of *V. albo-atrum* have been tested. One type of stem and rootstock have thus been used throughout. The stem-inoculation experiments are open to two criticisms. First, the reaction of one variety to two fungi may not necessarily be governed by the same mechanisms as the reaction of two varieties to one fungus. With hop wilt, however, the similarity of symptoms in the two cases suggests that valid comparisons can be made. Secondly, invasion from direct inoculation may differ from that through roots. Again, the symptoms produced suggest that this is not so.

GRAFTING EXPERIMENTS

These will be described and conclusions drawn from the results. The tomato grafts were made by Heinze & Andrus (1945), and their interpretation of their results differs from that now suggested by the writer. These divergences of view will be discussed later.

(a) Fusarium *wilt of tomato*

All four possible stem-root combinations were made of the varieties Pan America (PA) (high resistance) and Bonny Best (BB) (low resistance). The composite plants were then inoculated through their roots. Results (Heinze & Andrus, 1945), were as follows:

BB on *BB*. Vigorous growth of *Fusarium* in the stem xylem. Wilt symptoms severe.

PA on *BB*. The same as above.

BB on *PA*. Slight or no invasion of the stem xylem. Wilt symptoms slight or absent.

PA on *PA*. The same as above.

(b) Verticillium *wilt of hops*

All four possible stem-root combinations were made of the varieties OR 55 (high resistance) and Fuggle (low resistance). The composite plants were inoculated through their roots with the virulent race. Results (Keyworth, 1953) were as follows:

Fuggle on *Fuggle*. Vigorous growth of *Verticillium* in the stem xylem. Invasion extensive both longitudinally and laterally. Wilt symptoms severe.

OR 55 on *Fuggle*. The same as above.

Fuggle on *OR 55*. Slight and restricted growth of *Verticillium* in the stem xylem. Extensive longitudinal but little lateral invasion. Wilt symptoms slight or absent.

OR 55 on *OR 55*. The same as above.

Conclusions from the grafting experiments

Except for the differences in growth of the pathogen up the stems showing a resistant reaction it is clear that the results with both diseases were identical. They may be viewed as a test of stem resistance, since in each case they indicate the reactions of the stems of both varieties under similar conditions of growth and invasion. Two such types of condition were used, viz. on roots of varieties of low and of high resistance. Under either circumstance the stems of both varieties behaved in the same way. Thus on roots of a low-resistance variety the stem reaction was one of low resistance and on roots of a highly resistant variety the stem reaction was one of high resistance.

Two conclusions can be drawn from these results:

(i) The inherent resistance of the stems of the two varieties used in each experiment was the same.

(ii) The effective resistance shown by the stems differed under different invasion conditions. The change occurred equally in either stem however and was not related to their varietal status.

These experiments present the surprising situation that under some circumstances the stem of a variety of high resistance has as little ability to combat invasion as the stem of a variety of low resistance. Under other circumstances both show a highly resistant reaction.

It is also clear that the factors controlling the difference between the varieties in resistance to their wilt diseases are present in the roots and not in the stems. This raises the question whether the stems play any part in the determination of the rate of invasion of the plant—that is, whether they have any inherent resistance at all. This will be discussed after a consideration of the stem-inoculation experiments.

INOCULATION OF HOP STEMS

As already mentioned these experiments were made with one variety (Fuggle) and two races of *V. albo-atrum* (virulent and mild), to which the Fuggle variety shows respectively low and high resistance when inoculated through its roots.

The stem inoculations were made by two methods:

(i) Spore suspensions of the fungi were injected hypodermically directly into the xylem of hop stems (Isaac & Keyworth, 1948), It was possible to inject only a very small quantity of spore suspension in this way.

(ii) Spore suspensions in 0·5 % (w/v) water agar were injected into the pith cavity of an internode on each stem until the cavity was filled. A large dose, 1–2 ml. of spore suspension, was thus inserted (Keyworth, 1953).

The results of these inoculations were as follows:

Small dose. Both fungi grew upward in the xylem from the point of inoculation. They also grew downward for a few inches. Both races invaded the stems in an identical fashion, which was similar to that shown after root inoculation with the mild race. The fungi were restricted to a part of the xylem; fresh xylem was produced and leaf symptoms were almost entirely absent. After small-dose inoculation, therefore, the mild race behaved in what may be considered a 'typical' fashion and the virulent race in an 'atypical' fashion.

Large dose. Invasion was again mainly upward and both races again grew in an identical way. This, however, was the very vigorous attack typical of root inoculation with the virulent race and resulted in the complete death of the stem in a few weeks. In this case, therefore, the mild race was 'atypical' and exhibited the same potentialities of invasion as the virulent race.

Conclusions from stem inoculations

It is clear from the results of these inoculations that the type of invasion shown by the two races of fungus was conditioned not by the inherent pathogenicity of the races, but by factors associated with the method of inoculation. It is not possible to decide without further experiments which of the differences between the inoculation methods were responsible for the effects observed. The most obvious difference lies in the number of spores inserted. There were other differences however. The large dose was in agar, the other was not. In addition, the small dose was inserted directly into one side of the xylem and to reach fresh xylem the fungi would have had to invade laterally. The large dose was in the pith cavity, and on growing from this the fungi would invade a large area of xylem tissue. It also seems possible that there may have been considerable growth of the fungus within the pith cavity before xylem invasion occurred.

Whatever the differences between the methods it is clear that some action took place in the case of the large dose which enabled both fungi to invade vigorously. The cause of this may have been either an increase in the invasive power of the pathogens or a decrease in the resistance of the stem.

The stem-inoculation experiments give some information on whether the stems have any inherent resistance. This, as already indicated, is considered by the writer to refer to the resistance of the normal un-invaded plant. As soon as invasion starts, the pathogenic mechanisms of the fungus initiate processes which may result in the overcoming or reduction of the host resistance. The extent to which this occurs will determine the progress of invasion which will then indicate the actual or effective resistance. High effective resistance was shown only when small inocula were used. To invade from such small inocula the pathogens had presumably to rely on their ability to parasitize the normal or nearly normal tissues of the stem since there was no other food base available nor was there any extensive preliminary growth before invasion. Only when the dose was increased could vigorous invasion occur and it may be concluded, therefore, that the stem was exerting a positive resistance which had to be overcome. It may be presumed, therefore, that the normal stem had intrinsically a high resistance. It should be noted that this was so even when the virulent race of fungus was used, to which the whole plant had a low effective resistance.

If correct, these conclusions mean that although a hop plant may show low resistance to root infection its stem has high resistance to direct infection. This high resistance of the stem must be overcome before active invasion can take place.

Correlation between the results of the grafting and stem-inoculation experiments

In the writer's opinion the stem-inoculation results can be used to interpret the results of the grafting experiments. The identity of the symptoms produced in the two experiments support this view.

The large-dose inoculation corresponds to invasion from a low-resistance root and the small-dose inoculation to invasion from a high-resistance root. The fungus cannot establish the necessary conditions in the high-resistance root to overcome the high inherent stem resistance but can do so in the low-resistance root. This applies equally to stems of both high- and low-resistance varieties. It must thus be concluded that in a plant of low resistance, the full development of wilt occurs only because stem resistance is overcome. Thus the stem does not provide a purely inactive substrate through which the fungus can grow in an unimpeded fashion.

A further study of the operative differences between the stem inoculations would seem desirable. These differences can be controlled experimentally, whereas the differences between the roots of different varieties cannot. They may therefore indicate the types of difference which should be sought in the roots in the study of varietal effect.

Inoculation experiments on roots

So far as the writer is aware no detailed studies have been made on the effect of inoculum dose on root response. Isaac & Keyworth (1948) inoculated roots and below-ground parts of previous year stems of hops by small-dose hypodermic injection. These small doses produced different stem responses with the two races of *V. albo-atrum*, similar to those induced by the normal multiple inoculation presumably arising from soil inoculation. The roots, therefore, differed from stems in that their response was not affected by the inoculum dose but was affected by the race of pathogen.

The grafting experiments described herein also show that the part played by the roots was not influenced by the variety of stem grafted on to them.

OTHER THEORIES ON STEM REACTION

Heinze & Andrus (1945) considered that the active invasion of Pan America stems from Bonny Best roots showed that these stems were 'completely susceptible'. It would seem from this that they thought that the stems had no inherent resistance whatever. Although it was not stated they presumably also considered the Bonny Best stems to be 'completely susceptible'. These stems, however, were not vigorously invaded from Pan America roots. The possibility had thus to be considered of some increase in their resistance which might presumably have been caused by the translocation of a 'resistance factor' generated in the Pan America roots. To test this possibility Heinze & Andrus grafted Bonny Best stems on to Pan America roots and inoculated these stems through adventitious (Bonny Best) roots on them. The stems were then vigorously invaded above the adventitious roots. It was, therefore, concluded that no 'resistance factor' had been translocated from the Pan

America roots, and that resistance was confined to these roots. In the writer's view, the original conclusion that the Pan American stems were 'completely susceptible' was incorrect. They did show low effective resistance when invaded from Bonny Best roots, but not only they, but also the Bonny Best stems, showed high effective resistance when invaded from Pan America roots. Heinze & Andrus's results can be explained by a complete reversal of their hypothesis. The normal stems of both varieties had a high inherent resistance which was *lowered* on Bonny Best roots. The reason for their failure to detect any translocated resistance factor is apparent—the stems were inherently resistant any way. The Bonny Best stems inoculated through their own adventitious roots when grafted at the base on Pan America roots were responding to factors operative in the inoculated roots.

As indicated, the present hypothesis will explain the results obtained by Heinze & Andrus. It also answers the criticisms of the theories of Heinze & Andrus made by certain other workers (e.g. Snyder, Baker & Hansen, 1946). There is one piece of research, however, which has given results which appear to be completely incompatible with those of the experiments described above. This was performed by Scheffer & Walker (1954) who worked with *Fusarium* wilt of the tomato. They injected cut stems of high- and low-resistance varieties with standardized spore suspensions (the number of spores in the suspensions was sufficient eventually to cause severe wilt in the variety Bonny Best) and then re-rooted them. Tests for the presence of the fungus in the stems and roots were made at intervals throughout the experiments. No *Fusarium* was found in the roots of any variety at any time. The fungus was at first distributed throughout the whole length of the stems of all the varieties, but after 20 days it started to disappear from the stems of the highly resistant varieties and after 35 days was present only in the base. In contrast, it grew vigorously in all parts of the stems of the Bonny Best variety and induced severe wilt.

The results, which at first glance are strikingly opposed to those reported in the present paper, particularly to those obtained by direct inoculations of hop stems, would appear to suggest that the stems of the tomato varieties do differ in inherent resistance. Five points in connexion with these results are worthy of note however.

(1) Although it is stated by Scheffer & Walker (1954) that no *Fusarium* was isolated from the roots at any time, it is not absolutely clear at what times the tests were made. In a previous note the authors (Scheffer & Walker, 1952) state that the fungus was not present in the roots up to the time of appearance of the first symptoms. They give no evidence on

whether they became invaded subsequently. From their later publication, however, it must presumably be understood that they did not.

It appears to the writer that this point is so critical that it should be subjected to the most exhaustive tests. If Scheffer & Walker's results are confirmed by these tests it would appear that other explanations must be sought for the results of the grafting experiments. Some other explanations are theoretically possible, although the invocation of any of them suggests at first sight that the facts are being strained to fit the theory.

(2) As already emphasized, the present studies have not strictly been on roots and stems but on the above- and below-ground parts of the plants. Thus all the grafts were actually stem-stem and not stem-root, although in many cases only a small length of basal stem was involved. Even in the adventitious-root-inoculation tests of Heinze & Andrus a part of the stem was buried in sand to induce root formation. The results of all the experiments would be compatible if the differential effects occurred in the below-ground portions of the stems as well as, or instead of, in the roots.

(3) Scheffer & Walker suggest that the results of the grafting experiments can be explained by a blocking of the vessels in the low-resistance roots which did not occur in the high-resistance roots. It seems to the writer, however, that this explanation completely fails to explain the vigorous growth of the pathogen in the stems of either variety grafted on to low-resistance roots.

(4) The stem-injection experiments do not completely satisfy the requirements for comparative resistance tests, since the stems were grown on roots of differing varietal status. In the writer's opinion it is probable that the normal uninvaded roots exert no influence on stem reaction, but this still requires experimental proof.

(5) Finally, it must be noted that in the grafting and stem-inoculation experiments reported above the contrast between the two methods of inoculation was considerable. The methods gave symptoms which were identical with those observed after natural infection, and for this reason it is considered that valid conclusions on the mechanisms underlying such natural infections can be drawn from them. In spite of this it must be agreed that they may not provide sufficiently sensitive tests to detect lesser differences in the stem resistance. Possibly the inoculation method used by Scheffer & Walker was of intermediate effect and could do this.

The writer is of the opinion, however, that this was not so. If Scheffer & Walker's results are confirmed, the possibility that they are attributable to some action occurring in the stem base would best seem to repay further study.

The relation of stem invasion to the production of leaf symptoms

The severity of a wilt disease is usually assessed on leaf symptoms. Although these symptoms were already mentioned above in connexion with the demonstration of high and low resistance, the primary concern of this paper is not with leaf symptoms but with stem invasion. In order to correlate the present results with those from leaf-symptom records alone, it is necessary to consider the relationship between leaf-symptom intensity and the extent of stem invasion.

Dimond *et al.* (1952) and Keyworth & Dimond (1952), using the methods devised by Gallegly & Walker (1949), demonstrated that the extent of vascular browning in tomato wilt was closely correlated with the extent and severity of leaf wilting. The writer's observations on both *Fusarium* wilt of tomato and *Verticillium* wilt of the hop have shown that the leaves of these plants rarely wilt until the fungus has invaded the stem at least to the base of the petiole of the leaf in question. Sometimes the petiole itself is invaded before severe wilt occurs. The major differences between mild and severe hop wilt also show a close association between leaf-symptom intensity and the extent and vigour of the vascular invasion by the pathogen.

In the writer's opinion, therefore, the leaf-symptom intensity shown in the two diseases being considered must be related to the extent of stem invasion. This opinion is opposed to that of Gäumann (1950), who suggests that the leaf symptoms of wilt diseases are caused by factors similar to those operating in the silver leaf of plum. In this disease the fungus *Stereum purpureum* is known to generate diffusible toxins which affect the leaves at considerable distances from the localized invasion site in the base of the plant. The writer considers that toxins are at least partly responsible for the leaf symptoms of wilt diseases, but that they are probably effective at only short distances from the advancing mycelium. These views refer only to the diseases under consideration, but it seems probable that they may also apply to other wilt diseases. Conversely, there may be some wilt diseases in which toxins are diffused considerably in advance of the fungus. The toxins involved in wilt diseases are considered in another paper in this series. Mention must be made of another theory of wilt-symptom causation: that of vascular obstruction. This has been suggested for many years, but recently has received further attention. Ludwig (1952) investigated the subject in connexion with *Fusarium* wilt of tomato. He concluded that, although toxins might be partly responsible for leaf symptoms, an equal if not greater part was played by the obstruction of the vessels by the fungus and by deposits of gummy substances. It seems unlikely to the writer, however, that a simple plugging mechanism would completely explain the successive appearance of symptoms on leaves up the plant. It would also seem inadequate to explain the gradual desiccation of the leaves in hop wilt.

GENERAL DISCUSSION

As will be gathered, the subject of vascular wilts bristles with opposing theories and the results of experiments apparently contradict each other. The hypotheses put forward by the writer in respect of the two diseases considered can be briefly stated as follows:

(1) The site of differential resistance is the base of the plant (root or stem base or both).

(2) Although two plants show different degrees of resistance when infected through their roots the stems of these plants have the same inherent resistance to invasion.

(3) This inherent resistance is high and must be reduced or overcome before active stem invasion can take place.

(4) The extent to which such stem invasion occurs will probably determine the severity of the leaf symptoms.

If these hypotheses are correct they suggest that active stem invasion may be a cumulative process. The parasitization of the roots sets in motion a 'chain reaction' which first induces conditions which permit active growth of the fungus in the stem. The further growth of the fungus may continue this process which eventually culminates in the production of typical wilt symptoms. However, if the essential first step, the reduction or overcoming of stem resistance, does not occur, the fungus remains confined either to the roots or stem base in tomato wilt, or to a restricted part of the xylem in hop wilt.

In hop wilt, the confinement of the fungus and the stimulation of the xylem to produce new uninvaded tissue are particularly apparent. These phenomena suggest that the stem may have an active resistance response which it is unable to exert under certain conditions of root invasion. It seems likely that resistance to invasion may imply the inability of the fungus to invade the living xylem parenchyma and thus enter fresh xylem tissue. The resistance effect would be enhanced if new xylem was produced at the same time. Scheffer & Walker (1954) also noted the production of fresh xylem in stem-injected Pan America tomatoes. Of particular significance is the observation of Snyder et al. (1946) that there was the same amount of fungal growth per vessel in both Pan America and Bonny Best tomatoes inoculated by root injection with spore suspension. Only a few vessels of the Pan America plants were invaded, however, compared with many in the Bonny Best plants. They suggested that resistance was associated with the living host cell and not with the xylem fluids. If this is so it is possible that the mechanism whereby the fungus invades actively is enzymic in nature. The formation of pectin methyl esterase by *Fusarium lycopersici* has been reported by Gothoskar, Scheffer, Walker & Stahmann (1953), although they postulate only that this is responsible for browning of the vessels and the production of wilt symptoms. They suggest that cell parasitization may be due to other causes.

Finally, it should be emphasized that the studies reported herein deal strictly with fungal invasion. It is suggested that active invasion of the stems is an essential preliminary to wilting, but this is not yet firmly established. Certain authorities (e.g. Gäumann, 1950) postulate that leaf-toxin diffusion precedes stem invasion, and that this occurs only after the toxin has affected the host cells. In this case the toxin might be the 'invasion precursor' as well as the cause of the leaf symptoms. This, again, remains to be tested, but, in the opinion of the writer, it will be found that it is not so, and that active stem invasion depends on other factors which are generated in the root of low-resistance varieties and either lower the resistance of the stem or increase the invasive ability of the fungus.

REFERENCES

DIMOND, A. E., DAVIS, D., CHAPMAN, R. A. & STODDARD, E. M. (1952). Plant chemotherapy as evaluated by the *Fusarium* wilt assay on tomatoes. *Bull. Conn. agric. Exp. Sta.* no. 557.

GALLEGLY, M. E. & WALKER, J. C. (1949). Plant nutrition in relation to disease development. V. Bacterial wilt of tomato. *Amer. J. Bot.* **36**, 613–23.

GÄUMANN, E. (1950). *Principles of Plant Infection*, p. 70. London: Crosbie Lockwood and Son, Ltd.

GOTHOSKAR, S. S., SCHEFFER, R. P., WALKER, J. C. & STAHMANN, M. A. (1953). The role of pectic enzymes in *Fusarium* wilt of tomato. *Phytopathology*, **43**, 535–6.

HEINZE, P. M. & ANDRUS, C. F. (1945). Apparent localization of *Fusarium* wilt resistance in the Pan America tomato. *Amer. J. Bot.* **32**, 62–6.

ISAAC, I. & KEYWORTH, W. G. (1948). *Verticillium* wilt of the hop. III. A study of the pathogenicity of isolates from progressive and from fluctuating outbreaks. *Ann. appl. Biol.* **35**, 243–9.

KEYWORTH, W. G. (1953). *Verticillium* wilt of the hop. VI. The relative roles of root and stem in the determination of wilt severity. *Ann. appl. Biol.* **40**, 344–61.

KEYWORTH, W. G. & DIMOND, A. E. (1952). Root injury as a factor in the assessment of chemotherapeutants. *Phytopathology*, **62**, 311–15.

LUDWIG, R. A. (1952). Studies on the physiology of hadromycotic wilting in the tomato plant. *Bull. Macdonald Coll. P.Q. Canada.* no. 20.

SCHEFFER, R. P. & WALKER, J. C. (1952). Distribution of *Fusarium* resistance in the tomato plant (Abstr.). *Phytopathology*, **42**, 474.

SCHEFFER, R. P. & WALKER, J. C. (1954). Distribution and nature of *Fusarium* resistance in the tomato plant. *Phytopathology*, **44**, 94–101.

SNYDER, W. C., BAKER, K. F. & HANSEN, H. N. (1946). Interpretation of resistance to *Fusarium* wilt in tomato. *Science*, **103**, 707–8.